Human Nature

Human Nature

David Berlinski

Seattle Discovery Institute Press 2019

Description

Conventional wisdom holds that the murder rate has plummeted since the Middle Ages; humankind is growing more peaceful and enlightened; man is shortly to be much improved—better genes, better neural circuits, better biochemistry; and we are approaching a technological singularity that well may usher in utopia. *Human Nature* eviscerates these and other doctrines of a contemporary nihilism masquerading as science. In this wide-ranging work polymath David Berlinski draws upon history, mathematics, logic, and literature to retrain our gaze on an old truth many are eager to forget: there is and will be about the human condition beauty, nobility, and moments of sublime insight, yes, but also ignorance and depravity. Men are not about to become like gods.

Copyright Notice

Library Cataloging Data

Human Nature by David Berlinski

330 pages, 6 x 9 x 0.7 inches & 1.0 lb, 229 x 152 x 17.5 mm. & 0.445 kg

Library of Congress Control Number: 2019951015

ISBN: 978-1-936599-71-4 (Paperback), 978-1-936599-73-8 (Kindle), 978-1-936599-72-1 (EPUB)

HIS049000 HISTORY / Essays

SCI080000 SCIENCE / Essays

SCI075000 SCIENCE / Philosophy & Social Aspects

SCI027000 SCIENCE / Life Sciences / Evolution

Publisher Information

Discovery Institute Press, 208 Columbia Street, Seattle, WA 98104

Internet: http://www.discoveryinstitutepress.com/

Published in the United States of America on acid-free paper.

First Edition, First Printing, November 2019.

Dedication

Pour les pompiers de Paris

Advance Praise

Polymath David Berlinski's appraisal of a transcendent human nature is really a military history, a discourse on physics and mathematics, a review of philosophy and linguistics, and a brilliant indictment of scientific groupthink by an unapologetic intellectual dissident. Read it and learn something original and incisive on every page.
—**Victor Davis Hanson**, Senior Fellow, the Hoover Institution, Stanford University, author of *The Second World Wars*

Berlinski is a modern Hannah Arendt, but deeper, more illuminating and wittier (i.e., smarter). His ability to use science and mathematics to illuminate history is nearly unique. If I were assembling a list of essential modern books for undergraduates at my college or any college, this book would be number one. Not only would students learn a tremendous lot from this book; many would also love it. Likewise their teachers. Berlinski's gift to mankind is gratefully received.
—**David Gelernter**, Professor of Computer Science, Yale University

As the lights of Western civilization go out, it is nevertheless a treat to read these deep reflections on what we can be proud of, and where we went badly astray. Wonderfully unconventional and stimulating, with David Berlinski's characteristic wit and penetrating insight!
—**Greg Chaitin**, pioneer of algorithmic information theory and metamathematics, and Emeritus Researcher, IBM's Thomas J. Watson Research Center in New York, whose festschrift *Unravelling Complexity: The Life and Work of Gregory Chaitin* is forthcoming

Berlinski combines mastery of classical culture and deep knowledge of mathematics and the natural sciences with sharp, elegant, and insightful writing. The man is fearless in pursuing lines of reasoning that are considered taboo by current standards. A wonderful display of common sense and reason at a time of great confusions.

—**Sergiu Klainerman**, Eugene Higgins Professor of Mathematics, Princeton University

These essays represent a reflection on man and modern times as erudite as the finest history, as profound as the most searching philosophy, as beautifully wrought as the loveliest prose, and as shocking and indignant as the best journalism. The work of a magnificent mind.

—**Peter Robinson**, Murdoch Distinguished Policy Fellow at the Hoover Institution, host of Uncommon Knowledge

Another tour de force by David Berlinski. Few writers indeed, about science or society, can boast such a thoroughgoing command of the significant ideas of the past century, the confident mastery of every centrally significant scientific theory. Yet if Berlinski derives obvious joy from the great theories that unify the world, he is never more memorable than when he vividly displays its irreducible particulars, holding the quiddities of place and person more clearly before our imagination than we might even see them ourselves.

Indeed, if Berlinski glories in science's achievements, he is no less dismissive of those attempts to see pattern and abstraction born not of vision but of ignorance; and he repeatedly marshals his exceptionally deep historical and scientific knowledge (and his inimitable wit) to drive facile theories of man and the world into the shoals. He is a relentless and devastating enemy of all attempts to reduce the tragic, bizarre, glorious world that confronts us to simple answers or easy slogans at the expense of the facts. We will treasure this book.

—**Stephen McKeown**, Assistant Professor of Mathematics, University of Texas at Dallas

Contents

Introduction

I have lived within half a city block of Notre Dame for the last twenty years. I saw the spire from my bedroom window every morning, and on leaving my apartment, I could walk within a few feet of the cathedral walls, dark with grime on the tail-end of the rue du Clôitre, white and sparkling at the head of the street, the stones steam-cleaned and scrubbed. On mild winter days, I liked to wander through the Square Jean XXIII on the east side of the cathedral. The square was always carefully tended, a fountain and a lovely flower-garden at its center. When I needed to get home after the metro had closed, and I was too tired to walk, I told taxi drivers to head for Notre Dame, and even if they had never heard of rue Chanoinesse—my street—they knew how to get there. My father was great friends with Pierre Cochereau, the organist at Notre Dame, and he performed often on the great Cavaillé-Coll organ, water-logged now. My father sometimes let me sit in the organ loft during his recitals. From the loft, the organ seemed to boom and echo. In winter, when there were few tourists, I would go into Notre Dame and light a candle for my friend, M. P. Schützenberger. He told me as he was dying that he wished to return as one of the gargoyles, and, perhaps, he had. No building has ever been more a part of my life.

I saw the spire topple, slowly at first, and then quickly. The police forced me to evacuate to the other side of the Seine. All of Paris was there. I thought of myself as a Parisian, if not by birth, then, at least, by sentiment. Twenty years is a long time. The *pompiers* were in their glory that night, and, when I was allowed to return home as dawn was breaking, they were still there, red-eyed, exhausted, sooty, grim, and proud. The police, too. The enormous plume of smoke had already drifted to the west and south. Later that day, I saw the front of the cathedral. Its towers were still standing, but its great bells, which I had heard every day, were silent.

The fire did a great deal of damage to the cathedral; it could not be contained, and, in the end, it burnt itself out. The fourteen hundred year old oak timbers that had supported the roof were consumed, and the roof destroyed. President Macron spoke optimistically of rebuilding the cathedral within five years, but no one believed him. The structural stability of the north and south towers is still in doubt. International architects were quick to sketch their plans for the cathedral's restoration, and, without exception, they were, if not hideous, then grotesque. One firm proposed putting a swimming pool on the roof; another, a design in which the roof and spire would be made of glass. The destruction of Notre Dame evoked an almost universal sense of cultural horror. Everyone quite understood that a structure of comparable grandeur lay completely beyond our collective competence.

Tout passe, tout casse, tout lasse.

In the eleventh and twelfth centuries, there must have been men in Europe who doubted the Catholic faith, and who had little use for its consolations. If atheism was a real presence in the early and high Middle Ages, it was not one that the philosophers or the chroniclers remarked. The contrast to the Moslem world is striking. Many Moslem intellectuals undertook a journey from faith to doubt and from doubt to despair. For many years, his physician remarked, God had put a lock on Al-Ghazali's tongue. The astrologer, Abu Mashar, ended his days as an atheist. Doubt about the faith was never endorsed in the Moslem world, but it was understood. Europe was more conventional, its literate thinkers either in the service of the Church or captive to its control. Of all the twelfth-century philosophers, Peter Abelard came closest to skepticism. He provoked and was reprimanded. Having begun his life in Holy Orders, he ended his life in Holy Orders. He did not change.

When almost ten years ago I published *The Deniable Darwin*, I was struck by the fact that the contemporary scientific community resembled in its swaggering assurance the intellectual community of the high Middle Ages. A professor at Harvard in the early twenty-first century, finding himself at the University of Paris in the thirteenth, would require only a few days to get his bearings. Nothing more than the polarity of his beliefs would change. As an experienced intellectual, he would have been right at home. Had the same professor been returned to tenth- or eleventh-century Baghdad, he would have been flustered by its intellectual diversity. There is an irony in this that is worth remarking.

Faith in the twenty-first century is secular and scientific. If I sometimes write to deplore the faith, it is because I am among the faithful. My criticisms are *self*-criticisms. I am what I have always been: a secular Jew. We secular Jews accept an ostentatious commitment to logic, inference, irony, and skepticism: if they engender an ever-present sense of emptiness, that is the price that they command. It is the price that we are prepared to pay. In an elegant essay published in the last decade of the twentieth century, V. S. Naipaul made popular, or, at least, better known, the idea of a universal civilization. He wrote as the Soviet system was collapsing, a moment of triumph. There is little of that sense today. The idea of a universal civilization remains, something like a complicated Diophantine equation, one describing the modern technological societies of the West. We know how to solve the equation, and every society has solved the equation in the same way. The necessary parameters are plain. The universal civilization requires an elaborate bureaucracy and a rational legal system enforcing the law of contracts; it requires a scientific elite; it requires science as a source of awe; and it requires relatively free markets. A doggish form of secular humanism prevails throughout. These are ideas—all of them—that invite a certain cynical asperity. Whatever else it may be, the universal civilization is emotionally and aesthetically repellent. *All that is solid melts into air, all that is Holy is profaned.*

There is no society without its underlying ideology, and the ideology of a universal civilization is expressed by a universal theory, a Court of Last Resort. No matter the debate, whether a matter of gender identity or global warming, the terms are drawn from the vocabulary that the Court enforces. In arguing for a position, it is necessary to say that science supports it, and fatal to admit that it does not. The result is very often comic. The idea that there are any number of genders is championed by the mentally defective and sullenly tolerated by everyone else. On the rare occasions in which men persuaded that they are women are pressed in debate, they are remarkably confident in appealing to scientific authority. And for every good reason. There is no position that some scientists will not support, and some scientists will support any position. If in our day competitive appeals to scientific authority are as frivolous as they are unpersuasive, this has not always been so. Both the Nazi and the Soviet states were pleased to observe that their genocidal imbecilities were the overflow in action of what the scientific community had antecedently determined. In this they were largely correct. Racial science flourished in Germany and Marxist science in the Soviet Union.

The universal theory is a part of the great structure of theoretical physics, but it contains in Darwin's theory of evolution an ancillary rider, something like a carbuncle on the main body. There is no obvious connection, after all, between theoretical physics and Darwinian biology, and no esoteric connection either. A commitment to Darwinian theory is nevertheless as imperative among academics as a comparable commitment to the Nicene Creed is among Catholics. However insincere, some form of genuflection is required. Like any theory, the universal theory conveys a certain aura, one that cannot be found in either its axioms or its conclusions. It is an aura that thaws and resolves itself into a number of familiar propositions: *The universe is a physical object. It is nothing less, and there is nothing more. The emergence of life on earth may be explained by synthetic chemistry; it has already been entirely explained by synthetic chemistry. Religions are among the delusions of mankind and are responsible for its misfortunes. The mind is the brain in action. There is, on the largest scales, nothing distinctive about the earth or the abundant life it nourishes. Human beings and all of man's passions are inadvertent and accidental. Beyond the laws of nature, there are no laws. The universe is large, remote, indifferent, and strange. Human life may be enjoyed; it must, in any case, be endured.*

Even those ardent in defense of the universal theory, and the claims that it makes, wonder whether there is some radical point of incoherence in its structure, some fundamental deficiency that it cannot accommodate. Some hope secretly that this is so. I am among them. No one doubts that a great deal about the life that men lead must forever lie beyond the reach of any theory. Neither man nor machine has the power deductively to exhaust the premises of a theory as well-known as quantum field theory. The question is whether the universal theory commands its power as an ideal. In a recent essay entitled "The Trouble with Quantum Mechanics," Steven Weinberg suggests what is at issue. "We want to understand," he writes, "the relation of humans to nature."[1] He then draws a distinction between two ways of grasping that relationship. In the first, the laws controlling human life are incorporated into the universal theory as axioms. In the second, the facts of life are deduced from premises that make no reference to human life at all. It is in this prospect that Weinberg has invested his hopes.

My own view is that a structure from which everything about human life follows as a deduction, if impossible in practice, is also impossible in principle. Any theory must be interpreted in the reflective gaze of those who appeal to it. If the universal theory admits of *no* interpretation, then it remains ineffable, and if it admits of some interpretation, then only a part of the interpretative apparatus—its ideas, concepts, rules of procedure—can be represented within the universal theory. Something must be left out, and if what is left out is let in, then something new must be left out. This process of interpretation is never-ending. This logicians know. It is something that the physicists do not know. It is, this ignorance, a reason for their confidence.

This book ranges over many topics, and incorporates a number of different styles, but is unified, I think, by a common concern for what is an indistinct concept, and that is the concept of human nature. It is a concept severely in disfavor because it suggests that there *is* something answering to human nature, some collocation of ineliminable and necessary properties that collectively define what it is to be a human being. There are such properties. Of course there are. That men are men is an obvious example. Men are men is true because men are *necessarily* men. And the fact that there are such properties *does* involve a commitment to essentialism. No one disposing of essentialism in biology is disposed to disregard it in logic, mathematics, physics, or ordinary life. Human beings are not indefinitely malleable. There are boundaries beyond which they cannot change. We are not simply apes with larger brains or smaller hands, and the distance between ourselves and our nearest ancestors is what it has always appeared to be, and that is practically infinite. Human beings are perpetually the same, even if in some respects different.

In the preface to his *Dictionary of the English Language*, Dr. Johnson remarked that his dictionary "was written with little assistance of the learned, and without any patronage of the great; not in the soft obscurities of retirement, or under the shelter of academic bowers, but amidst inconvenience and distraction, in sickness and in sorrow."[2] These are memorable words, and if I find myself reaching for them for my own work as well, it is only because they are true of my own life as well.

—Paris, 2019

I. Violence

1. The First World War

And a strange light began immediately, but by perceptible gradations, to fall and grow upon the map of Europe.

—Winston Churchill[1]

The Orient Express left Paris from the Gare de l'Est just after 18:30 every Tuesday evening, and it arrived in Vienna shortly before midnight of the next day. Service had begun in 1883. The train's sixteen elegant wagon-lits were pulled by a powerful steam-powered locomotive, its mushroomed stack puffing powdery gray smoke into the parabolic sky. The Great Powers were at peace. An attitude of optimism, if not general in the nineteenth century, was, at least, widespread in the early twentieth century. The French revolution, the Napoleonic wars, and the Congress of Vienna, with its gathering of spidery clerical conservatives, had receded into the past.

Writing in 1830, Thomas Macaulay had looked to the future and found it good.[2] In 1850, the French engineer, Eugène Belgrand, had undertaken the modernization of the French sewer system, bringing those dark infernal tunnels to standards common in the Roman empire. Horse-drawn wagons set off for Paris from the countryside early each morning carrying peas, carrots, beets, turnips, great slabs of beef, fish, squawking poultry, all drawn centrifugally toward the city's center at *les Halles*.[3] The sewers reversed their flow, establishing the great equilibrium of civilization.

On her first voyage in 1854, the extreme clipper *Red Jacket* crossed the Atlantic in thirteen days. The steam engine had made train travel possible early in the century; and by the end of the century, the internal combustion engine had made possible the automobile. In 1882, the Edison Electric Illuminating Company lit up lower Manhattan, and interiors and streets both acquired a harsh radiance as gas lighting gave way.

The Second International Congress of Mathematicians was held in Paris in 1900. Three years before, the mathematicians had met in Zurich and they had been well satisfied by Swiss efficiency, if not by German food. July had been warm in Paris. Temperatures had reached thirty-five degrees Celsius. The Seine was filled with swimmers paddling through the raw sewage with gusto, their ears sealed beneath rubber caps. Attendance at the Congress was desultory. Charlotte Scott wore her biscuity brown hair pinned back in a bun. An Englishwoman by birth, Scott had scored very well on the Cambridge Tripos examination, but she was denied her award as an Eighth Wrangler because university officials, while appreciating her ability, could not abide her gender. Now she was in Paris to report on events. A Monsieur Raymond Poincaré, she reported, was elected President of the Congress, and a Monsieur Hermite, the *President d'honneur,* a position that he was unable to enjoy in person because honor demanded that he perform his functions *in absentia*. Having described the opening session of the Congress, which was held in the great Exhibition Hall, Charlotte Scott proceeded to discuss the separate sections, all of them held in the somnolent Sorbonne.

Speaking in German, David Hilbert had offered mathematicians a list of ten open problems, referring members of his audience to his full list of twenty-three problems, which he had published elsewhere. Hilbert, Scott observed, seemed much concerned with the axiomatic foundations of mathematics, asking in particular for an account of the natural numbers. An "objection was taken to M. Hilbert's remarks... by M. Peano," a hoarse, rasping bulldog of a man, who claimed that such a system had already been established. No wonder. He had established it. David Hilbert was followed to the podium by Riki Fujisawa, the official delegate from Japan, who gave "a very interesting account of the mathematics of the older Japanese school." Some five years later, Albert Einstein laid the foundations of quantum mechanics and special relativity.

By the time the Orient Express crossed the French frontier at Strasbourg, the sun had vacated the European continent, and passengers, seated in chairs covered by buttery Russian leather, could see the snowfields of the northern Alps reflected in the sky, pink and pastel, gashed by gold.

§

The nineteenth century came to its end in August, 1914, and with it, the ascending trajectory of European civilization.[4] "The War was an unprecedented disgrace to the human intellect," R. G. Collingwood remarked in his autobiography, but whatever the disgrace, the war was a disaster for the civilization that made it possible.[5] The European political order that had since 1815 and the Congress of Vienna seemed stable and robust was, as events revealed, neither stable nor robust. European powers had gone to war in the Crimea, Sardinia, Denmark, Austria, France, and in the Caucasus, and they had confronted, or contained, revolutions in 1830, 1848, 1871, and 1905, but, as blood dries quickly, they had learned little from their mistakes, and the Balance of Power, in which so many of their suave diplomats had vested their faith, served only to persuade European statesmen that their complicated and shifting system of alliances, no matter how many times they had failed to preserve the peace, would in the future prevent them from being again at war.[6]

For more than a century, historians have endeavored to discover the causes of the First World War.[7] No event in world history has been studied with more effort and less effect. The cause of the war was, after all, there in plain sight: the assassination of the Archduke Franz Ferdinand and his wife, Sophie, the Duchess of Hohenberg, in Sarajevo on June 28, 1914. Their murder was as much an accident as an act of fate, the Archduke and his wife losing both their way and their lives owing to the incompetence of their chauffeur. Bad luck. Their assassin, Gavrilo Princip, was an ardent Serbian nationalist, tubercular, dull, dim-witted, determined, and short.[8] That the First World War was a tragedy, no one doubts, but that it was caused by a nineteen-year-old nincompoop, no one can abide. It is too much. What is intolerable has for this reason often been begrudged. The assassination was not necessary, so one argument runs, since other causes were sufficient, and it was not sufficient, so runs a second argument, since other causes were necessary.[9] If it was neither necessary nor sufficient, how could the assassination have been the *cause* of the First World War?[10]

A cause is one thing. There it is. It is the cause. What of the historical conditions, circumstances and forces that made it possible, history's hidden hand?[11] In a bleak little book devoted to the moral history of the twentieth century, Jonathan Glover abbreviates an account that historians have already amplified.[12] European statesmen, and especially their foreign ministers, were crushed by a sense of their own impotence.[13] Their intentions were ambiguously expressed.[14] Mobilization, once it had begun in Germany and Russia, could not be easily reversed. The German railway schedule was inflexible.[15] An arms race prevailed between Great Britain and Imperial Germany.[16] And thereafter Glover's list becomes progressively more general until it includes nationalism, social Darwinism,[17] national honor, and something so simple as a stubborn unwillingness on the part of Europe's leaders to recognize that they were marching toward disaster.[18]

§

The Austro-Hungarian government considered the assassination of Franz Ferdinand an insult to its honor and a threat to its security. It was both. General Count Franz Conrad von Hötzendorf, the Austrian Chief of Staff, had for years thought to end every Balkan crisis by demanding that it be resolved by war. In July of 1914, he remained faithful to himself.[19] Determined to make war, but incapable of making it alone, Conrad endeavored to elicit the support, or encourage the acquiescence, of Count Leopold von Berchtold, the Austrian Foreign Minister. He need not have exerted himself. The door that he thought to push was open.[20] Berchtold had often been thought weak by the Austrian military. Now he was seized by a sense of resoluteness. He came to life; he commenced to breathe fire.[21]

Under the very best of circumstances, the Austro-Hungarian Empire could propel itself forward by doing what it always did; it required an effort to act with dispatch, and to act with celerity was beyond its powers.[22] Conrad and Berchtold were persuaded that war was necessary. Having secured one another's assent with gratifying ease, they required in addition the assent of Count István Tisza, the Prime Minister of Hungary.[23] Tisza had few illusions about peace, but many reservations about war. At the very least, Tisza believed, it would be necessary to enlist the monarchy's friends before engaging her enemies.

Serbia did not stand naked in the international arena. Russia had since 1909 extended the shield of stolid Slavic solidarity to those whom its foreign office regarded as their little brothers. Suspicion was current in Austria that the Russian Minister in Serbia, Nikolai Hartwig, had had a hand in inflaming the passions of men who needed very little encouragement to become as violent as they were vicious.[24] Hartwig died of a sudden heart attack four days after the assassination of Franz Ferdinand, circumstance that the Serbians assigned publicly to Austrian perfidy and the Austrians privately to God's mercy.

France had determined that it would be better that Germany and Russia should fight one another than that France should fight either; it sought to make solid an alliance that for separate reasons each party found as useful as it was unnatural.[25] France was, moreover, Serbia's international creditor, and so scrupled at compromising a state eager to borrow money and willing to repay it.[26] Although nominally a member of the Triple Alliance, Italy prompted in Austria the same sense of suspicious distaste that Austria prompted in Italy. The Austro-Hungarian monarchy had in the summer of 1914 a friend in Imperial Germany. It was imperative to appeal tenderly to the sense of *brüderschaft* that bound Austria to Germany by language, custom, and treaty.[27]

Well before the assassination of Franz Ferdinand, officials commanding Austria's foreign affairs understood that the Balkans represented a threat to the monarchy's stability. Regional and national identities were often at odds. Serbians felt themselves Serbian and wondered why so many notional Serbians should be national Bosnians. For the whole of the nineteenth and early twentieth century, no map of the Balkans appeared fundamentally stable. The receding and advancing tides of Ottoman, Austrian, and Russian influence, although always in motion were never in phase, and at moments of turbulence, they threatened to involve the great powers in a conflict that not one of them could justify and few of them could grasp.

During the spring of 1914, Austrian officials entertained the hope, if not the prospect, of subordinating the Balkans to the domination of an empire that itself had no identity beyond its own existence. Berchtold asked his foreign office for an informed appraisal; he had in mind a new Austrian foreign policy, one full of mastery. On June 24, Berchtold approved the memorandum that he had himself commissioned.[28] Named after its author, Franz von Matscheko, the memorandum was designed to allow Austrian diplomacy the scope to deal with Austria's problems in the Balkans; but its ostensible focus was Romania, and not Serbia, evidence that the Austrian foreign ministry was prepared to discount a danger in plain sight in favor of an alliance with a state that, then as now, had nothing to offer its allies beyond its wheat and nothing to frighten its adversaries beyond its space.[29]

In June of 1914, Romania seemed interested neither in the Triple Alliance nor in the Entente. It was content to loom large in the thinking of both without weighing directly in the calculations of either. Although it shared no border with either Austria *or* Hungary, Bulgaria appealed to the Austrian foreign office, if only because a case could be made for its strategic importance as a buffer absorbing and so dispersing the downward pressure of the Russian empire. Having been humiliated by Serbia in the second Balkan war, Bulgaria, it seemed reasonable to Austrian diplomats to suppose, was ripe enough to poke, if not to pluck, and in 1915, after a year spent in frustrating neutrality, it *did* fall overripe into the Triple Alliance. The Matscheko memorandum occupied itself in soliciting, if not the alliance, then at least the neutrality of a state having every reason to endorse, and no need to deny, its solidarity of interests with the Austro-Hungarian empire.

With the exception of its large and almost perfect irrelevance to current events, the Matscheko memorandum seemed providential to Berchtold; it had the great merit of having been written, a circumstance of greater weight in diplomatic affairs than commonly supposed. To the original document, Berchtold added a postscript, one in which he addressed the Serbian threat that the memorandum had either discounted or dismissed. This he withheld from Tisza on the grounds that if Tisza approved of his postscript, its disclosure would be unnecessary, and if not, unwise. He persuaded Franz Joseph I to compose a *handgeschriebene* letter to the German Emperor, Wilhelm II, remarking on what both men must have known in their bones: an attack on one monarch was an attack on them all. To this, Berchtold added his own *Denkschrift*, closing with a melodramatic assurance that the Austrian eagle was determined to tear the net in which it was being enveloped. This image, since it called on a bird to raise a claw above its head, was, perhaps, not inspired in conception. Count Alex Hoyos of the *Ballhausplatz*, Austria's foreign office, was dispatched to Berlin. He departed on the 5th of July, 1914.

Hoyos was charged with conveying the revised Matscheko memorandum to the German Foreign Office. He quite understood that his real task was to assure German officials that their suspicions of habitual Austrian *schlamperei* notwithstanding, this time the Austrians meant what they said when they said that they meant business. The Austrian ambassador in Berlin, Count Ladislaus Szögyéni, secured an audience with the Kaiser, who read Berchtold's memorandum and Franz Joseph's note over lunch, and to Szögyéni's surprise, remained both measured and calm—signs, court intimates knew, indicating that shortly he would be neither. In the early afternoon, the Kaiser offered to Szögyéni the sense of encouraging indignation that so conspicuously he had withheld at lunch.

For all their differences, there trickled a stream of shy life between German and Austrian diplomatic and military figures. Like Berchtold, Theobald von Bethmann Hollweg, the German Chancellor, was widely thought lacking in martial ardor. The German military had seen no action in Europe in more than thirty years, a deficiency it was eager to make good, if not by winning a war then by waging one. It was a policy that the German Chief of Staff, Helmut von Moltke, had reason to revise or to regret on marching the German military into defeat at the Battle of the Marne. Unwilling to appear vacillating before von Moltke's stern stupid gaze, Bethmann Hollweg gave his assent to Austrian action without asking overmuch what form it might take. Hoyos left Berlin with what he had come to fetch, and that was a blank check.[30]

This seems more forthcoming than really it was. The amount of the check could be filled in at will, but not the date. German thinking was obvious. A sharp sudden Austrian blow might well catch Serbia's allies unprepared to take action, and if delivered smartly enough, unwilling to take revenge. There would be a peace conference. Things would sort themselves out. But a delay would allow Russia to recall that having concluded an alliance with France, she had previously concluded an agreement with Great Britain, and was thus in the attractive position of being able to recall one lover while being fondled by another.[31]

Hoyos returned to Vienna on the 6th of July. A fog now settled over the city. The Germans had asked for quick action, but the Austro-Hungarian empire was by nature slothful and by habit dilatory. Recognizing his power to impede war while doing nothing to promote peace, Tisza suggested to Conrad and Berchtold that before it be confronted by a military strike, Serbia be presented with a diplomatic ultimatum, one that should it be accepted would avert the need for military action and that should it be rejected would justify it. Sensing that the demand was dubious, neither Conrad nor Berchtold could determine how it should be denied. They thought to satisfy Tisza by preparing an ultimatum designed to be rejected, an exercise in low cunning obvious enough to be regretted by Austria's sympathizers and resented by her enemies.

Two weeks were occupied in the preparation of this squalid document. Although written by a reputed stylist, Baron Alexander von Musulum, the document that emerged was clumsy in its language and pointless in its effect, conveying not cool resolution but injured pride. Having scrupled over their ultimatum, Austrian officials neglected the fundamental caution of keeping what they were doing to themselves. They could see the need for secrecy, but while they could see the need, they could not satisfy the demand. Apprised of events taking place in Vienna, English officials, vexed as they were by the issue of Home Rule, were indifferent to their implications, either failing to grasp Austria's intentions or discounting them entirely; but Russian officials were determined to prevent an Austrian ultimatum from being delivered to Serbia, and to act on Serbia's behalf should it be delivered and then rejected. Russian foreign policy was hardly a model of steadfast lucidity. Sergei Sazanov, Russia's foreign minister, had acquired influence as Pyotr Stolypin's brother-in-law, and in his access to power, he had been pushed from below as well as pulled from above.[32] If his supporters were unable, and his detractors unwilling, to admire his previous accomplishments, this was because he had few that they could note and none that they could admire. To some members of the Imperial Duma, he seemed preferable to his predecessor, Alexander Izvolsky, and to others worse. Izvolsky had achieved an understanding with Great Britain, but he failed to appreciate, or adroitly oppose, Austria's annexation of Bosnia. His political opponents had regarded Austria's Bosnian *démarche* as a provocation and were able to use a diplomatic provocation as a political pretext. Sazanov was energetic and dapper, but he was sometimes erratic and often a blabbermouth, and while as a professional diplomat, he understood very well the ropes in play in the international arena, all too frequently he pulled on them at once, and if he did not do so in fact, he gave the impression that he was doing so anyway.[33]

Historians have remarked that Sazanov did much to provoke, while doing as much to prevent, the outbreak of war. Both judgments are correct. Informed of the Austrian ultimatum, now emerging in stages from various anxious or eager Austrian pens, Sazanov subjected Austria's ambassador, Count Frigyes Szápáry, to a peevish and hectoring interview in which he warned of war, alluded ominously to Russia's steadfastness in support of Serbia, and suggested incoherently that by withdrawing its ultimatum, Austria might yet achieve all of its diplomatic goals without ever employing any of its diplomatic means. The interview served no obvious purpose beyond persuading Szápáry of Sazanov's emotional lability.

At the moment of its crisis, the European balance of power reposed in the hands of diplomats whose skill might have sufficed in peace, and would prove entirely irrelevant in war, but were demonstrably inadequate during the interregnum between peace and war in July of 1914. The men who made the First World War, or who allowed it to be made, were curiously modern in their outlook, their temperament, their education, and their training. They were mediocrities.[34] British diplomat Sir Edward Gray had read classics at Oxford, but unlike Britain's Prime Minister Herbert Asquith, who had, at least, obtained a classical scholarship to Balliol, he was able, given the demand to translate from the Greek and Latin on sight, to progress no further than a few spastic barks. He wisely concluded his education in another field of study.[35] Berchtold had determined to be resolute well before resolution was required, and if his policies led to the destruction of the empire that he was charged with defending, he would remain, he remarked to an acquaintance, an aristocrat after he ceased to be an Austro-Hungarian.[36] Bethmann Hollweg was by nature gloomy and saturnine, and during the spring and summer of 1914, he was apprehensive about his wife's health and then saddened by her death. Having the Tsar's ear and thereafter his confidence, Sazanov was in his element, but he had set himself the difficult task of advancing Russia's interests *in* the Balkans while at the same time assuaging

Austro-Hungarian anxieties *about* the Balkans. A more adroit diplomat might have achieved both aims and a more forthright diplomat just one of them. Sazanov was able to achieve neither.

Berchtold and Bethmann Hollweg were men, like Gray, trained in, or exposed to, the subjects of law and political administration. They were ignorant of nineteenth-century science; they had no strong religious commitments; and beyond representing their country's interests, they had no other interests, and so no other commitments to which they were dedicated. Like Izvolsky, Sazanov was a graduate of the Tsarskoye Selo Lyceum, an institution similar to the French École Polytechnique in its attitudes and ideals, and like the École, the Lyceum afforded its graduates the entirely unjustified sense that by having spent three years in its classrooms, directly they would be able to master events beyond its halls. Poincaré entered French political life as a hard, shrewd, bombastic provincial attorney and economist, a master of a peculiarly French oratorical style, at once empty and fustian; but alone among his peers, Poincaré could boast of propinquity to genius, since his cousin was Henri Poincaré. Had the cousins reversed their roles, French political life might well have been improved. The foreign ministers of the great powers were in July of 1914 not so much helpless as unimaginative. They could, and sometimes they did, appreciate the fact that they were running risks, but not one of them, until it was far too late, had the power to appreciate the magnitude of the risks that they were running.

Throughout the July crisis, England appeared to the other great powers as a ship in the fog. They could sense that she was there. They could not determine where she was going. Secure in the thought that in the event of war with Germany, it would have a Russian ally and an English friend, France was belligerent, an attitude that allowed its military leaders, who had not by themselves prevailed in conflict since the Napoleonic era, to abandon all measures to defend France by advancing various schemes to attack Germany.[37] Russia was throughout vainglorious; Austria, insecure; and Germany by turns bombastic, concerned, morose, and fatalistic.

Not one of the great powers was shrewd, and none understood its own interests well enough to defend them.

The Austrian ultimatum was delivered to Serbian officials late on the 23rd of July, almost a month after the assassination of Franz Ferdinand. European diplomats had resigned themselves to his loss, the European public, to his absence. Flustered Serbian officials were unwilling to accept the Austrian ultimatum in person and unable to read it in German. It is a pity that they did not try harder and try harder at once. Austria was asking little enough of Serbia, so little that one wonders, in fact, why they bothered asking anything at all.[38] The ultimatum made no demands that the Serbian government could not evade with ease or ignore with impunity.[39] A show of Serbian compliance would have left Austrian officials fuming in frustration. There is some evidence that a few members of the government of Prime Minister Nikola Păsić thought originally to accept the Austrian ultimatum without demurral, until Sazanov, in a careless but characteristic gesture of irresponsibility, encouraged them peevishly to scruple at one or two Austrian demands.[40]

Păsić delayed acceding to Austria's ultimatum as he searched for a way in which he might delay acceding to anything at all. He had not survived unwounded in the jungle of Serbian politics by acting vigorously. In moments of crisis, he preferred to scuttle. The response the Serbians finally offered the Austrians on the 25th of July was as incompetent as the ultimatum that the Austrians had presented the Serbians, an exercise in cunning as low as the original. Having *agreed* to eight of the ten Austrian demands, Serbian officials hoped that Austria would overlook the other two and regard its note as a gesture of compliance. On noting that the Serbians had *rejected* two of its demands, the Austrians discounted the other eight and regarded the Serbian note as a gesture of defiance. Each side got not what it wished, but what it deserved.

Russia had during the same week begun what it called partial mobilization, a charade designed to persuade the Germans that despite the fact that the Russian state was sopping wet, it was unacquainted with water. No one was fooled, least of all the Germans. The Russian military, as short-sighted as it was over-confident, began to preen itself in the glow of its imagined victories.

On the 23rd of July, Poincaré, the President of the French Republic, and his foreign minister, René Viviani, found themselves in St. Petersburg on a state visit, one lasting until the 26th of July. They were thus in St. Petersburg as Austria and Serbia handed matches to each other under circumstances that made it likely that one of them would be lit. The exchange between French and Russian officials was obviously of importance, but there is little in the documentary record of either state that affords the historian a sure sense of what took place when private meetings were held. Poincaré offered the Russians nothing by way of substance, but after every one of his speeches, he was gratified to imagine, their souls had felt him like the thunder's roll.

Viviani was out of sorts during what was in every respect a state visit, and he discharged some obligations while appearing ill and avoided others by appearing green. He seems, in fact, to have suffered a nervous breakdown and was seen muttering incomprehensibly to himself. A martial and a festive air prevailed throughout. A twittering group of beautiful young women in the Tsar's entourage were overheard urging war on young French officers eager for their favor. The beautiful young women were destined within just a few years to die violently or disappear into exile. Although nominally the head of an autocratic state, the Tsar found himself unable to resist the swell of military enthusiasm and, alternately hectored or cajoled by his advisors, agreed to actions that he could not control.[41]

It was not in Vienna but in Berlin that a window briefly opened and was as quickly shut. Kaiser Wilhelm II was known to his critics, and appreciated at his court, as a statesman who under ordinary circumstances tended to be bombastic to the point of moral witlessness. Serbian officials had managed to answer the Austrian ultimatum within the forty-eight hours given them as a deadline, and so required one-seventh the time to express their regret at the assassination of Franz Ferdinand as the Austrians had required to express their indignation. They devoted to their reply a kind of frantic care. Passages were crossed out, re-written, or written over. On reading the Serbian reply to Austria, the German Kaiser was not only moderate but perceptive, seeing at once that if properly understood, it removed the causes of war by offering Austria what it most required, and that was a salve to its honor. Of all the political sentiments, a sense of injured dignity is the most difficult to assuage, and Germany was faced with diplomatic imbroglio requiring great skill if it were to persuade the Austrians to allow their dignity to be soothed by appearances instead of being jeopardized by force. German statesmen, the Kaiser included, briefly contemplated the absurdity of defending a cause in Austria that the Serbians had apparently ceded, but no one in the German foreign office had the nerve or the resoluteness to force the Austrians to back away from a conflict that the Germans had themselves carelessly encouraged. Until the very moment that Austria declared war on Serbia, Bethmann Hollweg had conveyed to the Kaiser the impression that the crisis that he had done so much to inflame, he could manage to deflame, an undertaking violating both the laws of politics and physics, but his idea of fire control had all along been to encourage the Austrians in their convictions while suggesting to the Kaiser that he was discouraging them in their resolutions.

Austria declared war on Serbia on the 28th of July, 1914. It was a declaration that conveyed menace but that did not express force. The Austrian army, Conrad explained patiently to his colleagues, would require a further two weeks to gather itself, and could not take the field before the 12th of August. Why during the previous four weeks, it had not prepared itself at all, his colleagues did not ask, and Conrad did not say. Austria's declaration of war allowed Serbia to conduct its own mobilization in almost perfect tranquility, and when later in August, Austrian troops invaded Serbia, they were shocked that Serbian troops were well-entrenched and willing to defend what Austrian officials considered a terrorist state and Serbian officials a site of national redemption.

With the Austrian declaration of war, the Kaiser was at last disabused. Germany faced an unenviable choice between dishonor and war. Whether the war would be one waged among Russia, Germany, and Austria or would engage all of the great powers was a matter in German hands.

The decisive moment had arrived.

§

If Germany acted without hesitation, and apparently without reflection, this was owing to the morbid, indeed, the fatal, disjunction between the imbecility of its strategic appreciation and the sophistication of its tactical deployments. In looking at the map of Europe, some German politicians, and all of its military leaders, had concluded with alarm that Germany was surrounded, an observation that, since Germany's position as a central European state was undeniable, was both trivially true and strategically irrelevant. In order to avoid a war on two fronts, German military planners, under the direction of Alfred von Schlieffen, had determined to overcome their enemies by attacking them one after the other. To strike at Russia, Germany would first attack France. The Schlieffen plan accumulated weight in the years from 1891 to 1914; it became entrenched in German military thinking. And it contained a dreadful flaw. To strike at France, the German military would need first to violate Belgian neutrality.

The state of Prussia had in 1839 been among the European powers guaranteeing Belgian neutrality, an obligation that the German empire, since it had absorbed the Prussian state, had acquired and then accepted. Whatever the military advantages of a flanking attack on the French army, they were outweighed by its liabilities. To attack France through

Belgium would be to invite war with England. In order, thus, to avoid fighting against two enemies at once, German military planners anticipated a war in which they would be obliged to fight against three of them. This consideration was understood; it was recognized; and it was ignored. On the 30th of July, the Tsar, torn between a prudent sense that he was inviting disaster, and a morbid unwillingness to appear weak before his advisors, issued and then cancelled and then re-issued an order for general mobilization.

The nerves of the sluggish Russian military bureaucracy began to respond. The great beast came to sullen life. Showing every indication that they did not quite know what they were doing, or why they were doing it, German officials demanded that the Russian mobilization be reversed by issuing an ultimatum as likely to be effective as the Austrian ultimatum to Serbia. Full of the bounce of misplaced self-confidence, France ordered its own forces to a general mobilization on the 1st of August, 1914. It had invested all of its prestige and some of its confidence in the Russian Behemoth, now gathering force behind the screen of the Russian border. The thought that under the circumstances doing nothing might be preferable to doing anything did not occur to any French diplomat.

Germany, its ultimatum to Russia having been ignored or otherwise rejected, followed on the same day. Men in the German foreign office who a week earlier were concerned but not yet alarmed by events, now undertook that odd maneuver that was to become common to all diplomatic services: they gave up any rational appreciation of events by appealing to the impression that the die had somehow been cast. There is no evidence whatsoever in the diplomatic record that the Germans had wished for this day, but if the day was not wished for, the Germans were nevertheless prepared to seize it, and so German policy found itself best expressed by two Latin maxims: *alea iacta est*, and *carpe diem*, the first an observation, the second, an injunction. On the 1st of August, Germany declared war on Russia. German statesmen, liberated from the constraints of rational policy and free thus to dream, saw Europe at their feet, and if not at their feet, then under their heel. The European state system began to smolder ominously.

By August of 1914, Europe was either in flames, or about to be so.

§

The political and military leaders of both the Alliance and the Entente proved themselves largely incapable of conducting the war that they had done little to avoid and much to provoke. Nine million combatants, and at least six million civilians, died in the First World War.[42] States that had in the nineteenth century prided themselves on their statistical sophistication found themselves unable accurately to count their dead, a pattern that was to continue as the century advanced.

The First World War ended in an Armistice, one signed on November 11th, 1918. While the Allied powers were convinced that they had won the war, the Axis powers were not persuaded that they had lost it. They were relieved of their illusions at the Paris Peace Conference of 1919. The consequences of the First World War were ramified throughout Europe and the world. Four world empires had advanced into battle during the beginning of the war and withdrawn into oblivion at its end.[43] If the Axis powers failed properly to calculate the cost, or the nature, of defeat, the Allied powers neglected to consider the price, or the consequences, of victory. The global economic order stood compromised. Free trade did not return to pre-war levels until the late twentieth century. The European standard of living declined after the First World War, and in Russia, Germany, and the Balkans, it declined dramatically.[44] Civil liberties within the Allied countries were abridged to ensure victory, and among the Axis powers, to avoid defeat. They did not recover.

In central Europe, multi-ethnic empires had once protected from their enemies, and as often from themselves, states that were now independent, or wished to be so: Austria, Poland, Czechoslovakia, Slovenia, Hungary, Bosnia, Herzegovina, parts of the Ukraine, parts of the Italian Tyrol. These were states that, while proud of their identities, had no means of protecting their integrity. Throughout the Middle East, as the hand of the Ottoman Empire fell lifeless, the map designating territories from Morocco in the west to Turkey in the east acquired a lurid glow, one inviting European statesmen to create states whose borders had no justification in terms either of history or tradition, and whose identity seemed certain to guarantee that all they could expect in common would be conflict, war, bitterness, and rancor.[45]

If the Austro-Hungarian and Ottoman empires had been tested in war and found wanting—they lost, after all—the nation states of Europe were both weakened and corrupted by the war. No one thought to repose their confidence in the Balance of Powers, but when attempts were made to subordinate national interests to larger European institutions such as the League of Nations, it was discovered that states with common interests had no reason to appeal to the League, and states without, no reason to fear it.

When the war ended, Allied and Axis political and military leaders rushed to the lamp in order to compose their memoirs. Each statesman assigned responsibility for the outbreak of war to his opposite number, and each military leader determined that the war would have been more rapidly concluded had his advice been better followed.[46]

If the historical literature about the First World War is vast, it is also profoundly unsatisfying. "Life can only be understood backwards," Søren Kierkegaard remarked, "but it must be lived forward." The history of the First World War offers a counter-example. Historians understand very well how the war came about, but they have not grasped and cannot fully fathom why it did. What makes analysis so frustrating is the multiplication of counter-factual conditions. The steps are there in plain sight: the assassination in Sarajevo, the Austrian ultimatum, the blank check, the decision to violate Belgian neutrality; but while these steps collectively give the impression of causal sufficiency—they did the job, after all—they fail to give the impression of causal necessity.[47] Things might have been otherwise. What a pity that they were not.

Citing the work of the English statistician, Lewis Richardson, Steven Pinker is concerned to argue that the First World War, and all of the others, as well, occurred for no good reason whatsoever. At "every instant," he writes, "Mars, the god of war, rolls his iron dice, and if they turn up snake eyes, he sends a pair of nations to war."[48] But the First World War was made by men and not gods, and no examination of any of the events leading to its occurrence indicates in the slightest that the actors in the drama were throwing dice. How, then, did randomness enter into their affairs?[49]

An analysis of the First World War fully adequate to its magnitude would require a work comparable to St. Augustine's *The City of God.* Augustine quite understood that no tracery of causes and their effects could begin to explain the historical catastrophe enveloping the Mediterranean world as an ancient and profound order among men underwent dissolution. Augustine could grasp what he could not otherwise explain only by a radical reinterpretation of human history. The categories to which he appealed are no longer available to historical analysis. And this, too, was a fact expressed by the First World War and ratified thereafter by its historians.

The First World War was a catastrophe for European civilization because it destroyed its moral structure. The war demonstrated to European statesmen and their military leaders that they had misjudged, and misjudged profoundly, the ground over which they were walking. They had imagined that their system was so conceived as to be continuous in its fundamental aspect and that a general European war among all of the great powers would be like a local European war among some of them. They were mistaken. The First World War was nothing like the Balkan wars. Or any other war in European memory. It was more terrible. Like Charles Darwin, writing sixty years before, they had placed their confidence in continuity, a law of proportionality, and so they had vested their hopes in the idea that by a progressive augmentation or withdrawal of force in battle, they could come to master the brute contingencies of violence. They failed to understand that violence has a life of its own. The affairs between the great powers were subject to *no* law of proportionality.

Those who had survived the First World War and who were in a position to compare what had vanished with what had remained were consumed by a sense of bitter historical nostalgia. Before the First World War, both the Austro-Hungarian and the Ottoman empires were thought to be tottering, decrepit, and corrupt political structures. Writers disposed to ridicule or otherwise dismiss them when they existed were equally disposed to lament their disappearance when it was too late to encourage their revival. In his appreciation of the vanished Austro-Hungarian empire, *Die Welt von Gestern*, Stefan Zweig recalled the sense of *sicherheit* that it provided, its solid and enduring institutions placidly occupying space and continuously occupying time. The word *sicherheit* is translated into English as security, but it has in German an additional epistemological connotation, *sicherheit* designating a form of certainty, as well. *Sicher ist sicher* means that what is certain *is* certain.

If bitter nostalgia was one response to the First World War, dread was another, and as the first was appropriate, the second was prophetic. The war allowed the sewers of nineteenth-century history to break the surface of European life and for thirty years they foamed and bubbled over every European institution, blighting whatever they touched with their own ghastly iridescence.[50] In both Nazi Germany and Soviet Russia, novel forms of political organization appeared, and while historians may have exaggerated their resemblance to each other, both were radically unlike any structures that had appeared in the past. When the twentieth century stands condemned, it is not simply because of the terrible, the unpardonable, things that took place within its ambit, but because it introduced into the human imagination possibilities of political organization that were bleak and unrelieved and terrible. Once seen, these possibilities could not be unseen.

No one doubted that European society had been weighed in the balances and found wanting.

2. The Best of Times

They were men enough to face the darkness.

—Joseph Conrad[1]

In the early years of the fifth century AD, a Spanish priest named Paulus Orosius had occasion to publish a work entitled *Historiarum Adversum Paganos Libri VII*— Seven Books of History against the Pagans. Orosius was a disciple of Saint Augustine. It was the purpose of the seven books to provide a defense of Christianity against the common pagan charge that Christianity accelerated, if it did not cause, the decline of the Roman Empire. Orosius met this dubious challenge by reversing its polarity. If things were in the fifth century bad, he argued, once they were worse. His book is a tedious account of the violence, brutality, and stupidity of the pagan past.[2]

Saint Augustine, who had initially welcomed Orosius as a collaborator, in short order rejected him as a schnook.

§

The twentieth century began in August of 1914.[3] It has not been a century that has enhanced the dignity of the human race. Only five years after it began, the Russian poet Anna Akhmatova asked whether it was worse than any of the others.[4]

It was *much* worse.

Two hundred and thirty-one million men, women, and children died violently in the twentieth century, shot over open pits, murdered in secret police cellars, asphyxiated in Nazi gas ovens, worked to death in Arctic mines or timber camps, the victims of deliberately contrived famines or lunatic industrial experiments, whole populations ravaged by alien armies, bombed to smithereens, or sent to wander in their exiled millions across all the violated borders of Europe and Asia.[5] The Holocaust and the Gulag have become symbols of the twentieth century, but if they are prominent as symbols, they are not unique as abominations. The Chinese Civil War took place from 1927 to 1936 and, after an interregnum in which those belligerents who had previously fought one another found reason to fight the Japanese, resumed with undiminished industry in 1945; it caused millions of deaths, no party to the conflict much burdened by the blood that had been shed. John King Fairbank's *China: A New History* offers no death tolls, an omission that would be unthinkable in the case of the Holocaust.[6]

A generation of scholars has made the Ukrainian famine of the early 1930s—the Holodomor—if not well known, then, at least, known well, but the earlier Soviet famine of 1921 has slipped out of the stream of memory, and the Soviet famine of 1947, in which at least one million Soviet citizens starved to death, is neither well known nor known well.[7] The Federal Republic of Germany has been willing to acknowledge the crimes of its predecessor; but in east Prussia, the Red Army, in its revenge, destroyed a society fully as old and as rooted in the European experience as the Jewish society of eastern Europe. Thereafter between twelve and fifteen million ethnic Germans were expelled from their homes, properties, and the lives they had known, and over the course of the two years between 1945 and 1947, sent into exile in the withered German state in which they had never lived and to which they were bound only by the decayed tie of the German language.[8] Yet the expulsion of the ethnic Germans from eastern and central Europe bears comparison to the partition of India and dwarfs completely all population expulsions in the Middle East.[9]

At the end of *The Struggle for Mastery in Europe*, A. J. P. Taylor remarked of the period between the Congress of Berlin in 1878 and the outbreak of the First World War that "Europe had never known such peace and tranquility since the age of the Antonines."[10] One would not have imagined in the nineteenth century that the world could spare so much blood or that it would have conceived the desire to shed it.[11]

§

Robert Southey was a poet, a dreamer, and a dunce. Born in 1774, he died in 1843. Like Wordsworth, he had been a supporter of the French revolution; and, like Wordsworth, he had been disappointed by the revolution that he had supported. He was determined not to be disappointed again. In 1824, Southey published *Sir Thomas More, or Colloquies on the Progress and Prospects of Society.* Profoundly attached to the English countryside, and especially the Lake District, Southey used his *Colloquies* to express a fastidious objection to the degradation of rural life.

To Thomas Babington Macaulay, Southey appeared a man at once out of place, out of touch, and, so far as *he* was concerned, out of time. Southey? Pooh-pooh. The man had been wrong about the past. How could he be right about the future?

> It is not strange that, differing so widely from Mr. Southey as to the past progress of society, we should differ from him also as to its probable destiny. He thinks, that to all outward appearance, the country is hastening to destruction... [W]e rely on the natural tendency of the human intellect to truth, and of the natural tendency of society to improvement.[12]

Why the tendency is natural, Macaulay did not say, and that it exists, he did not demonstrate.

The response to Macaulay came late, but it fell heavily. In 1931, the historian Herbert Butterfield published a little tract entitled *The Whig Interpretation of History.* The book is an indictment of various Whig historians, but Butterfield managed the difficult trick of faulting them by reputation largely without mentioning them by name. Butterfield was sly and, beyond the criticisms that he made of the Whig interpretation of history, he managed to suggest that, like Southey, the Whig historians were in their own way sentimental provincials.

Where had they gone wrong? Southey had seen the early nineteenth century as part of a long historical decline. Things had gone badly and they were getting worse. The Whig historians reversed his error without cancelling its effect. They sought to

> impose a certain form upon the whole historical story, and to produce a scheme of general history which is bound to converge beautifully upon the present—all demonstrating throughout the ages the workings of *an obvious principle of progress*. [emphasis added][13]

It is a principle that has had a deforming effect on historical narrative. "A caricature of this result," Butterfield adds, "is to be seen in a popular view that is still not quite eradicated: the view that the Middle Ages represented a period of darkness when man was kept tongue-tied by authority—a period against which the Renaissance was the reaction and the Reformation the great rebellion."[14]

Almost one hundred years later, this caricature of medieval history retains an unquenchable vitality.[15]

And so does the Whig interpretation of history.

§

If it is difficult to look at the twentieth century with a steady eye, so terrible are its crimes, the temptation is great to allow one's eye to wander. Steven Pinker is, in this regard, one step away from clinical strabismus. Things are today not so bad, Pinker writes in *The Better Angels of Our Nature*, and since they were once worse, they must have been getting better.

> Believe it or not... violence has declined over long stretches of time, and today we may be living in the most peaceable era in our species' existence... it is an unmistakable development.[16]

This thesis, Pinker believes, has been widely overlooked, or as often denied, because historians, lacking access to the perspective vouchsafed Pinker, have failed to see the Big Picture, the one that emerges in the majestic sweep of centuries. *The Better Angels of Our Nature* has not been warmly embraced by historians, but neither has it been coldly rejected.[17]

Pinker maintains, of course, that his conclusions are scientific and quantitative.[18] Whether they are for this reason *true* is another question.

The years between the end of the Second World War and 2010 or 2011, Pinker designates the long peace.[19] It is a peace that encompassed the Chinese Communist revolution, the partition of India, the Great Leap Forward, the ignominious Cultural Revolution, the suppression of Tibet, the Korean War, the French and American wars of Indochinese succession, the Egypt-Yemen war, the Franco-Algerian war, the Israeli-Arab wars, the genocidal Pol Pot regime, the grotesque and sterile Iranian revolution, the Iran-Iraq war, ethnic cleansings in Rwanda, Burundi, and the former Yugoslavia, the farcical Russian and American invasions of Afghanistan, the American invasion of Iraq, and various massacres, sub-continental famines, squalid civil insurrections, bloodlettings, throat-slittings, death squads, theological infamies, and suicide bombings taking place from Latin America to East Timor. Alone, broken, incompetent, and unloved, the Soviet Union lumbered into oblivion in 1989. The twentieth century had come to an end.

§

Violence is not an uncontested idea. The dictionary, which defines violence as "behavior involving physical force intended to hurt, damage, or kill someone," is of no help. Behavior is no necessary part of violence since laws, institutions, attitudes and judgments may all be violent, and physical force is no sufficient condition for violence, since the threat of violence is often as effective in compelling behavior as its administration. Violence is neither exhausted nor expressed very precisely by any obvious measure. If the idea is allowed to encompass a stellar explosion as well as an animal attack, then it is too broad profitably to allow historians to draw the distinction between a violent battle and a violent crime, and, if not, then too narrow to describe them both. An act may be violent in degrees; or it may be violent in effect; violence may be obvious or disguised; systematic or haphazard and even incidental; it may be overt or subtle; there are violent states and violent societies, and whether violence is a matter of action or the disposition to action, violence by itself is not obviously an ordinary cause leading to an ordinary effect. A man may simmer with violence for years without acting, and another may act violently for years without simmering.[20] Some men may be disposed to violence. Cross them at your peril. But if, preceded by their reputation, these men are never crossed, what remains to be assessed? If a violent act is violent only in virtue of some antecedent violent intention, it is equally true that an intention to do violence is revealed only when someone acts violently. How else would we know? Violence appears analytically as a state or emotional condition, but also as an act or disposition to action. It may simmer, boil, erupt, explode, seethe or subside; or seep, ooze, infect, derange, madden, escalate or intensify; it may be confined, regulated, distributed, sealed off; or liberate, intoxicate and purge; it may be insensate, demented, irrational, careless or incidental; or muted, indirect, verbal, or hidden; and as these constructions might indicate, there is nothing obvious or isolated that *by itself* answers to the name of violence. Like greed, generosity, love, cupidity, cunning, or artfulness, violence is a part of a dense matrix in which everything is held in suspension by the reciprocating pistons of human nature.[21]

These are circumstances to which sociologists believe that they are adequate. "For the last few years," Gerd Schwerhoff observed, "the homicide rate has been regarded as a quantifiable indicator of the degree of violence in a particular period."[22] Is it? A society in which homicide rates are very high is a violent society, but the reverse is not obviously true, and in the twentieth century, societies of almost incomprehensible violence were often in a position to observe that if their concentration camps were full, their streets were safe. German homicide rates fell to their lowest level since 1882 in 1939; they have remained relatively stable for more than 70 years.[23]

In 1937, Stalin reduced the Soviet Union to a state of gibbering terror.[24] In his account of the Great Terror, *Moscow 1937*, Karl Schlögel argued that some 1.5 million men and women were shot or died in miserable captivity in the Gulag.[25] To paralyze a large and complex society by fear is itself an achievement in violence, for those paralyzed are afraid of violent death. Violence is not simply a matter of what is done but what might be done. No account of twentieth-century violence that does not encompass this distinction can be judged very sophisticated. Soviet *homicide* statistics for 1937, when execution cellars in the Lubyanka prison were crowded and fields outside of Moscow began bubbling with decomposing corpses, are notoriously unreliable, but given the Stalinist regime's determination to re-describe even public urination as counter-revolutionary hooliganism, purely apolitical homicides, if they were recorded at all, must have been low, the occasional ax-murderer much appreciated for his willingness to balance the books.[26]

§

Homicide rates are expressed as the ratio **H/P** of the number of homicides **H** to the population **P** of a city, region, state, county, country, or even the world. The rate is most commonly given per annum, and the ensuing ratio normalized: **H/P** x 100,000. In the ratio **H/P**, **H** designates a reference attribute, and **P**, a reference class. Both are necessary. To say that there are, or were, five dead men without providing a reference class would be like saying there are, or were, three fat women.[27]

The reference class in homicide statistics is inevitably an historical, social, or legal artifact. Homicide rates are, for this reason, arbitrary, a point evident in a number of examples. Suppose that an imaginary region or city **C** is partitioned into five smaller regions R_1, R_2, R_3, R_4, and R_5. Homicide and population figures are as follows:[28]

R_1 = 200,000; **H** = 50.

R_2 = 50,000; **H** = 0.

R_3 = 50,000; **H** = 0.

R_4 = 50,000; **H** = 0.

R_5 = 50,000; **H** = 0.

The homicide rate assigned to **C** is **H/C** = 12.5 per 100,000. What is unclear, because it is ambiguous, is the homicide rate assigned to R_1. This is where the dead are stacked. Should **H/**R_1 be 12.5 per 100,000? R_1 is, after all, a part of **C**. This would seem a reduction in violence achieved by a sleight of hand. The dead are still the dead, and they have not been diminished. Since $\mathbf{H/P} \to 0$ as $\mathbf{P} \to \infty$, homicide rates may always be reduced by an expansion of their reference class.

Albert Reiss has, on the other hand, argued that so far as homicides go, what is required is "a measure of [the] population that is exposed to the events, or is at risk of being involved in events, such as offenders or victims."[29] This might suggest that, far from being 12.5 per 100,000, the homicide rate assigned R_1 should be the one that measures *its* victims: **H/**R_1 = 25 per 100,000. This tactic, once encouraged, has a tendency to get out of hand as well. It is always possible, after all, to partition a reference class P into two classes P_1 and P_2, such that $\mathbf{P} = P_1 \cup P_2$, $P_1 = \mathbf{H}$, and $P_2 = \{\mathbf{P{-}H}\}$. It follows that $\mathbf{H}/P_1 = 1$, and $\mathbf{H}/P_2 = 0$. No statistic serves better than **H** to measure the "population that... is at risk of being involved in events," and no statistic serves better than **{P–H}** to measure the reverse. (These issues appear again a few pages below. There is no getting rid of them.)

The arguments just given suggest that, so far as R_1 is concerned, its homicide rate should be 25 *or* 12.5 per 100,000. It cannot be both; and no one, I presume, is tempted to say that it should be neither.

Homicide rates are compelling as a statistic because they convey risk as a probability. Selected at random from some reference class **P**, an individual may observe that his risk of death by homicide is **H/P**, which is another way of saying that he stands an **H** in **P** chance of being killed. The problem lies with the definition of the appropriate reference class. Without a reference class, there is no measure of risk; without a measure of risk, no way to persuade a man to watch his back. But to talk of risk, death, and chance in terms of **H/P** is already to assume that **H/P** has been assigned to **P** as its homicide rate. That is just the question: Has it? And, if so, how?

These questions are an encouragement to what Hans Reichenbach called reference-class ambiguities. "If we are asked to find the probability holding for an individual future event," Reichenbach wrote, "we must first incorporate the case in a suitable reference class. An individual thing or event may be incorporated in many reference classes, from which different probabilities will result."[30]

Many reference classes? Yes, certainly. One and the same man may be resident in Corleone, Sicily, Italy, Europe, and, beyond that, the world; in endeavoring to measure *his* chance of violent death, *he* finds himself confronted by an embarrassment of risks. It all depends. It depends on whether *he* is described as a citizen of the world, Europe, Italy, Sicily, or Corleone. Described as a citizen of Corleone, it then makes a considerable difference whether he is described as a Mafioso or as a mortician. These dependencies suggest that homicide rates are unstable as statistics, and, if so, unreliable as indicators of violence.

§

For anyone wishing to argue that once things were worse than they are now, the Middle Ages are ideal. It is widely supposed that having gotten out of them was one of the accomplishments of modern civilization. No contemporary *scholar*, one might think, would make such a mistake in judgment. A one-man multitude, Pinker champions the case to the contrary. "The people of the middle ages were, in a word, gross."[31]

Gross?

They ate with their hands, blew their noses with their fingers, belched copiously at table, and "took only perfunctory measures to keep their coitus private."[32]

In time freed from public fornication, the men of the thirteenth and fourteenth centuries were occupied in killing one another in tavern brawls or over tavern wenches; at the dinner table, lacking access to the fork, they used their knives to settle slights as well as scores.[33]

How they made time to eat remains a mystery.

In an essay entitled "Interpersonal Violence in English Society: 1300-1980," Lawrence Stone argued that homicide rates in Britain were in the past very much higher than they now are.[34] Crime is not the historian's habitual prowling ground; Stone's essay served to anoint criminology with the oil of his unexpected approval.[35] What had caught Stone's eye was an essay published in 1981 by Ted Gurr, "Historical Trends in Violent Crime: a Critical Review of the Evidence."[36] Gurr wrote as a scout for scholars, and in his interpretation of thirteenth-, fourteenth-, and fifteenth-century English history, he relied upon two sources: James Given's Stanford Ph.D. dissertation, *Society and Homicide in Thirteenth-Century England*,[37] and Carl Hammer's essay, "Patterns of Homicide in a Medieval University Town: Fourteenth-Century Oxford."[38] The incidence of homicide in Britain, Gurr argued, Stone wallowing manfully in his wake, "has fallen by a factor of at least ten to one since the thirteenth century."[39] Gurr illustrated his essay by a brilliantly simple graph. No one could fail to appreciate its meaning. When it came to murder, what had been up had come down. Some twenty-two years after Gurr published his essay, criminologist Manuel Eisner reported that he could see just what Gurr had seen: a striking 800-year decline in the English homicide rate. Gurr's original essay, Eisner remarked, "easily qualifies as one of the most influential studies in the field of history of crime research."[40]

Gurr's essay has by now become that rarest of things in historical scholarship: it is its own best source.

The thesis that there has been an 800-year decline in homicide owes much to the peculiar circumstance that Gurr's essay has been widely read but rarely studied. Beyond arguing broadly that down is down, Gurr did not argue much at all. The curve that connects Gurr's data points was, as Gurr suavely affirms, drawn by hand. It has no statistical justification. Data points between the fourteenth and fifteenth centuries are missing. Both Oxford and London diverge widely from what would appear to be the mean homicide rate for the thirteenth and fourteenth centuries, and London in the fourteenth century diverges from itself by a factor of three. Although Gurr's diagram covers eight hundred years, it lacks intra-century markers. To the right of the diagram, there is an incomprehensible squiggle. Of the diagram's twenty-one data points, only four are labeled. None is sourced, Gurr appealing both to Given and to Hammer, as if *they* shared joint ownership of *his* graph. Given based his study on medieval Eyre court records; Hammer, on medieval coroner rolls. There is "no other medieval document," Hammer commented in defense of his choice, "which can bring us closer to the truth of the matter."[41] The methodological discrepancy between Given and Hammer is not one that Gurr mentions.

Of the cities represented on Gurr's graph, it is fourteenth-century Oxford that has caused a number of eyebrows to hoist themselves up: **H/P** = 121 per 100,000.[42] This figure brings medieval Oxford into companionship with various exhilarating Latin American drug domains. A careful scholar, Hammer understood that these figures were absurd. Medieval Oxford was a young man's town; murder is a young man's game. Hammer addressed this problem by asking what the homicide rate for Oxford would have been were Oxford's population represented by an age-adjusted population?

> If, on this basis, we were to calculate a revised or adjusted homicide rate (victim) we would arrive at a figure of 60 to 80 per 100,000 for a normal population, still very high but exceeding experienced rates in large American metropolitan areas by no more than about three or four times. *No doubt there are neighborhoods in New Orleans, Atlanta or Detroit, many times larger than medieval Oxford, the homicide rates of which match or exceed that of the medieval borough.* [emphasis added][43]

Since they were less alarming in fact than they became in fiction, homicide rates in medieval Oxford have become grimmer in the telling. To Hammer, the original sources suggested a neighborhood of New Orleans, Atlanta, or Detroit; to Gurr, "a society in which men... were easily provoked to violent anger and were unrestrained in the brutality with which they attacked their opponents";[44] to Stone, "the highest homicide rates recorded anywhere in the west";[45] and to Pinker, no doubt, a region of Gehenna.

§

James Given wrote as a student of thirteenth- and fourteenth-century English Eyre courts.[46] Instruments of royal justice, Eyre courts convened in English shires at intervals ranging from months to years. They served to settle on terms favorable to the Crown both civil and criminal pleadings, and, as Donald Sutherland has observed, their eagerness to see where money could be got lent to their proceedings an air of frank extortion.[47] Introduced into the English legal system in the late twelfth century, Eyre courts disappeared at the end of the fifteenth, replaced for the most part by courts of Assize. Whatever their role in the complex administrative machinery of the English Crown, Eyre courts were not, with respect to homicides, close to the ground. They served a recapitulative function, leaving to local officials, coroners among them, the business of poking at the dead. Written in medieval legal Latin, Eyre court records were often written in different hands and in different inks, and they were covered with legal scribbles and annotations—the work, obviously, of clerks pressed for time and under pressure from the Crown. Presiding over the London Eyre court of 1271, Roger of Seyton was frank about the quality of his rolls: "I cannot vouch for them for various reasons, because sometimes one thing is done and another thing more or less is written in the rolls by the clerks, who continually fail to understand the lawyers and litigants correctly."[48]

Given's dissertation records his assessment of seven Eyre records: Bedford, Bristol, Kent, Norfolk, Oxford, Warwick, and London. The first record dates to 1202, and the last to 1276. It is Warwick in 1232 that is recorded as having the highest thirteenth-century homicide rate (**H/P** = 64 per 100,000), and Bristol in 1248 the lowest (**H/P** = 4 per 100,000). These rates depend on population estimates, and so on a choice of reference class. In the case of Bedford, Norfolk, Oxford, and Warwick, Given's estimates were derived from the Domesday Book of 1086; and for London and Oxford, from Josiah Cox Russell's *British Medieval Population*[49] and Rodney Hilton's *A Medieval Society* respectively.[50] To make use of the Domesday Book, Given first multiplied its figures by five, and then by 2.5% per annum. This is in agreement with contemporary demographic analysis only to the extent that, if no one knows whether these figures are correct, no one knows that they are not. Russell's population estimates were, on the other hand, based on the poll tax returns of 1377.

Medieval homicide rates are very sensitive to population estimates. Of course they are. In his study, *Plantagenet England*, Michael Prestwich found reason to revise previous population estimates for medieval London; and with previous population estimates, previous homicide rates.[51] One estimate of London's population in the mid-fourteenth century puts the figure between thirty-five and fifty thousand: **H/P** ≈ 44 per 100,000. The true population of London, Prestwich argued, was somewhere between one hundred and one hundred and seventy-six thousand inhabitants: **H/P** ≈ 18 per 100,000.

In an essay entitled "Peacekeepers and Lawbreakers in London, 1276-1321," published in the most recent volume of *Thirteenth Century England*, Henry Summerson, having examined the roll of crown pleas from the London Eyre of 1321, concluded that with respect to medieval London, **H** ≈ 15 per annum.[52] This makes for a homicide rate **H/P** ≈ 37.5 *on the assumption* that **P** = 40,000; **H/P** ≈ 15, *on the assumption* that **P** = 100,000; and **H/P** ≈ 8.571 *on the assumption* that **P** = 175,000. These uncertainties are ineliminable.

In 2012, the homicide rate in the District of Columbia was **H/P** ≈ 13.9. No one quite knows the population of medieval London, but the population of Washington, DC, is known to the last miserable miscreant.

There are sufficiently many population estimates at work in the study of medieval homicides to comprise a bouquet of them. And, of course, the various population estimates do not coincide. Why should they? They are each inadequate; but each is inadequate in its own way. Given alone reaches two quite different conclusions about thirteenth-century homicide rates: one based on his own estimates, the other, on Russell's. The differences are dramatic. On Given's population estimate, **H/P** = 64 per 100,000; and on Russell's, **H/P** = 30 per 100,000.

This is hardly a trivial difference.

§

Bludgeoned, stabbed, bopped on the head, knifed, run through with a pike, pushed out of high windows, trampled in a frenzy, strangled, stuffed into wells, poisoned—the dead, in short, and so the reference attribute in any homicide rate. How many of them were there in a given year?

If it is not possible reliably to assess the size of thirteenth-century populations, then neither is it possible reliably to assess the number of thirteenth-century homicides. Given's own estimates do very little to support the lurid thesis that "murderous brawls and violent deaths... were everyday occurrences in medieval England."[53] They do nothing at all. Between 1227 and 1248, Given's figures indicate that there were 16 murders in Bristol, a homicide rate of 4 per 100,000 per annum—hardly an everyday occurrence, and rather less than stimulating Miami's murder rate of 15 per 100,000 between 1948 and 1952, or even Philadelphia's homicide rate of 5.7 per 100,000 over the same four years. It hardly helps Given's case that his arithmetic is incorrect. If the population of Bristol was 17,000 in 1248—his own figure—the five homicides he cites from the 1248 Eyre Court make for an annual homicide rate of 1.4 homicides per 100,000, and *not* 4 homicides per 100,000. The eleven homicides reported in the 1227 Eyre court record would make for an annual homicide rate of 3.8 homicides per 100,000, *if* they spanned twenty years; but since the 1227 Eyre court records homicides only *up to* 1227, the reader, consulting Given's treatise, cannot know how many years were at issue before the previous Eyre court.

There were six, as it happened; but the 1221 Eyre court, the subject of a famous study by Frederic Maitland, was held in the county of Gloucestershire, and not in the city of Bristol. About the reliability of the rolls, Maitland very sensibly remarked that "as to the amount of crime that there has been very accurate statistics must not be expected, for it is clear that the same case is sometimes presented by more than one jury, and there are other obvious difficulties in the way of a precise computation."[54]

In Table 1 of his dissertation, Given lists seven Eyre court records, together with their archival location. Eyre courts were held in London in 1244 and again in 1276, a lapse of thirty-two years. But, oddly enough, Given asserts that only twenty-four years elapsed between the Eyre court of 1276 and the previous Eyre court. In recording the number of homicides, Given sets **H** = 145, so that **H/P** = 15 per 100,000, but this figure is correct only if the time elapsed since the previous Eyre court is understood to be twenty-four years and not thirty-two years. If the latter, then **H/P** = 11 per 100,000, a difference of almost one-third.

In fact, an Eyre court *was* held in London in 1251. Given thus *counted* homicides between 1276 and 1244, but *estimated* homicides between 1251 and 1276. Is the difference statistically significant? We have no idea.

Records for the Eyre court of 1251 have disappeared.

§

The thesis that thirteenth- and fourteenth-century homicide rates were 30 times higher than contemporary rates owes much to the correlative conviction that men and women of the thirteenth and fourteenth centuries were emotionally labile, quick to anger, childish, and for this reason, since they were adults with weapons, prone to violence.[55]

Medieval court records and chronicles exert a lurid fascination on otherwise sober historians. Criminologists are worse. They cannot leave the stuff alone: "Symonet Spinelli, Agnes his mistress and Geoffrey Bereman were together in Geoffrey's house when a quarrel broke out among them; Symonet left the house and returned later the same day with Richard Russel his servant to the house of Godfrey le Gorger, where he found Geoffrey; a quarrel arose and Richard and Symonet killed Geoffrey."[56]

That *was* bad luck, Geoffrey.

The story, Eisner goes on to say, "is typical of the situational structure of lethal violence in thirteenth century London—a disagreement, a quarrel leading to a fight, and a fight resulting in a death."[57]

If the story is typical of the situational structure of lethal violence in thirteenth-century London, it is also typical of the situational structure of lethal violence in the contemporary United States.

At random:

- A south Florida man charged with murdering his girlfriend admitted to disemboweling her with his bare hands after she twice cried out her ex-husband's name during sex.
- A Christian rapper fatally struck a Washington, DC, area man in his car after an argument about a music deal.
- According to a Laramie Police Department affidavit, a fight took place at a party on the 700 block of North Seventh Street where Williams admitted to punching Joe McGowan once. Friends of Joe McGowan took him to Ivinson Memorial Hospital with severe head trauma after they found him lying in the gutter unconscious. Joe McGowan was taken to Medical Center of the Rockies in Loveland, Colorado, where he died from his injuries around 2 p.m. Nov. 1.

These crimes are typical of the crime of manslaughter, circumstances that would be evident to criminologists and historians alike were they to spend more time by the lamp reading the *Daily Mail*, the *Daily News*, or the *National Enquirer*.

Or *The Evening Whirl*, which is little known at Harvard or at Oxford, but very well known in St. Louis. "We are among the most savage and brutal people on the face of the earth," the newspaper's editor Anthony Sanders observed, apparently with professional satisfaction. "We are killing people indiscriminately. It doesn't always have to be gang or drug related. There are people just going off and killing people. That happens all over the country."[58]

§

Running a hand the size and shape of a butcher's block through his iron-gray hair, a grizzled old homicide detective in Akron, Ohio reflects on a persistent methodological mistake in the analysis of homicide statistics.

"Nothing," he says heavily, "declines from anything."

"I don't know, Chief," his assistant remarks, "Minneapolis homicides are way down."

"Down from what?"

"Down from here."

"You're a dull boy, Stevie," the grizzled old detective remarks. And he has a point. A *difference* in homicides is no very good evidence of a *decline* in homicides. Or the reverse, of course. The population of Akron, Ohio is 200,000: **H/P** = 11.6. The population of Minneapolis, Minnesota is 400,000: **H/P** = 2.5. Homicide rates in Minneapolis have not plummeted from their Akron level. Nor have they declined, dropped off, trended downward, or been diminished.

"You tell me," the grizzled old detective remarks, "you figure homicides are way down there on a cause of what here?"

"The way I figure it, Chief, I figure the lowlifes are getting hold of themselves, working for Google and all."

"Sort of like lowlife self-control. What do you see, makes you figure the lowlifes are getting control of themselves?"

"Well, the homicides up there are way down, Chief."

All that one can say is that homicide rates in Akron and Minneapolis are different. But so are homicide rates between thirteenth- and twentieth-century Oxford.[59]

That is the end of it.

"I'm too old for this job," the grizzled old detective remarks. "Been at it too long."

§

Poorly defined problems very often lead to absurd solutions, the ensuing circle having, in the case of homicide rates, the virtue, at least, of long-term stability. Imagining an 800-year decline in homicide rates, criminologists looked naturally for an 800-year explanation.[60] They were pleased to discover the work of Norbert Elias.[61] Published in 1938, his masterpiece, *The Civilizing Process*, has enjoyed a late-in-life success among criminologists and even a few historians. Steven Pinker has welcomed his views for the narrative comfort that they provide.[62] Elias was a fine German stylist and a man of exuberant imagination. Although expressed at great length, his theories admit of severe compression. Men acquire their differences from their societies: human nature is second nature. Elias regarded primitive life with fastidious distaste.

In Europe, at least, the civilizing process began in the late fifteenth and early sixteenth centuries, and it began in various European courts. Having been accustomed to take by force what they could not otherwise obtain by guile, warriors at court were obliged to wheedle, charm, and flatter, and since there were many of them, the imperatives of court life demanded that each develop the self-control needed to participate in a system designed to punish men unable, or unwilling, to control their impulses.[63] Court manners spread from the aristocracy to the middle class. Immersed in an ever-expanding network of commercial and professional relationships, merchants and traders had reason to subordinate their impulses to the demands of *geschäft,* their well-being contingent on a finely developed sense of mutual obligations, and as they became honest enough to honor commercial contracts, self-interest was promoted from a commercial to a moral virtue. In time, the civilizing process spread downward to peasants and artisans, who, if never before eager for improvement, now adopted with some reluctance, or resentment, the imperatives of civilization.[64] The ensuing refinement encompassed table manners, comportment, gesture, dress, standards of elegance, child rearing, sexual relations, personal hygiene, and, above all, self-control.

This is vividly imagined, and, since it assigns to society as a whole the same system of constraints that every parent imposes on a child, it is *easily* imagined. It is incorrect in every particular. Elias drew on fifteenth-century instructional manuals for his impression of late-medieval civility, and he was moved and influenced by Johan Huizinga's study of Burgundian court life.[65] These are limited sources. The improvements to which Elias attended may be found four hundred years earlier in various Benedictine monasteries.[66] Cluny was notable for its elegance, the refinement of its table, its manners, and its courtliness.[67] They may be found, those improvements, in the behavior of canon and civil lawyers, university teachers, monastic scribes, medieval physicians, poets, musicians, and singers. The hard shrewd administrators who built the Norman empire in the eleventh-century were not careless primitives, slapping together tax rolls, nor was the Vatican under Innocent III an organization manned by men likely to yield to impulse. The architects who constructed the cathedrals at Notre Dame or Chartres planned their work for years, executed them over decades, and built for eternity.[68]

The high Middle Ages marked the emergence of a noble and self-confident civilization. From the battle of Bouvines in 1214 until almost the end of the thirteenth century, Europe was largely at peace. If in the Catholic Church, Europe lacked a ruling power, it had in Catholic doctrine a unifying ideology.[69] A warming trend promoted abundant harvests. Populations everywhere increased. On the Continent, there was a revival of Roman law; in England, the emergence of common law. Art, philosophy, literature, music, jurisprudence, and, above all, architecture, flourished and became great; and if medieval kingship was frequently exercised with hesitation, the men of the thirteenth century had every reason to suppose that they were better governed than they had been governed. Having acquired some measure of felicity, the medievals were in no need of a civilizing process to obtain what they already had.

Norbert Elias published *The Civilizing Process* in German, a gesture of optimism that in retrospect has acquired a tragic grandeur. Elias quite understood that in the twentieth century, the civilizing process had somehow gone into reverse. He could see what was in front of his eyes. Across the Swiss border, civilization was grinding to a halt. His theories and the facts of life were in conflict. He was unwilling to give up his theories, and unable to disguise the facts. In 1989, Elias published a volume entitled *Studien über die Deutschen*.[70] The Germans, he argued, who had since Roman times been universally viewed with some anxiety, were in virtue of their *peculiar* history exceptions to the civilizing process. This may well be so. No one has ever doubted that the Germans have always been peculiar, and certainly not the Germans. But of what use is the civilizing process as a theory if it fails somehow to include the largest, most powerful, and most populous of European states?

When Norbert Elias published *The Civilizing Process*, he dedicated the volume to the memory of his parents. His father died in 1941; his mother's date of death, Elias did not know. She perished at Auschwitz.

§

Di talem terris avertite pestem![71]

The twentieth century is terrible because, terrible though its warfare has been, its crimes have been worse. In 2010, Timothy Snyder published a book entitled *Bloodlands: Europe between Hitler and Stalin*.[72] The Bloodlands encompassed Poland, the Ukraine, Belarus, Russia, and the

Baltic States during the twelve years from 1933 to 1945. Fourteen million men, women and children were murdered. Steven Pinker does not, of course, deny the magnitude of these crimes; he scruples at their relative importance. "If I were one of the people who were alive in a particular era," he asks, "what would be the chances that I would be a victim of violence?"[73] The question provides its own answer. There is safety in numbers.

Is there? Is there *really*?

An individual x selected at random is a commonplace in the theory of probability, where x is who he is and S is the population in which he is embedded. In the twentieth century, just what risk was he running to—or fleeing from? It was, Pinker affirms, the risk of being "a victim of violence." This comes close to cant. If the *victims* of violence are left undefined, they tend to multiply uncontrollably, the more so if *violence* is treated as a sinister, but shapeless, force. The Holocaust, the Nuremburg court affirmed, was a crime against humanity. The judgment was morally correct because morally unavoidable, but if the entire human race has, for this reason, been a victim of violence, there are no statistical distinctions left to draw.

There remains the grisly category of violent deaths. The dead are dead. They can be counted. The world's population in 1940 stood at roughly two billion. In 1840, it was roughly half as large. If a man selected at random must run the risk of violent death, who would not prefer running it in 1940?

This is Pinker's question.

And his point.

Violence in the twentieth century has had a lurid, but characteristic, shape. Located in the heart of Europe, Germany and Switzerland share a border. From 1941 to 1945, extreme state violence was common in Germany, but not in Switzerland. Is there a measure adequate to both countries? To have assigned to Switzerland Germany's rate would have afforded the Swiss an unrealistic sense of their danger, and to have assigned to Germany Switzerland's rate would have afforded the Germans an unrealistic sense of their safety. To have assigned to both Germany and Switzerland an average of their rates would have astonished the Germans while alarming the Swiss.

Unlike the Bloodlands, the gross violence of the twentieth century was not confined to a simply bounded geographic area. A retreat to abstraction is required. Let $s_1, s_2, \ldots, s_n$ represent the various sites where extreme violence *did* take place. The requisite abstraction is a matter of seeing these sites as sets—perhaps sets of individuals.[74] $S = \{s_1 \cup s_2 \cup \ldots \cup s_n\}$ then emerges as a complicated dead zone: large, irregular, blood red.

Violent deaths make for homicide in the largest sense, and murder in the plainest. Thus a return to a symbol of old in $\{\mathbf{H}\}$, sheathed now in set theoretic parentheses, and looking uncommonly like a scaffold. The juxtaposition of **H** and S leads to three probabilities: $\mathbf{PrH}/S$, $\mathbf{Pr\ H}/S^c$, and $\mathbf{Pr\ H}/S \cup S^c$.

Of these, *which* should be assigned to a randomly selected x as a measure $\mathbf{Pr}(x = \mathbf{H})$ of *his* risk of violent death? Not $\mathbf{PrH}/S$, since this would assign to anyone beyond S the risk of death of everyone within S. Nor $\mathbf{Pr\ H}/S^c$, since $\mathbf{H}/S^c = 0$. Violent deaths are, by definition, concentrated in S. $\mathbf{Pr}(x = \mathbf{H}) = \mathbf{H}/S \cup S^c$? But $\mathbf{Pr\ H}/|S \cup S^c| = \mathbf{H}_1/S + \mathbf{H}_2/S^c$ for some choice of $\mathbf{H}_1$ and $\mathbf{H}_2$. Inasmuch as $\mathbf{H}_2/S^c = 0$, it does not count. If $\mathbf{Pr}(x = \mathbf{H}) = \mathbf{H}_1/S$, then any x in S^c both runs some risk of violent death and none whatsoever.

There is no consistent way in which to assign $\mathbf{Pr}(x = \mathbf{H})$ under these assumptions. This should hardly be a surprise.[75]

A lighthouse in Italy, Albertus Magnus remarked, does not affect a lighthouse in England.

There remains an empirical point, and so a matter of fact. According to Pinker's own source, the proportion of excess deaths to the world's population—**H**/$S \cup S^c$—was far smaller in the nineteenth than in the twentieth century.[76]

All formulas were tried to still
The scratching on the window-sill,
All bolts of custom made secure
Against the pressure on the door,
But up the staircase of events
Carrying his special instruments,
To every bedside all the same
The dreadful figure swiftly came.[77]

§

In the face of its crimes, what can one say about the twentieth century beyond what Elias Canetti said: "It is a mark of fundamental human decency to feel ashamed of living in the twentieth century."[78] What one is not prepared to say, and still less to encounter, largely because it is, at once, absurd and obscene, is the view that the great crimes of the twentieth century were, all things considered, not so bad. This is the view that Pinker defends: the crimes of the twentieth century were not among the greatest of crimes because other crimes were greater. In *The Better Angels of Our Nature*, Pinker offers a list of the worst atrocities in human history.[79] His source is Matthew White, a librarian with a morbid interest in atrocities and a marked talent for publicity. White has deduced his conclusions by an assiduous survey of secondary sources, each citing the other for authority. The greatest of the great atrocities, White argues, is the An Lushan revolt in eighth-century China. Thirty-five million Chinese lost their lives. This is the figure cited originally on White's website, but on more diligent reflection, White revised thirty-five to thirteen million, almost a threefold reduction. This might have suggested to a more scrupulous scholar than Pinker that White is no reliable source.[80]

Whatever the truth, it is incontestable that the times were bitter.

"Earth fades, Heaven fades, at the End of Days. But Everlasting Sorrow endures always."[81]

§

The coordination of crimes over centuries requires some consideration of their natural reference classes. "For comparisons across vast ranges of times and places (such as comparison of the atrocities of the 20th century with those of earlier centuries)," Pinker writes, "I generally use the population of the entire world at the time."[82] In assessing the An Lushan revolt, Pinker accepts the figure of thirty-five million dead. Thirty-five million dead in the eighth century, he argues, is comparable to 429 million dead in the mid-twentieth century. Calculations are straightforward. $\mathbf{H}_1/\mathbf{W}_1 \approx \mathbf{H}_2/\mathbf{W}_2$, where $\mathbf{H}_1$ designates death tolls in the An Lushan rebellion, and $\mathbf{H}_2$ refers to presumptive death tolls had the An Lushan rebellion taken place in the mid-twentieth century. $\mathbf{W}_1$ and $\mathbf{W}_2$ are eighth-century and mid-twentieth-century population totals. Following White (blindly, as it happens), Pinker assumes that $\mathbf{H}_1/\mathbf{W}_1 = 1/6$, whereupon there is $\mathbf{H}_2 = 429{,}000{,}000$.[83] This is a figure intended to shock, and, of course, it does. Had the An Lushan taken place today, Pinker remarks, it could "hold its head high amidst twentieth century atrocities."[84] A sense for the tone appropriate to his subject is not among Pinker's stylistic accomplishments. These meditations must now be interrupted by an obvious question: If the An Lushan rebellion had taken place today, would the ensuing death toll be greater than it was or would the world's population be smaller than it is? Both counter-factual claims are compatible with the assumption that $\mathbf{H}_1/\mathbf{W}_1 \approx \mathbf{H}_2/\mathbf{W}_2$.[85] This macabre argument goes backwards as well as forwards. Six million Jews were murdered in the Holocaust. The world population in 1940 stood at roughly two billion; and the world's population in 1300, at roughly one hundred million. Had the Holocaust taken place in 1300, would death tolls have stood at 300,000 or would the world's population have been two billion? In response to the objection that the world's population in 1300 was *not* two billion, there is the counter-response that neither did the Holocaust take place in the fourteenth century. Which is it to be? There is no way of telling: evidence, if any were needed, of the homicidal projection is intrinsically unstable because it is unavoidably counterfactual.[86] That the An Lushan revolt killed thirty-five million people is, or may be, a fact; that the An Lushan *would have* killed 429 million people in the twentieth century is not. The Holocaust, the Atlantic slave trade, and the An Lushan revolt cannot be projected into the past or into the future. They are what they are. We are left with what we always knew. The An Lushan revolt killed, or may have killed, thirty-five million Chinese; and the Holocaust most certainly killed six million Jews.

Both were terrible.

A correlative error at once follows, this one closer to frank fallacy. "If the population grows," Pinker affirms,

> so does the potential number of murderers and despots and rapists and sadists. So if the absolute number of victims of violence stays the same or even increases, while the proportion decreases, something important must have changed to allow all those extra people to grow up free of violence.[87]

Nothing of the sort is true in the case of homicide statistics; and nothing of the sort is true in the case of atrocities either. The supposition is backwards. The correct question is rather what changed in Nazi Germany, or Stalin's Russia, or Mao's China, or Pol Pot's Cambodia, to allow crimes never before seen to take place *there*?

If the question is obvious, so, too, the answer.

We have no idea.

§

In contemplating the twentieth century, contemporary criminologists enjoy or, at any rate, evince, a sense of optimism somewhat at odds with their immersion in the inky details of their professional calling—murder, after all. Like Eldorado in a somewhat different context, London in 1950, Eisner argued, "may serve as a benchmark for the lowest level of interpersonal lethal violence as yet attained in any known Western society."[88] Interpersonal lethal violence? What Eisner had in mind is *murder*; and what he observed was that, for a time in London, there was not much of it going around.

Whereupon that sense of optimism.

Given the correlative assumption that the homicide rate is a quantifiable indicator of the degree of violence, criminologists might be forgiven a sense of giddiness.

Historians of the twentieth century, like anyone with his eyes open, might wonder about interpersonal lethal violence elsewhere in Europe just a few years earlier. From Eisner's buoyant "long term declining trend in homicide rates," one would expect the data to reflect a series of homicide rates converging sedately to **H/P** ≈ 1/100,000. They did nothing of the sort. Look to Kiev, Amsterdam, Westerbork, Salonika, Treblinka, Majdanek, Chelmno, Sobibor, Krakow, Lachwa, Zazlaw, Potulice, Soldau, Stutthof, Lublin, Kelice, Wilnow, Bedzin, Bialystock, Nowogrodek, Ponary, or Warsaw, and another picture emerges, one in which homicide rates converged to the near certainty of death.

During the German occupation of France, the French police, demonstrating an efficiency never revealed in the pursuit of their daily activities, deported 50,000 Jews from Paris to their deaths.[89] *La rafle* is today well-remembered in French political history, but *la rafle* was one incident in a series of deportations, *les rafles*. Let me see. The population of Paris in 1940 stood at **P** ≈ 1,000,000. Neglecting entirely the ordinary Parisian murder in which a drunken sot at last settled the score with his nagging wife, **H/P** ≈ 1,250/100,000 per annum.[90] The presumptive homicide rate in Oxford in 1343 was 121/100,000. In the middle of the morally improved twentieth century, Parisian homicide rates were *ten times higher* than they were in mid-fourteenth century Oxford. Almost all Jews in Paris *lacking* French citizenship were killed.

There were roughly nine million Jews living in Europe in 1939. Of these, six million were murdered, making for a homicide rate **H/P** ≈ 66,000/100,000, or 14,000/100,000 per annum for each of the four years between 1941 and 1945. A refinement in reference class so that it refers *only* to Jews murdered in various cities, such as Lachwa, Zazlaw, Potulice, Soldau, Stutthof, Salonika, Budapest, or even Amsterdam, yields a homicide rate much higher than the overall European homicide rate, even as the overall European homicide rate during these years was higher than the European homicide rate *at any time* in the history of Europe.

Should these dead not be included in European homicide figures?

Are they not dead?

Were they not murdered?

Criminologists understand that terrible crimes took place in the twentieth century. They are disposed to ignore them. Homicide is one thing, genocide, another.[91] Their business is the first; let others deal with the second. The distinction is entirely artificial. Homicide is murder, and genocide, mass murder. When the statistics pertaining to mass murder in the twentieth century are acknowledged, they bleed through every calculation, forming a ghastly but ineradicable spike in the otherwise humdrum human record of murders undertaken in some sordid hotel room or in the alleyway behind the *Bannhof* or in a field of winter wheat.

"If thou doest well, shalt thou not be accepted? and if thou doest not well, sin lieth at the door. And unto thee shall be his desire, and thou shalt rule over him."[92]

If mass murders are not included in the homicide rate for the twentieth century, then the homicide rate is no very good measure of violence; and if they are included, then the homicide rate does not indicate a long-term declining trend in violence.

It indicates the opposite.

It is by virtue of its crimes that the twentieth century has achieved a terrible form of immortality. "It is in the very nature of things human," Hannah Arendt observed, "that every act that has once made its appearance and has been recorded in the history of mankind stays with mankind as a potentiality long after its actuality has become a thing of the past." No matter how remote, great crimes have a living power to influence the future. Tradition and taboo are unavailing.[93] "No punishment," Arendt wrote, "has ever possessed enough power of deterrence to prevent the commission of crimes." On the contrary, "whatever the punishment, once a specific crime has appeared for the first time, its reappearance is more likely than its initial emergence could ever have been."[94]

It is in this sense that the twentieth century, having introduced into human history crimes never before imagined, or if imagined, never before undertaken, is immortal, and will, like the crucifixion, remain a permanent part of the human present.

It is simply there, an obelisk in human history: black, forbidding, irremovable, and inexpugnable.

3. The Cause of War

It is right to know that war is common and justice strife, and that all things come to be through strife and are so ordained.

—Heraclitus[1]

Some things happen because they must. *Nulla fata loco possis excludere.* And still other things happen because they might have happened. *Time and chance happen to them all.*[2] Fate and chance divide the world. The distinction between them is embedded in all of the physical sciences, but whether it is a distinction that encompasses historical events is rather less clear.

The proximate cause of the First World War was the assassination of the Archduke Francis Ferdinand by Gavrilo Princip. As a cause, it was both necessary and sufficient: had it not taken place, the war would not have occurred; given that it did take place, the war must have occurred.[3] "When the agent and patient meet suitably to their powers," Aristotle remarked, "the one acts and the other is acted on of necessity."[4] From the proximate cause of the First World War, various causal chains can be followed backward in an ever-ramifying series, one running from the Balkan wars of 1913 and 1912 to the Congress of Berlin in 1878, and after that emptying into an ever-widening tangle of causes and their effects.

No one is satisfied by this, if only because the causal chain is defective. If e_1 is the cause of E, and $e_1 = e_2$, then e_2 must be the cause of E as well. The principle of extensionality ratifies causes and events as things taking place in the world. The Austrian annexation of Bosnia and the assassination of Archduke Francis Ferdinand are connected only by the friable tissue of Princip's emotional state, his commitment to Serbian nationalism, his uninformed appreciation of Austro-Hungarian politics, and his stupidity.

These states were both intermittent and uncertain. Had Princip believed the Bosnian annexation a gross provocation, he might have acted as he did; had he believed it an irrelevance, he might not have acted at all. Whether described as a provocation or an irrelevance, one event is at issue. In that case, $e_1 = e_2$, but while e_1 might have been the cause of E, not so e_2. A cause is a cause no matter how it is described. Princip had his reasons for what he did, and in this sense, it is possible to rationalize his actions, but it is exceptionally difficult analytically to interpolate his reasons into a causal chain that began before Princip acted and ended as he acted. Only some version of fatalism, in which Princip acted as a cause because he acted as an effect, would do justice to this analysis; but Princip was not compelled to assassinate the Archduke Francis Ferdinand and his imperial consort. He might have walked away. The other conspirators did.

None of the Great Powers were compelled to go to war. They could have walked away. If these considerations are admitted, the causal chain that was designed to explain the outbreak of war is less a chain than a series of unconnected links. None of them are properly causes because each could have occurred without effect, depending on how they were described or what the various actors believed. If the assassination of Franz Ferdinand was a part of a transitive chain in which one thing led to another, it could not have been extensional, and if it could not have been extensional, how could it have been causal?[5]

History is like that.

Every attempt to construct a philosophically impeccable chain of causes leading to the outbreak of war faces its difficulties, and while none of them is entirely defective, neither is any of them entirely successful. It is for this reason that historians have wondered whether the outbreak of the First World War might have been an accident. "No other human activity," Clausewitz remarked, "is so continuously or universally bound up with chance."[6] This is an idea fully as old and as suggestive as the correlative idea that wars are the effects of their ancestral causes, inevitable, and so fated. At "every instant," Steven Pinker writes, "Mars, the god of war, rolls his iron dice, and if they turn up snake eyes he sends a pair of nations to war."[7]

Does he? And do they go when they are sent?

I can call spirits from the vasty deep.

Why, so can I, or so can any man;

But will they come when you do call for them?[8]

In the mid-twentieth century, the English statistician Lewis Fry Richardson studied war under the aspect of two different statistical distributions.[9] The relationship between the frequency and the intensity of warfare, Richardson argued, followed a power law. And he argued again that the inception of war from 1820 to 1950 followed a Poisson distribution.[10] Political scientists were well pleased with Richardson's work.[11] They have devoted an industry to its study. Historians have remained skeptical.[12]

A power law function has the form $f(x) = \alpha^{-\gamma}$, and power law functions are among the Mandela of elementary functions.[13] A power law distribution has the form $\mathbf{Pr}[X \geq x] \sim \alpha^{-\gamma}$, and in the discrete case,

$$\mathbf{Pr}(k) = \frac{k^{-\gamma}}{\zeta(\gamma)}$$

where $\zeta(\gamma)$ is the Riemann Zeta function. There is a good deal of evidence in favor of Richardson's thesis that a power law distribution coordinates the frequency and intensity of warfare. Whether the evidence is any good is another question. One difficulty is obvious. Data before the twentieth century is poor, and data during the twentieth century is not much better. Given a patchy data series, political scientists have often used a power law distribution to interpolate the missing data points. The ensuing series is then used in favour of the hypothesis that it is a power law distribution that governs events. The circle is closed to argument. No matter the power law distribution, the First and Second World Wars remain the most terrible wars in European history. Aaron Clauset accepts the figure of roughly sixteen million deaths during the Second World War; Steven Pinker, the figure of fifty-five million deaths.[14] Both Clauset and Pinker are persuaded that their figures may be accommodated by some power law distribution, but whether there is a *single* power law that does justice to them both is rather less clear.[15] If this is so, what is the relevance of a power law distribution, and if it is not so, why did these wars occur in the way that they did? Whatever the details, power law distributions are stationary. Had the Second World War commenced in 1839, and not 1939, the relevant power law distribution would have retained the same explanatory value, which is to say, none whatsoever.

The Poisson was promoted to prominence when Ladislaus Bortkiewicz used it with remarkable success to explain the distribution of fatal horse kicks in the Prussian cavalry. Up went the horse, down went the cavalryman, the industrious Bortkiewicz adding his tick of doom to the statistical record. Like the power law distribution, the Poisson belongs to the broad and noble class of probability distributions:

$$\mathbf{Pr}(\mathrm{X}, \lambda) = \frac{\lambda^k e^{-\lambda}}{k!}$$

where X is a random variable; λ, the mean rate at which events occur; and *k*, the number of trials.

The Poisson distribution distributes; it is what distributions do. It does not count. The expression $\mathbf{Pr}(\mathrm{X} = k; \lambda t)$, by way of an improvement, designates the probability that X counts the number of events expected to arrive, or occur, during fixed intervals of time. Whence

$$\mathbf{Pr}(\mathrm{X} = k;\ \lambda t) = e^{-\lambda t}\,\frac{(\lambda t)^k}{k!}$$

the probability that up to the interval *t*—days, weeks, hours, years—precisely *k* events will have occurred: one war, two wars, *many* wars. Like horsekicks, traffic accidents, and the arrival of e-mails, the inception of war follows a heavy-tailed distribution.[16] It is there that rare events may be found, as when a great many horses take it into their heads to kick their owners at the same time.

A data series is one thing. It is a finite numerical record. A Poisson distribution is another thing. It is an abstract function $f(X, \lambda)$. A Poisson *process* is otherwise. It is a description of some undertaking in the world, a connection to the place where things happen. Suppose that $H(t)$ designates the number of events occurring in the interval $[0, t]$, when $H(t) = 0$. A process is Poisson if

1. the number of events in disjoint time periods is independent;
2. the probability of a single event for δt is $\mathbf{Pr}\ [H(t + \delta t) - H(t) = 1] = \lambda\delta t + o(\delta t)$, where $o(\delta t)$ tends to 0 as δt goes to ∞; and
3. the probability that two or more events occur in the same small time period is $\mathbf{Pr}\ [A(t + \delta t) - A(t) \geq 2] = o(\delta t)$.

The relationship between a Poisson process and a Poisson distribution is straightforward in one direction, but not the other. If P is a Poisson process, then P satisfies a Poisson distribution. All is well. But if P satisfies a Poisson distribution, it does not follow that P is a Poisson process.[17] A close correspondence between the distribution on the ground and the Poisson distribution in the air may be misleading. Some other process may account for both distributions, and often it does.

The fact remains that a homogeneous Poisson distribution *does* seem to describe the inception of war very well, and because it does, it makes for a division of labor. Randomness is a property of a Poisson distribution as a whole. It is global. Historical events are local. They take place at given times and places, and each Poisson episode encompasses events with causes all their own. "Shallow men," Ralph Waldo Emerson observed, "believe in luck or circumstances; but strong men believe in cause and effect." Given a Poisson distribution, they can double their beliefs without incurring a contradiction. The historian may study the causes of war; the statistician, their inception.[18]

There remains a certain bleak irony in the thesis that the inception of war is governed by a Poisson distribution. In a homogeneous Poisson process, the rate parameter, λ, is fixed from the first, and it does not change.[19] Things could not be getting better, gentler, or kinder, because they are not changing at all.[20] This is a conclusion that Steven Pinker is unwilling to accept, and so one that he is eager to reject. The inception of wars may, indeed, be governed by a Poisson process, but this does not imply the inescapability of conflict. The Poisson rate parameter may itself be changing. The result is an *in*homogeneous Poisson process; and if λ is itself changing stochastically, a Cox process. Pinker assigns the change in λ to various moral, social, and political improvements. The analysis that results is bound to seem circular to skeptics since the evidence that human beings have recently undergone moral improvement is chiefly the fact that λ is changing.

There remains the question whether λ *is* changing. There is no question that the sixty years from 1950 to 2010 were less violent than the thirty years that preceded them.[21] Short of a nuclear exchange, they could hardly have been more violent. Whether 1950 represents a turning point in the history of warfare, and so the beginning of a trend, is less obvious. Statisticians have grown hoarse warning political scientists not to confuse expected statistical fluctuations in a stationary process for some very good thing.[22]

The historical data is unrevealing. It is what it is. The long peace is either an expected fluctuation or a statistical anomaly. Some sense of moral optimism turns on the issue. If the long peace is an expected fluctuation, there is no reason to imagine that the underlying process is apt to cease fluctuating; if an anomaly, there is some reason to hope that it is the beginning of a trend. The past cannot be replayed and, in this regard, the statistician is as helpless as the historian. What *is* within the statistician's remit is the question whether comparable processes admit of sixty-year periods of relative peace. Only one historical process is at work in the world. Comparisons must be made by the expedient of constructing those comparable processes as model variations. In an interesting paper entitled "Trends and Fluctuations in the Severity of Interstate Wars," Aaron Clauset constructed three models of the primary data. His conclusions do not inspire a sense of optimism:

> However, the analysis here demonstrates that periods like the long peace are a statistically common occurrence under the stationary model, and even periods of profound violence, like that of and between the two World Wars, are within expectations for statistical fluctuations. Hence, even if there have been genuine changes in the processes that generate wars over the past 200 years, data on the frequency and severity of wars alone are insufficient to detect those shifts. The long peace pattern would need to endure for at least another 100 to 150 years before it could plausibly be called a genuine trend.[23]

Too bad.[24]

This point of view expands, but it does not dilute, the initial disjunction between determinism and randomness. Either changes to λ are determined or they are random. If they are determined, we are returned to an older fateful view of war as a manifestation of strife, and if the amount of strife in the cosmos is changing, while that may be to our benefit, it remains beyond our power. To assign the amelioration of strife to various Good Thoughts is frivolous. It is beyond human power to change the great chain of causes that stretches back to the throat of time; and if it *is* within our power, then the disjunction between determinism and randomness must be incomplete. If λ is itself a stochastic variable, the argument is without relevance, because it removes the claim that wars are random events from rational assessment. Any finite set of data points, no matter how determined (or determinate), can be approximated by *some* Cox process.

Quite beyond these issues, an interpretation of warfare in terms of a Poisson process raises questions within the historian's remit. So far as Poisson processes go, William Feller remarks, "The probability of any particular event is the same for all time intervals of length *t*, independent of where this interval is situated and of the past history of the system."[25] It is here that the historian demurs. A *particular* event can no more take place at two different times than at two different places. A Poisson process demands a ruthless subordination of events to their number, and within a given count, wars are indistinguishable, like bosons in Bose-Einstein statistics. Given a warlike series, the probability that some war or other will break out is everywhere the same, regardless of which temporal interval is which. This is not a plausible assumption. It implies that the probability that combat might begin on the day that it has ceased is the same as the probability that combat might cease on the day that it began.

It is implausible in a larger sense. Two events A and B are independent if **Pr**(A&B) = **Pr**(A)·**Pr**(B). Events undergoing a Poisson process are independent by definition. So long as men have memories, nothing done in the present can *ever* be independent of the past. Having been concluded, the Congress of Berlin lowered the likelihood of another Russo-Turkish war; and, indeed, Europe remained largely at peace for the thirty years that followed. The first and second Balkan wars raised the likelihood of a larger European war because both wars provided evidence that some issues of European concern could not be settled short of war. At the end of the First World War, Ferdinand Foch remarked of the treaty then under construction, that "it was not peace but an armistice for twenty years." He was correct, and for the same reason that anxious statesmen could see that the Balkan wars presaged the First World War: some business had been left unfinished. If the history of warfare does not suggest a series of *independent* events, neither does it suggest a series of independent *events*. An event, if the concept is to have any content, must be found within some definite region of space and time; and for this reason, events belong to the class of countable things. How many wars were fought during the inter-war years? And fought where? The Russian Civil War was fought from the Baltic in the north to Odessa in the south, and from the Urals in the east to the gates of Warsaw in the west. It had no sharp temporal boundaries, sputtering to begin with, guttering to end with. How many events did it encompass? The Russian historian interested in the long sweep of history may justifiably count the Russian Civil War as a single event, and the Polish historian, too; but the events that they are counting had different spatial and temporal boundaries. They cannot be the same. The question *how many events* admits of no rational answer because the count is entirely determined by context; it is determined locally; and, beyond the descriptive concerns of various historians, it is unstable.

Richardson understood these points perfectly. In considering the question of just when wars break out, he remarked, in a phrase of great power, that "thinginess fails."[26] It does.

The events of July 1914 proceeded as they did, but how did randomness enter into European affairs? In striking a metaphor, no man is under oath, but if the god of war was busy throwing down his iron dice in July of 1914, it was not with any notable effect. European statesmen did it to themselves, and they did it by themselves. Richardson persuaded several generations of political scientists that his was a scientific attitude toward war. The research that has resulted has the very great merit of having occupied many political scientists in an undertaking that is as innocent as it is irrelevant. Nothing has been discovered about the onset and seriousness of war that was previously hidden from common sense.

Men go to war when they think that they can get away with murder.

II. Reason

4. Relativism—A Fish Story

A dark Prince of the English department at Duke University has brought his pen to bear in the defense of multiculturalism, affirmative action, gay rights, and ethnic studies.[1] It is, some might think, a gesture undertaken after the issue has been decided. The Army of Indignation to which Stanley Fish now offers his allegiance has already triumphed wherever it has taken the field. Leaping to the cannon's mouth, Fish runs the risk of leaping too late. It is no surprise that the elegant essays that result are informed, and, as often, sanctified, by an appeal to large but somewhat anachronistic philosophical principles. In his acquired sympathies, Fish is devoted to the interpretive turn, a maneuver undertaken by theorists committed to the thesis that far from being subordinated to the world of facts, it is language that brings facts into being. Those troubled by the turn, Fish acknowledges, take it to imply that "words have no intrinsic meaning, values are relative, rationality is a social construct, everything is political, every reading is a misreading," and argue by contraposition that the interpretive turn is a mistake. Fish accepts the inference but revels in its conclusions, regarding them as commonplaces.

"There is no such thing as literal meaning," he buoyantly affirms, "a meaning that because it is prior to interpretation can serve as a constraint on interpretation." But what Fish writes in the course of denying the existence of literal meaning is meaningful in English and not in Farsi, circumstances that might suggest constraints on interpretation of precisely the sort that Fish thinks inexistent. The point is well-known, if not well-taken, and from time to time, Fish himself appears in the literary journals, arguing earnestly that on this matter, what he said, he did not mean, and what he meant, he did not say.

In reading Fish, skepticism starts early and it never flags. If literal meanings go in one essay, transcendent truths disappear in another. Whatever they are, these truths "would not speak to any particular condition or be identified with any historical production, or be formulated in terms of any ethnic, racial, economic, or class traditions." Lacking these identifying caste marks, they would be humanely (but not divinely) inaccessible. Yet if there are no transcendent truths, there are nevertheless transcendent *statements*—those that *fail* to mention history, class, race, and gender, and of these, there are many. Fish's book is full of them, and it is only the fact that they are false that robs these transcendent statements of their role as transcendent truths; but if they are false, their negations must be true, and thus one and the same argument affirms what it was intended to deny.

If Fish is wrong about the transcendent truths, he is wrong again about truths that are *not* transcendent. "The truths that any of us find compelling," he writes, "will all be partial, which is to say that they will all be political." This is a thesis still advocated ardently by the low-browed faithful at Mongahela Community College—or at Yale, for that matter; elsewhere, Fish's line is apt to elicit only a few polite murmurs of assent. And for obvious reasons. I, for one, am completely compelled by the truth that tin is softer than molybdenum, and while this is only a part of the truth about tin, it is not necessarily a *partial* truth, the very form of words suggesting incoherently that a particular truth might, like a Chevrolet Camaro, be broken down into parts, and not even partially a political truth, if the political and metallurgical truths are, in any reasonable sense, distinct. Fish's animadversions on transcendence constitute a clean sweep: every argument is invalid and every premise false.

Essentialism represents another tempting but dangerous target. "The essential," Fish affirms in his preface, "is a rhetorical category whose shape varies with the contingencies of history and circumstance."

Confidence in this familiar declaration, another Mongahela lunchroom staple, does not survive a confrontation with examples, as when one says that while Fish might have been a lawyer rather than a literary critic, he could not have been a seal rather than a man, some essential part of what it is to be Fish having been irretrievably and thus poignantly lost were he to emerge dripping from the waves, sleek fur receding over his phocine head. This judgment appears to owe nothing to the contingencies of history or circumstance. Might Fish have been a seal in another time or place? Under *what* other circumstances? It is again a contingent fact that cats do not have pink fur and lack the capacity to play the oboe, but not a contingent fact that cats are mammals rather than reptiles or amphibians. It is a part of the *essence* of literary criticism that it is not dentistry. Whatever a critic's position on essentialism, and the issue is yet vexed and has long been vexed, the distinctions embodied by these commonly made and intuitively plausible judgments need either to be enforced, or, if rejected, explained convincingly as artifacts. This Fish does not do.

Atheistic on essences, Fish is radical on epistemology, arguing in the course of the otherwise sensible "Being Interdisciplinary is So Very Hard to Do," that "knowledge… cannot grasp, or name the grounds of, its possibility, and whenever it thinks to have done so, those grounds are elsewhere than they seem to be," an affirmation calling to mind nothing so much as a fraternity brother's astonished discovery that try as he might, he can never catch sight of his own well-upholstered rear-end, it swiveling as he swivels and all. If the objects of knowledge are propositions, the grounds of any proposition constitute, on one reading of Fish's assertion, the set of propositions necessary, but not necessarily sufficient, for its truth. The thesis of radical epistemology, then, is that one could never know on pain of infinite regress the set of sentences necessary for every sentence that one knows. This thesis is true so long as no sentence is necessary for itself, which is to say, not obviously true at all; and, indeed, if the truths are taken to be points in the closed unit ball in Euclidean *n*-space, and its grounds are expressed by continuous functions, then demonstrably false by Brower's fixed-point theorem.

Epistemology is not a strong subject for Fish, but neither is ontology or metaphysics. Together they function as Burmese finger-traps. Writing in the book's introduction about the difference between the sociology of science and science itself, Fish argues that incompatible doctrines should, like sleeping dogs, be allowed to live where they lie. "Acting scientifically," he writes, "means acting on the assumption of a determinate nature waiting to be described by a neutral observation language; acting sociologically means acting on the assumption that nature is socially constructed by the very speech acts of which it is supposedly the cause." Expatiating on this theme, Fish remarks that "it is no longer taken for granted," and surely not taken for granted by *him*, that "molecules and quarks come first," in the scheme of things, "and scientists' models of molecules and quarks come second." These theses taken literally, it follows that so far as sociologists of science are concerned, *a speech act* such as "Arise, Dumbo" could bring an elephant into being; and that molecules, and so the materials they compose, did not exist before the molecular theory of matter, the Cathedral at Chartres thus acquiring, on Fish's account, its molecular structure eight hundred years after its construction.

This is not a conclusion that inspires confidence.

It is Fish's conviction that an older, insufficiently flexible generation of scholars has rejected the interpretive turn because it is unfamiliar. He is sympathetic to their plight: "One cannot blame those who entered the academy thirty years ago for feeling discombobulated and dispossessed by developments they could not possibly have predicted." The photograph on the cover of his book persuades me that if Fish is not yet middle-aged, he is, at least, a man of certain years, and if he has managed to retain the intellectual suppleness necessary for a fine appreciation of the interpretive turn, it cannot be age alone that keeps other scholars sitting on the sidelines.

§

In the title essay of his collection, "There's No Such Thing as Free Speech, and It's a Good Thing, Too," Fish forsakes philosophy in order to suggest suavely that it might be a good thing to shut some people up. Who would argue? Not me. But those whom Fish wishes to silence, I am prepared to encourage; those that he encourages, I would see silenced. Controversy over cases inevitably remains, prompting the corrosive suspicion that if there is no agreement on who is to be silenced, it might be the better part of wisdom to leave off silencing anyone.

Free speech is among the pious virtues. It is upheld because it is a virtue, and denied even though it is a virtue. That freedom of speech *is* a virtue imparts a certain characteristic shape to arguments in its defense. No one, Justice Holmes remarked, has the right to shout fire in a crowded theater. The exception implies the right. Difficulties arise because exceptions themselves have exceptions. Anyone has the right to shout fire in a crowded theater if the theater is on fire. The cry is then welcome. The place is, after all, on fire. Even this exception has a tendency to fission. No one has the right to shout fire in a crowded theater that is on fire if by shouting fire, he is apt to exacerbate the general panic. The place is on fire. Why is that idiot yelling? To say that the ensuing panic was the result of the fire, and not the cry, is pointlessly to divide panics. And while no one has the right to shout *fire* in a crowded theater that is not on fire, murmuring the words, or whispering the words, or writing them down—these are quite all right. Had he considered them, Justice Holmes could not have scrupled. This makes it seem as if the objection to shouting *fire* in a crowded theater were less a matter of what was said and more a matter of how loudly it was said. A loudly shouted exclamation in favor of the Smoot-Hawley tariff might well have evoked a panicky response, as well.

The traditional defense of free speech, Fish believes, rests on a flabby distinction between speech and action. A distinction denied is a distinction discarded, and if speech is a species of action, it falls, it must fall, under the scope of rules and regulations, speech crime arising at the busy intersection of a public prohibition and a provocative utterance. It is, of course, trivially true that what a man says is a part of what he does. Contracts are created, hearts are broken, and marriages are made on the strength of what is said, and Fish's efforts to suggest that he is alone in recognizing this elementary fact engender a false air of *Fish v. Foul, et al.* Investing speech with the attributes of action is yet compatible with the observation that much that a man says, or might say, is said quite without effect. Still, if some things are said without effect, others plainly are not. The law recognizes libel, slander, and blackmail, and common sense recognizes, as well, what Fish earnestly affirms, namely that "speech-related injuries may be grievous and deeply wounding," even if as offense taken multiplies on every university campus, the objective evidence for offense given tends to dwindle and then disappear. Cases remain in which offense is both given and taken.

No set of explicit and specific rules, Fish admits, can inform the deliberations of campus censors addressing racist, sexist, and homophobic speech, but Fish is well-disposed to a principle of expected utility expressed succinctly by Judge Learned Hand: "Ask whether the gravity of the 'evil' discounted by its improbability justifies such invasion of free speech as is necessary to avoid the danger" (*U.S. v. Dennis 183 f 2d 212*).

As a principle, I see no way to fault this. Who would argue *for* the imposition of a likely iniquity? But Justice Hand is appealing to a dangerous evil and Fish to speech-related injuries, and however galling it may be for people of color to be called colored people, the imposition of the epithet hardly jeopardizes the distinction between two quite different categories of sin. The principle of expected utility is, in any event, too strong to do Fish much good, going as it does beyond what is false inadvertently to proscribe and then purge what is true. There are, after all, plenty of statements that it would be better for humanity never to have uttered or having uttered them never to have heard: $E = mc^2$ comes readily to mind; that, and in view of the cholesterol count of the dish that results, the recipe for *fettuccine Alfredo*. I leave the development of this argument as an exercise.

The concept of a speech crime suggests something like a rule of three specificities. No speech crime without a specific baleful effect, of course, but also no speech crime not tied to a specific utterance and a specific form of words. Absent the effects, and there is nothing to talk of; absent the specific form of words, and there is no speech crime, the misdeed indistinct, passing from something hard-edged and glittering to a crime marked as a crime only by the circumstance that an offense has been conveyed by words. What is *streng verboten*, campus speech codes or Facebook censors must affirm, is *saying*—and there follow the forbidden words, phrases or sentences: the specific sentence, for example, that women are low sloppy beasts. But absent the specific circumstance of *utterance*, there is no speech *crime*, the charge lapsing, for example, if I merely *mention* but do not use specific forbidden words, as Fish himself does, or if I *deny* publicly that women are low sloppy beasts, or if I *doubt* that they are, or if I *speculate* or *entertain* the thought that they are, or if I *accept for purposes of argument* that they are, only assertion, avowal, or declaration carrying the requisite intentional commitment necessary to bring about a crime.

But as the circumstance of utterance is fixed, specificity in the form of words unavoidably disappears. Attitudes such as assertion, avowal, or declaration take propositional objects, something indicated by their grammar as forms of indirect discourse, and propositions are constitutionally dissociated from any specific choice of words used to express them. I may affirm that women are low sloppy beasts without ever once using those very words, as when I express the thought in French or in German, or when overhearing Fish—of all people!—indecorously affirm that women are low sloppy beasts, I agree publicly with him, or murmur "Attaboy Stanley," or say simply "Way to go, Chucklenuts," this imaginary case altogether too close for comfort to cases that have already passed into the personal scrapbook of proud campus censors, as when professors of American literature are brought low by quoting from *Huckleberry Finn*. Conveying the thought that women are low sloppy beasts by using the words "Way to go, Chucklenuts," I may well induce "speech related injuries" that are both grievous and deeply wounding, my offense the more vexing in virtue of its obliqueness.

The requirement that words be used assertively means that uttering a specific form of words on a particular occasion is never *sufficient* for the charge of speech crime. The argument just given implies that uttering a specific form of words on a particular occasion is never *necessary* for speech crime either. And if uttering a specific form of words is neither necessary nor sufficient for speech crime, it is hard to see that any independent content remains to the concept. What does remain is the general impression that it would be a good thing to shut some people up. It is because freedom of speech is so piously held a virtue that no one is ever prepared to say this, although everyone is prepared to think it.

§

It is in "Reverse Racism" that Fish comes to the defense of affirmative action, a cause that evokes his assent in proportion, one might suspect, to the extent that it has never jeopardized his career. To the objection that affirmative action is reprehensible because racist, and racist because based on color, Fish responds that a racist policy and a "policy designed to remedy that plight" are not, after all, the same thing, an assertion trivially true, skeptics will observe, in view of the fact that they have just been described as having different *aims*.

But differing in their aims, apartheid and affirmative action may nonetheless be alike in appealing to reprehensible *means*. To point out the mistake is to see a variant promptly embodied. "Reverse racism," Fish writes, "is a cogent description of affirmative action only if one considers the virus of racism to be morally and medically indistinguishable from the remedy we apply to it." Not so. If racism and its remedies differ in any number of respects, the good intentions of those urging the remedies the most obvious, it may yet remain true that reverse racism is a cogent, an *inescapable*, description of affirmative action, Fish's assertion to the contrary falling to an invocation of *modus tollendo tollens*.

An issue larger than logical incompetence infects Fish's argument. Is affirmative action to be simply a remedy for past injustice, nothing more? Fish is uncertain. "It is a travesty of reasoning," he writes, "to argue that affirmative action, which gives preferential treatment to disadvantaged minorities as part of a plan to achieve social equality, is no different from the policies that created the disadvantages in the first place." The pairing of preferential treatment and disadvantaged minorities resurrects a remedial concept of affirmative action, one that issues in a familiar and explicit recommendation: That those who have been injured by an unacceptable social policy should be compensated by the society that injured them. The objection to affirmative action thus described is well known. Extending reward on the basis of race, affirmative action benefits those who have not been injured and injures those who have not benefited. It is unfair, and as time goes on, it becomes progressively more unfair, tending in the limit to acquire the frank aspect of a racket.

Affirmative action collides with the ancestral moral doctrine that two wrongs do not make a right, a collision that evokes no sympathy whatsoever from Fish, who champions the contrary doctrine of compensatory injustice. The black experience in the United States having been bitterly *unfair*, it follows, Fish reasons, that fairness "as a resolution no longer to discriminate against blacks legally" is inadequate as a remedy for their historical misfortune. But the fact that fairness is insufficient as a remedy hardly implies that it is not *necessary*. And this, the charge of unfairness, is the gravamen of the case against affirmative action. It would, no doubt, provide a salutary shock for those infected, or afflicted, by the residue of racism, were a few white men flogged and then lynched each year as either an example or as a warning. *Strong illness, strong remedy*, as Fish might say, as Fish, in fact, *does* say in defending affirmative action; but if Fish would scruple at such injustice, it is hard to see that he would have any better defense than the one he derides in the case of affirmative action, namely that two wrongs do not make a right. There are certain principles that, indeed, one gives up at one's peril.

The inclusion of affirmative action in a "plan to achieve social equality" points Fish toward the badlands that lie beyond any remedial scheme, *social equality* functioning in his text, and in life, as a coded description of a spoils system, one based on skin color or gender. If fifteen percent of the physicists at the Institute for Advanced Study must be black, and fifty percent women, skill in solving differential equations will not by itself remain a standard of merit and so a criterion for advancement. Fish is sensitive to this point. Raising the possibility early on that merit may itself be a contested category, Fish himself contests it cheerfully, arguing that inasmuch as "diversity will be an important factor in the educational experience," race must count for something. What holds for blacks, holds again for women, but unlike blacks, who need to achieve minimum scores to pass muster in race norming at the University of California at Berkeley, merely the "very presence" of women in a department, say, of microbiology, Fish believes, "makes a difference," and although he does not say what kind of difference it is apt to make, he is in favor of the result.

The thesis that Fish embraces with some residual diffidence, others endorse with a hearty sense that they have seen the high ground and propose to command it. "The world is changing, higher education is changing, our definitions of *quality* are changing," Robert Wolf, the director of the Western Association of Schools and Colleges Accrediting Commission, boisterously affirmed in a recent edition of the *San Francisco Chronicle*. Contrary to Fish's view that professors of English carry little influence in the world at large, doctrines that arise in departmental colloquia often survive to become principles of practical dogma. The policy that Fish commends carries consequences that he might otherwise deplore. At least some blacks who entered the freshman class at the University of California as the beneficiaries of affirmative action left some years later as its victims, the standard of merit by which they gained admission suspended at some point between their introduction to the Afro-American experience and their introduction to the Calculus, diversity appearing to everyone but affirmative action bureaucrats as a policy that is cruel by its very nature.

Diversity as a moral command is incompatible with any conception of affirmative action as a form of remedial relief. And vice versa, of course. If diversity is an end in itself, there is no reason to exclude from consideration mesomorphs, those who lisp, Hakkas, the congenitally retarded, men who are left-handed or six-toed, the morbidly obese, those who suffer from hemorrhoids, Swiss-Chinese lesbians—there are more minorities than members in any society, and so, as the demand for diversity grows, places available to satisfy the demand must dwindle; but if every minority is entitled to some representational share of the spoils, diversity cannot be a remedy to the black community for the *particular* injustices that *it* has suffered. Rights are general; remedies are not, and in the face of a declaration that diversity is a very good thing, members of the black community may well ask, what's in it for *us?* On the other hand, if affirmative action entitles the black community to a specific, a *remedial,* share of the spoils, some aspect of diversity as a social good must inevitably be compromised since one portion of the available spoils will be set aside irremovably for one minority in virtue of what they have suffered and not in virtue of who they *are.* This is a dilemma sensed by many representatives of the black community; when proposals are made to diversify the college campus, or anything else, their response is often a very tepid grunt of enthusiasm.

§

In "The Common Touch, or, One Size Fits All," an essay devoted to the much-contested canon of great books, Fish comes to the defense of "those for whom matters of class, race, ethnicity, and gender are of paramount importance and abiding concern, that is, those who are poor, black, Hispanic, Asian, female, gay, etc." Without his advocacy, Fish is persuaded, class, race, ethnicity, and gender may for a moment go unmentioned, a prospect that, for those familiar with the shape of campus controversies, will seem richly preposterous. And as for those who are poor, black, Hispanic, Asian, female, or gay, their endless *geschrei* fills the academic presses and campus podiums, striking evidence, if any were needed, that whatever attempts have been made to exclude these groups from discourse have been unsuccessful.

The position that Fish advocates on the canon is at odds somewhat with his practice, which reveals, as he is the first to admit, that whatever the outcome of the debate, *he*, at any rate, is not going to get caught teaching feminist hermeneutics to walnut-eyed women, or spend time reading the works of various third-world worthies. Nonetheless, Fish is provoked beyond measure by appeals to common ground in the humanities, by appeals to common *anything*. "Someone who says to you," he writes, the crust of indignation on his lips, "'This is *our* common ground,' is really saying 'This is my common ground, the substratum of assumptions and values that produces my judgment, and it should be yours, too.'" This demand for an uncorrupted canon, Fish continues, is nothing more than "the authoritative imposition of one group's very particular tastes in the name of the common and the transcendental." But the categories of the common and the transcendental appear in the equation algebraically to cancel one another. The burden of Fish's objurgations is carried by his assumption that it is a bad thing that one man's tastes are being imposed upon another man.

If the argument over the canon, whether in literature, philosophy, the arts, or music, is a matter mostly of *taste*, it is hard to credit the conflict with much content. Tastes issue in preferences and preferences may be different without revealing disagreement, the fact that one man prefers Milton to May Angelou compatible with the fact that another man prefers Maya Angelou to Milton. If the conflict does have content, judgments must come into conflict. And if two judgments are in conflict, it follows as a point of logic that they cannot both be true.

What, then, is the diagnosis? Does the dispute over the canon describe a divergence in taste or a disagreement in judgment? The voluptuousness of Fish's indignation suggests the stouthearted commitment of a man who may know nothing about literature, but knows what he *likes*. The implications of this adopted pose are plainly distasteful to the Fish who recognizes that everyone party to the dispute is compelled to his or her own version of the truth. "No one in the field," Fish reminds us, "is aligning himself with falsities." But if truth is of the essence, there is no point in talking of tastes. And no point either in complaining that the champions of the traditional canon propose to put their principles into effect. "When the present shape of truth is compelling beyond a reasonable doubt," Fish writes, "it is our moral obligation to *act* on it and not to defer action in the name of an interpretive future that may never arise." Having warmly welcomed the truth with one hand, Fish proposes coldly to reject it with another. "What are these *truths*," he asks, "and how and *by whom* are they to be identified?" Of these three questions, the first is being asked rhetorically, and the second is unanswerable since beyond the sciences, no one knows how the truth is ever reached. It is the last of these questions that expresses the dissenting Fish, *by whom* functioning as a way of suggesting that the truth or various truths have been corrupted by a partisan, a political, agenda, and so do not count as truths at all.

This is an argument by insinuation, to give it a name and assign it a rhetorical category, and comprises the expectation that a series of slight doubts will sum to a substantial deficit. It is an argument that cannot survive a confrontation with a counterexample. Proponents of a core curriculum in arithmetic, to take the obvious case, often stress that the natural numbers follow one another in a certain order, so that ten is indisputably a greater number than nine. Greater for *whom*, one might ask, following Fish? The appropriate answer must surely be that it does not matter. The argument by multiculturalists in favor of a system according to which the number two is followed by the all-purpose many, or the denunciation by feminist epistemologists of a number system, given the prominence of the *prime* numbers, that is inescapably phallocentric—these we dismiss as an idiotic irrelevance.

We? Everyone.

§

I would not leave the reader with the impression that the reprehensible Fish is a representative Fish. He makes for good company, and if he is unreliable in his argument, he is throughout literate in his expression. He very seldom babbles, and having taken in the reader, he is himself very rarely taken in. Still, the space between being caught up in a rhetorical pose and being caught out by a rhetorical pose is not very wide. It is thus that Fish recounts his own experience with affirmative action. Passed over for some high-level administrative position, he attributes his bad luck to a preference for women or minorities on the part of the institution that might have hired him. "Although I was disappointed," he writes, "I did not conclude that the situation was unfair." Anyone who has come this far in Fish Studies will recognize this declaration as a form of feigned humility. Had Stanley Fish really been rejected for some senior position in favor of a less-qualified woman or black, he would not have yielded gracefully in the name of remedial affirmative action.

Strong illness, strong remedy? Not a bit of it. He would have been outraged.

5. The Dangerous Discipline

Reason does not err.

—Kurt Gödel

There was a certain rabbi in the town of Yehupetz. He had a long thin nose from which a drop was always trembling and a yellow beard that fell in tangles to his waist. Behind his back, the urchins of the village called him Zogn Gornisht, for his habit of hardly ever speaking. Young men about to be married would come to him for advice. The rabbi would sigh deeply, stare up at the ceiling of his study, lock his long fingers together, and mutter to himself without saying anything. When the elderly felt the wings of the Angel of Death beating about their bed, they would call for the rabbi. He would sit silently by their beside, but beyond intoning the blessings, he refused to say anything more.

At home, his wife had long despaired of hearing the rabbi enter into normal conversation. "That one," she would say, tapping her forehead significantly, "has been struck dumb by the Evil One himself."

It had not always been thus. The rabbi had been famous for his ingenious interpretations of Talmud. He would read a section from the tractate Bava Metzia, which deals with finding and giving gifts, and ask his students whether the right hand could give the left hand a gift.

"Nu?" he would ask, his eyes twinkling. His students sat there, concentrating on the question, but before any of them could answer, the rabbi would argue that if a man could give to others, then surely he could give to himself.

The students nodded.

Then in the next minute, the rabbi argued that this view was completely mistaken. "Nu, blockheads," he said, "Can a man be taller than himself? Then how can he give himself a gift?"

His reasoning was so clever, and his thin tenor voice so persuasive, that his students were once again forced to nod their heads in agreement.

But then the rabbi would say, "On the other hand," and show that everything he had just said was wrong as well. Dancing from foot to foot in impatience, his earlocks flapping as he moved his head vigorously, the rabbi explained that even if a man gives something to himself, some time must go by between the giving and the receiving of a gift, and in that time a man becomes something other than he was. If one of his students mentioned a commentary by Akiba, the rabbi would, at once, bring up another commentary by Yohanan ben Zakkai.

The Evil One, cursed be his name, corrupts each man according to a special plan. One day, later in the afternoon, a peddler carrying a sack appeared in Yehupetz. He was a short, broad-shouldered man, somewhat stooped from carrying his heavy sack. He had no more hair on his head than a pumpkin, but he had enough hair growing from his nose and ears to cover two heads. He took his supper in the kretchma, eating a bowl of kasha and groats mixed with curdled milk, and afterwards he visited the bathhouse. His fingernails were long and yellow, and when he took off his shoes, the men of Yehupetz noticed that his toes were long and monkeyish. That night, he slept with the other schnorrers on a wooden bench in the study hall.

The next day, he set off to peddle his wares. Unlike other peddlers, he did not stop and make small talk with the matrons who answered the door when he knocked.

"I have pots, two groschen," he would say brusquely.

"Your tongue, it would split in two if you said a few words more?"

"If tongues had wings, peddlers would fly."

To the pious Jewish matrons of Yehupetz, who covered their heads with kerchiefs, the peddler sold tin pots, scullery knives, darning needles, thread, and tailoring wax, but when he knocked on a door and a Polish serving girl answered, he would plunge his monkeyish hands into his sack and pull out colored ribbons or embroidered handkerchiefs or tortoise-shell combs.

The serving girl would look at these treasures and shake her head.

"But darling, there are many ways to pay me," the peddler would answer in perfect Polish.

His sack seemed to be bottomless. For the men of Yehupetz, he had a device for removing ear wax, a brass ball shaped like the head of a lion that could be placed over walking sticks, warm gloves lined with rabbit fur, and a variety of ointments for chilblains, night sweats, and haemorrhoids; for the urchins of the town, he had pennywhistles, candy, and cut beads, and for the young girls, silver bells, dolls with glass eyes, and tiny mirrors made of brass.

And for the rabbi's Talmud students, he had something special. He accosted them on the dusty street as they were going to the study hall. Holding up his hand, he said, "The Messiah has waited this long, a little longer he can wait."

The students stopped. The peddler reached into his sack and fished out a deck of playing cards. The oldest of the rabbi's students, a tall youth named Itche Bunzel, with a prominent Adam's apple and a long, thin nose like the rabbi's, took one look at the cards and spat into the street.

"My fine young gentlemen," the peddler said, "these are special cards."

"The devil himself deals such cards in Gehenna," said Itche Bunzel.

"Can the devil's cards do this?" the peddler asked, and riffled the cards in his hand. As the cards jumped under his fingers, a plump woman wearing absolutely no clothes appeared on the card backs, as if by magic.

A sudden blush shot through Itche Bunzel's cheeks. He turned on his heel, and stalked off, the other students following. Later that day, Gimpel the Goatherd observed Itche Bunzel sitting on a rock in the field above the village mill. He was trying to riffle through a deck of cards.

By the end of the week, the peddler was able, as the saying goes, to keep two kopeks company in his pocket. On Saturday morning, he attended services, and placed five groschen in the poor box. After fasting all day, he took his evening meal at the kretchma, where he ordered a carp head boiled with turnips, pickled beets, stewed onions, and pears in honey with almonds. The rabbi's students reported to him that the peddler no longer slept with the other schnorrers on the study hall benches, but had asked for a bed at the kretchma.

The rabbi asked Reb Avigtor to summon the peddler to his study.

"At once, Rabbi," said Reb Avigtor, and rushed off.

The rabbi was seated at his long wooden study table when Reb Avigtor knocked and opened the door slightly.

"We're here, Rabbi," he said.

"So I see."

The rabbi motioned the peddler to a chair. The peddler sat facing the rabbi, fingering his beard, and now and then poking at his ears. The rabbi coughed decorously.

As if he were reading the rabbi's mind, the peddler asked abruptly, "So where is it written that a man must be poor?"

The rabbi said, "Where is it written that cows must walk on four legs? Nevertheless, cows can't fly."

The peddler said nothing in response, but it seemed to the rabbi that there was something mocking in his thin smile. Then he reached into his sack and withdrew a leather-bound book and placed it on the rabbi's desk.

Even though the windows were closed, the flame on the rabbi's candle sputtered. The rabbi felt a pain in his nose and then he felt a pain in his ear. His hands and feet tingled. He felt the urge to cough. Drawing out his handkerchief, he sneezed violently instead. And then in an instant, the pains in his nose and ear vanished. It was revealed to him that everything was as it should be. A feeling of joy came over him. The peddler continued to sit where he had been sitting.

The very next day, the peddler was seen departing Yehupetz, his heavy sack slung over his shoulder. A week went by and then another. When the rabbi returned to his students, he observed a new power of analysis in himself. Passages in the tractates that had long been mysterious were suddenly clear. He saw meaning behind meanings. Aramaic words would form and reform themselves on the printed page. Arguments sprouted from his mouth like teeth. It appeared that if the whale had swallowed Jonah, then Jonah must have also swallowed the whale. Where before, the rabbi had been very orderly in discussion, so that a study of the Bava Batra would follow a discussion of the Bava Metzia, now he was frequently struck by new thoughts so that in a discussion of a difficult passage in the Bava Batra, which deals with damages, he would suddenly ask why King Solomon said that "a righteous man falls down seven times and gets up." One student would appeal to Rashi and another student to Rabbi Eleazer of Worms. The rabbi would listen impatiently. "So he gets up," he said. "Nu Blockheads, why seven times? Why not eight?" His students could barely follow the intricacies of his thought. He would pose the simplest of questions, and then reveal complexities behind the plain meaning of the Aramaic words. "Why is it written that Angels have two wings? Why not four?"

The students would grope for an answer. "Blockheads," the rabbi cried, "do you not see that the Almighty created being out of nothingness with only two numbers?"

In time, word of the rabbi's powers spread far beyond the town of Yehupetz. Students came to listen to his discourse from as far away as

Chelm and even Warsaw. He would no longer enter into disputations with his students, but carried on both sides of the discussion by himself, saying, "On the one hand," and "On the other hand," as if he were two people instead of one. More and more, the rabbi came to study the Talmud in order to formulate arguments, rather than formulating arguments in order to study the Talmud. He designated certain students for special study. Meeting with them in the study house after he had dismissed the others, he would demonstrate all manner of unusual propositions, showing how by means of logic, words could be made to deny what they seemed to assert, and assert what they seemed to deny. His eyes seemed to burn with a strange fire.

One afternoon, he walked home through the dusty streets of Yehupetz. As was his custom, he took only bread and an apple with honey for his evening meal. Afterwards, he mounted the narrow wooden steps to his study.

Beyond the study window, fruit trees were in bloom. Birds were twittering in the orchard. Insects whirred and chirped in the warm evening air.

The rabbi peered at the familiar surroundings of his study, the bookcases with their leather-bound volumes, the silver candlesticks, the wooden candleholder on his study desk, where his wife had lit a sputtering taper, the worn woven rug on the oak floor. He felt a pain in his nose and then again in his ears. There was a burning underneath his heart. The silver candlestick that his father, the rabbi of Yehupetz before him, had bequeathed to him, stood upright as a sentinel. It seemed to the rabbi that all the things in the world were symbols and that the universe was arranged as a gigantic argument. The pale stars just beginning to shine in the sky beyond his study window were asserting, "On the one hand," and the crescent-shaped new moon was replying, "On the other hand." The leather-bound books in the bookcase were making one claim and the very smoke in the air was answering with another. Everywhere things were in dispute and everywhere there was an argument, every part of the world talking, observing, contradicting, defining, mocking, saying "nu?," looking in feigned astonishment, pointing things out.

When the rabbi awoke, the candle had burnt itself out.

The next morning, the rabbi called his initiates together. "There is no truth," he said, "only argument."

His initiates looked at him uneasily. "Where is written," the rabbi asked, "that there must be truth?"

The rabbi then proceeded to argue that there could be truth in the world only if it were true that there was truth in the world.

His students nodded.

"Blockheads," the rabbi said, "should a man fish for carp if he needs a carp to fish?"

His students nodded again.

From that day forth, the rabbi devoted himself to arguing against every interpretation of the Talmud. There was nothing he could not do, no position he could not uphold. Whenever he reached a particularly puzzling interpretation, he showed that, contrary to expectation, it really was in accord with the tractate and with what Rabbi Akiba and the other commentators meant to say. Then he would say, "On the other hand," and show that Rabbi Akiba and the commentators were wrong and that Rashi was right all along.

His students nodded again.

As the rabbi spoke, he paced back and forth in the study hall, his earlocks flapping, his black gabardine coat open. He stabbed at the air with his forefinger and pulled on his earlobes. He spoke so rapidly that several times, he seemed in danger of swallowing his tongue.

His arguments grew more and more outrageous. He argued that there was no obligation to keep holy the Sabbath and that if there was no obligation to keep holy the Sabbath, then God has never made a covenant with Moses. He argued that the dietary laws could only be kept if they were violated. He argued that women who were unclean were clean and that women who were clean were unclean.

His disciples and his initiates were troubled, but they were afraid of his ridicule and the power of his tongue. Reb Avigtor said to him, "There are things that are given us to know and things that are given to us not to know." The rabbi turned and in a torrent of words showed that what was known was false and that what was not known was true. Reb Avigtor blanched.

In truth, the rabbi lived only for the moments that he could appear before his initiates. He slept little and ate less and less. He ceased attending to his conjugal duties and spent most of his nights pacing in his study, and then falling asleep in his chair. His beard grew more and more tangled, and his eyebrows bushy. Small insects appeared in the pockets of his gabardine coat. At night, a strange fire seemed to glow in his study, and bats beat about the study's windowpanes. In the morning, when he walked to the study house, the village cats woke from their slumber and hissed at him before slinking across the street.

Before his initiates, he now argued that the pious man was wicked and the wicked man was pious. He argued that if nothing was forbidden, then everything was permitted, and then he argued that nothing was forbidden. He argued that the Messiah had come and that the Messiah would never come.

That evening he continued to dispute with himself in his study. From far away, he could hear an owl hooting. "Hoo Hoo," it said. "Nu Blockhead," the rabbi said, "where is it written that owls should hoot?" The rabbi paused for a moment in his pacing. "On the other hand, where is it written that owls shouldn't hoot?" He answered his own question with a question. "If owls don't know Torah, why shouldn't they hoot?" The owl continued to hoot: "Hoo Hoo." The rabbi returned to his study table and lit the taper that his wife had set in his candlestick. The smoke tickled his nose and he sneezed. "Where is it written," he said out loud after wiping his nose with the back of his hand, "that a man should sneeze when he smells smoke?" The owl hooted again, a long low strange hoot. The rabbi said, "So hoot." And then he said, "May your hoots be happy." He sat himself in his study chair and looked at the walls of his study. He began to say, "On the other hand," but then he could not think of anything to add. "On the one hand," he said, holding up his left hand, "and on the other hand," he said, holding up his right hand. "So nu, Blockhead," he said to himself.

The next day, he asked his initiates to comment on a section in the Bava Batra that begins "so that I can hide from you." He was struck by the words, "so that I can hide from you." Itche Bunzel said that by mehetza, the sages meant a division, not a partition, since in Numbers 31:43, it is written that "the mehetza of the congregation was," and this must mean a division, not a partition. The rabbi nodded, but he did not say anything else. Another of his initiates took up the discussion, and then another.

That evening, his wife told him his eldest daughter had scraped her knee. "So nu?" the rabbi said. His wife waited for him to say, "on the other hand," but the rabbi did not say anything and resumed eating his soup. And thereafter the rabbi began to say less and less in study hall. Little by little, Itche Bunzel began to lead the discussions, and when Reb Avigtor asked him why, Itche Bunzel pointed to his temple with his index finger, and said, "God has put a lock on his tongue." Later that day, Reb Avigtor told the rabbi what Itche Bunzel had said. The rabbi looked at Reb Avigtor and then he looked beyond him.

"If there is a God," he finally said.

6. Necessary Nature

I imagine that all of us want to ignore—when possible—the contingent, and seize the essential, aspect of any idea.

—Barry Mazur[1]

Whatever the x, certain propositions are true of x; others not. Some philosophers have flirted with the idea of a bare particular, an individual existing before the assignment of its properties; but there is no particular x so bare that nothing is true of it, and if something is true of x, then it is no longer bare. Truth is by itself a weak fixative, one imposing no distinction between the fact that Pluto is cold and the fact that Pluto is self-identical. Facts are facts. Modal concepts are needed to animate the distinction. That Pluto is cold is contingently true. It might have been warm. That Pluto is self-identical is necessarily true. It could not have been, or be, otherwise. Pluto's sense of self-identity is crowd-sourced: $\Box(\text{Pluto} = \text{Pluto})$ because $\forall x \Box (x = x)$.[2] Philosophers who draw and then endorse these distinctions have acquiesced in Essentialism, the view that individuals have some properties accidentally, and others necessarily.

In the social and political sciences, no philosophical position has been more vigorously abused. An example, chosen at random: "The concept of Essentialism states that there are innate, essential differences between men and women. That is, we are born with certain traits."[3] This particular quotation comes close to parody in suggesting that human beings might be born *without* certain traits, but the animadversions that it reveals, or otherwise suggests, are so widespread as to amount to a contemporary academic dogma. An unthinking commitment to Essentialism is thus often seen as a convincing explanation, or a convenient excuse, for structures of control or oppression. When large-scale differences in privilege, income, or longevity are attributed to necessary features of certain groups, a white-hot heat emerges from the ensuing discussions.

Essentialism is a full-bodied doctrine. Men, Aristotle argued in the *Nichomachean Ethics*, are rational animals: $\forall x(Mx \supset Rx)$. The thesis was common throughout antiquity and the Middle Ages. What is true of all men is surely true of any particular man—Capeheart Haskins, say. Haskins is a man, after all, whence the rational Haskins by instantiation in $\forall x(Mx \supset Rx)$ and *modus ponens*. This is not an inference calculated to vex the empiricist. But neither does it say very much about whether in thinking about the manly *essentials*, one should look toward rationality. *Yes*, contingent on a pair of inferences: (i) If $\forall x\Box(Mx \supset Rx)$ then $\forall x(\Box Mx \supset \Box Rx)$; and (ii) if M(Haskins) then $\Box$(M(Haskins). *No* otherwise. The law of distribution (i) is a theorem of modal logic; but whether in being a man Haskins is necessarily a man is another question entirely.

Is there a possible world in which *he* is not?

It is with questions such as this that recondite issues in metaphysics acquire a lurid contemporary relevance. "For the current wave of gender-fluid artists," one reads in the *Guardian*, "it's not about dressing up, but about expressing their core identity. Ezra Furman muses about gender in the song "Wobbly":

> I've just been changing genders fluidly
>
> Because they'll never pin me
>
> Down in the pages
>
> Like a bug or bumblebee
>
> Never classify me, don't try.[4]

The idea that gender-fluid artists are committed to expressing their *core* identity suggests that they have a core identity to express. If this is so, it is only the width of cigarette paper that separates them from a variety of Essentialism. The question, of course, is which variety. Almost everyone today rejects brute masculinity as part of any convenient core.

It is fashionable to do so.

If Haskins is masculine, he is masculine as Pluto is cold. It is just one of those things. Thus fashion. It is rather more difficult to say of Haskins that his origins are as fungible as his masculinity. In this, the real world, Haskins figures in quite a specific line of descent; he has a history. One can imagine Haskins enjoying the usufructs of gender fluidity. But given the fact that Haskins is who he is, could he be who he was not?

It is not easy to see how.

This is an argument with a considerable amount of carrying power. If it indicates that Haskins as an individual has, at least, something by way of an essence, when generalized just slightly, it also indicates that men, considered now as a set, have an essence of their own, too. Not rationality. That cause is lost. But while {M} is not necessarily rational, it is necessarily, one would think, the kind of thing that it is—something like an animal, according to Aristotle, so that $\{M\} \subseteq \{A\}$. Is there a world in which $\{M\} \subseteq \{A^c\}$, so that men are found among the paper clips, but not the animals? If not, then this *is* something essential about men.

Human origins are one example of strong and controlling modal intuitions; they are in some sense essential to human nature. Equally compelling are considerations of composition. If *x is* a human being, there is a limit to what one might discover about how *x* is composed or made. Given that *x* is a human being, could any discovery indicate that he or she was composed of ice? Sea water? Pure sodium? Not being made of ice, sea water or pure sodium is an essential feature of human nature.

Being made as human beings are made—*yes*, this is an essential part of human nature.

Identifying individuals is often a matter of pointing them out—there he is, *that's* Haskins. Specifying groups of them (contract lawyers, professional archers, anarchists, ax murderers, human beings) is a matter of specifying the sets to which they belong. The set {E} of even numbers may be defined by enumeration, in which case it is one number after the other {E} = {2, 4, 6, 8, ...}. But a definition by enumeration does not specify {E} uniquely. Enumeration can go no further than the specification of some initial segment in {E}. The set {2, 4, 6, 8, ...} is an initial segment of both {2, 4, 6, 8, 10, ...} and {2, 4, 6, 8, 9}, leaving {E} unsaturated.[5]

{E} may be defined once and for all only by an explicit specification of the even numbers—$\{k \mid \exists n: (n \in Z \;\&\; k = 2n)\}$, for example. Specification does what enumeration does not: It makes for a saturation of {E}, whereupon it involves the mathematician (or anyone at all) in a full-blooded commitment to Essentialism. If Essentialism involves necessity, then specification rules out ambiguity by insisting that $\Box(\{E\} = \{k \mid \exists n: (n \in Z \;\&\; k = 2n)\})$. If this were not so, there would be a possible world in which {E} denoted the even numbers but in which there was a $k \in \{E\}$ such that for no n was it true that $k = 2n$. {E} would again be unsaturated. On some versions of the even numbers, {E} would include k; on other versions, not.

It is worth noting that $\Box(\{E\} = \{k \mid \exists n: (n \in Z \;\&\; k = 2n)\})$ is itself necessarily true: $\Box[\Box(\{E\} = \{k \mid \exists n: (n \in Z \;\&\; k = 2n)\})]$. This is, in fact, a theorem when expressed in S4, since $\Box\Box A$ is one of its defining axioms. This is another way of expressing the price exacted by successful specification.

The argument just given shows why this is so.

Writing in the second volume of his *Principles of Geology*, Charles Lyell asked "whether species have a real and permanent existence in nature; or whether they are capable, as some naturalists pretend, of being indefinitely modified in the course of a long series of generations."[6] This disjunction suggests a dramatic inference. If species have a real and permanent existence in nature, they could not be indefinitely modified over the course of evolution; thence by contraposition, if species *are* indefinitely modified over the course of evolution, they could not have a real and permanent existence in nature. This inference, more than any other, has been the historical fulcrum by which Essentialism has been displaced from its position of historical prominence. What is Darwin's theory, *au fond,* if not the claim that *something* can be indefinitely modified over the course of evolution? If that something is not a species, it is hard to know why Darwin entitled his book as he did; but there is no doubt that in reflecting on his own work, this is what Darwin meant: *No species:*

> Systematists will be able to pursue their labors as at present; but they will not be incessantly haunted by the shadowy doubt whether this or that form be in essence a species... In short, we will have to treat species in the same manner as those naturalists treat genera, who admit that genera are merely artificial combinations made for convenience. This may not be a cheering prospect; but we shall at least be freed from the vain search for the undiscovered and undiscoverable essence of the term species.[7]

This is not an easy argument to overlook, or to rebut. It is perfectly true that sets are not dynamic objects. They cannot add or shed members and remain the same. They are what they are. Given the Axiom of Extensionality, that is all that they are. A set is completely determined by its members. Ditto a species, at least to the extent that it is a set. Dogs form a biological species—*Canis lupus familiaris,* in fact—one would think, if anything does. The very first member of this species has been lost to the injuries of time; but whatever the species, it must have had a ragged beginning. No one able to trace the dogs backward could possibly say of a given dog that that is where the species began. On some accounts, the set $\{D\} = \{d_1, d_2, d_3, \ldots, d_n\}$ began with one initial member, d_{1i}, and on other accounts, with quite a different initial member, d_{1k}.

If this is so, are there for this reason two species?

Who knows? There are certainly two sets.

If evolutionary biologists wish to say that there is yet only *one* species—those damned dogs—then they must offer a principled reason to reject either one initial beginning or the other. But just how could one set be ruled inadmissible? In virtue of what? The tendency to remark that one progenitor of the dogs is not really a dog because it is insufficiently dog-like is, of course, very strong. How dog-like must something like a dog be to be reckoned dog-like? Any organism whatsoever will share some qualities with the dogs, after all, but if what is really wanted in this context is a standard of similarity contingent on the dog's *essential* qualities, there is no need to bother looking for that proverbial first dog at all. The sets of dogs are those creatures that are necessarily dogs. Darwin might have said as much had he not persuaded himself that the search for such essences was somehow in vain.

If the set of dogs, and so the species, is ragged at one end, it is incomplete at the other. Dogs are not yet extinct, and the set of them is growing. Enumeration works to the same disadvantages in evolutionary thought as in number theory. Where the set begins, no one knows; but how it ends, *if* it ends, no one knows either. The greater part of the set is unavailable for inspection. For all anyone knows, there may be infinitely many dogs waiting in the wings of time.

Specification of the sort that defined the even numbers is needed to saturate {D}. Since it is dogs and not numbers at issue, the kth dog, like all his predecessors, needs to be defined in terms of some characteristic other than being a multiple of two.

A recursive definition? $\{D\} = \{k \mid \exists n: (n \in Z \,\&\, \mathbf{Des}(n\text{-}1\ k) \,\&\, \mathbf{Dog}(n\text{-}1)\}$. The set {D} comprises those individuals descended from dogs. This definition depends, of course, on some ground plan specifying the dogginess of the base case. In view of the ragged nature of the dogs, this is just what is lacking. An explicit definition is thus mandatory: $\{D\} = \{k \mid \mathbf{Dog}(k)\}$. Whereupon experts will wish to expand $\forall x(\mathbf{Dog}(k) \equiv P_1(k),\ldots,P_n(k)$ in all sorts of expert ways. The question at hand is whether the resulting definition $\{D\} = \{k \mid \mathbf{Dog}(k)\}$ is necessary or whether it is simply a contingent truth, a fact about some dogs? If it is not necessary, the various properties expertly affirmed of dogs are among their accidents, and not their essence. If this is so, $\{D\} = \{k \mid \mathbf{Dog}(k)\}$ cannot resolve a point of ambiguity between two competitive versions of {D}, both unsaturated inasmuch as they do not (and cannot) encompass dogs not yet born. In some possible world, one version of {D} incorporates pooches for which $\forall x(\mathbf{Dog}(k) \equiv P_1(k),\ldots,P_n(k)$ fails, and another, pooches for which it does not. Lacking a principled way of distinguishing between them, biologists are forced to a double welcome.

This means that insofar as species are sets, dogs do not form a single species.

Why not leave it at that and make do with a completely nominalist program in evolutionary theory? This is, if not the hidden urge, then, at least, the hidden logic of Darwinian thought. It represents a position that would seem to rule as incoherent commonly made evolutionary claims—that dogs are descended from wolves, for example. Biologists would surely wish to claim that dogs not yet born will still be descended from wolves. It is an aspect of their nature. Large principles of Linnaean taxonomy become incoherent as well. And for the same reason.

All of the old metaphysical dodges may be invoked at this point. Individual dogs, *yes*, species *no*, but in writing a textbook about the anatomy or physiology of the dog, what harm is there in basing the book on the fact that dogs are in some sense similar? What harm? Philosophers know how this ends. Dogs are in some sense similar, but they are in some sense similar in being dogs. If their similarity makes it into the textbooks, why not their dogginess? And what is their dogginess if not their essential part? And if their essential part exists, is this not what biologists have always meant by a species?

When it comes to the dogs, specifying their species is intimately involved in their analysis; and Essentialism is intimately involved in specifying their species. These discussions have by no means come to an end. In studying human origins, Ian Tattersall, writing in an issue of *Inference*, has given his assent to human species—many of them; but he has declined to invest himself in their genera.[8]

To be an essentialist about *human* nature, one must believe that necessarily if *x* is a human being then *x* has some property (or properties) P. Human essences have, as one might expect, come and gone. Almost every political theorist over the past 200 years has suggested something about the essentials. (And, of course, the essentials of the essentials, to adopt a Plotinus-lite point of view.) Descartes, Locke, Hobbes, Hume, Voltaire, Diderot, Rousseau, Madison, Herder, Goethe, Jefferson, Vico, Marx, Weber, and Freud all presented forthrightly, or hinted at obliquely, some doctrine of human nature. Philosophers or sociologists most interested in avoiding traditional concepts of human nature almost always appear on analysis to have embraced what they most wish to avoid. Human nature, Norbert Elias remarked, is second nature. This is wonderfully suggestive. Human nature is neither innate nor essential, but acquired, like an overcoat. But inasmuch as no other animal seems able (or willing) to acquire any aspect of human nature as *its* overcoat, the revised Elias may still be seen wandering in all the old familiar circles. Such items as self-control become second nature in certain societies; and self-control is thus an accidental human characteristic. What is essential to human nature is the power to acquire the camouflage of local coloring. To read this as a denial of human essentialism would be a little like assuming that the ability of the puffer fish to blow itself up reflects nothing fundamental about its biological nature. René Girard, by way of contrast, had no illusions on this score. He was, he acknowledged, writing about human nature; and he was writing about the way in which human nature endowed human history with its meaning.

Various claims on behalf of human nature admit of only one form of radical rejection. Writing in 1859, Charles Darwin denied there was any such thing. This is very much of a piece with his denial of a human species. One denial follows from the other. If human beings have an *unlimited* capacity to change, they could not form a species; and if they cannot (or do not) form a species, what is the subject of human nature? Or the point in studying it?

This is not quite a compelling argument. There is a loophole. If human beings or dogs *do* form species, then Darwinian change, if those species exist at all, must represent discontinuities between them. The last of our simian and the first of our human ancestors are members of separate sets. This makes for a very awkward reconciliation between Darwinian theory and ordinary modal intuitions, but not one that is philosophically impossible. Many species; many sets. When Noam Chomsky was asked about human nature, he responded equably that exposed to precisely the same stimuli, his granddaughter, but not a kitten, could acquire English. But as a linguist prepared to defend Darwin, at least to the extent that he is persuaded of a natural explanation for the existence of human language, Chomsky has also argued that human language has a one-time only character. A powerful, brain-changing mutation occurred in a specific individual. One time only! It was acquired by his descendants, and then spread rapidly throughout a small breeding population. If human language is, in fact, an essential aspect of human nature, and not simply an accident, then the first individual to possess the requisite faculty and his immediate ancestors (mother and father, obviously) must belong to different species.

This hardly seems reasonable, but it does not seem a position amenable to rational rebuttal.

It is one thing to show that with respect to human beings certain properties exist and that they are essential; and it is quite another to show that they are unique. The number nine is necessarily greater than the number eight, but so is the number ten. Much of the anxiety about human essentialism turns on questions of uniqueness, and not existence. Nonetheless, as one might imagine, questions about uniqueness and questions about essentialism are related.

According to mainstream evolutionary theory, human beings and chimpanzees evolved from a common ancestor some five or six million years ago. This understanding of human origins has been widely assumed to undermine the belief in a qualitative difference between human beings and our presumed closest relations. Human beings differ from chimpanzees in degree, but not ultimately in kind. This argument is very difficult clearly to state. The sequences 0001 and 1000 are both derived from the sequence 0000 by a one-letter permutation. This does not yet suggest that 0001 and 1000 differ in degree but not kind, the more so since 0001 and 1000 are further from each other than either is from 0000.

One line of evidence that has tended to support the Darwinian claim comes from comparative genomics. Numerous textbooks, scientific articles, popular science books, and even the policy statements of major scientific organizations such as the National Science Foundation, have claimed a remarkable genetic similarity between human beings and our nearest simian ancestors. But this argument, if valid, depends on the further assumption that there is a universal mapping h: G → O between an organism's genome G, and the organism O itself, such that that if G_1 is close to G_2, O_1 is bound to be close to O_2.

Is there such a mapping? It is hard to avoid the conclusion that the existence of such a homomorphism is precisely what is at issue in discussions of this sort. The assertion that differences between human beings and other animals are differences of degree and not kind has persuaded biologists that differences in kind are really differences in degree. Hannah Arendt was impressed by *homo faber*, man as maker; and ever since Darwin introduced his theory in 1859, biologists prepared to reject Essentialism in all its forms have argued that while men make their tools, so do other animals. Crows bend wires, chimpanzees use sticks. The tool-making powers of crows or chimpanzees rather resemble a dog walking on its hind legs. What is surprising is not that it is done well, but that it is done at all.

The real threat to human uniqueness does not arise in the animal kingdom at all. As machines do more and more of what human beings used to do, including tasks that previously only human *minds* could do, the uniqueness of essential human traits seems queerly undermined, if only because a century ago, no one saw any threat coming from *that* direction. Stephen Hawking has recently suggested that intelligent machines will eventually take over from human beings as computers begin to express their own purposes and accomplish their own ends. Proponents of strong AI, such as Marvin Minsky, have long thought that consciousness could exist on a silicon platform. Like Ray Kurzweil, he may well be encouraged to download his consciousness to a computer chip no larger than the head of a pin—a perfect fit, as his phrenologist would say. If machines do imitate or eclipse the capacities of human mind, some widespread sense of human uniqueness will be lost.

But *not* the correlative sense that an individual *x* must have certain properties in order to be a human being.

These are distinct issues.

"We are more insignificant than we ever could have imagined," the physicist Lawrence Krauss has written. "So we're insignificant on a scale that Copernicus never would have imagined," he added, lest anyone should fail to understand his drift.[9] This view is interesting because it functions as an axiom among physicists, who almost to a man believe (or say) that human life is insignificant because the earth is not the center of the universe. This is an argument as persuasive as the comparable claim that London played no significant role in the British Empire because it wasn't the Empire's geographical center. Discoveries in astronomy showing the privileged position of earth within our solar system (and of our solar system within our galaxy) have further challenged any strong version of the Copernican principle.

There are, speaking very roughly, three separate issues at work in these discussions:[10] (i) the relationship between essential human properties, if they exist, and human significance on a cosmic level; (ii) the relationship between human uniqueness, if human beings are unique, and human significance on a cosmic level; and (iii) the relationship between Essentialism and the structure of the cosmos. It is quite clear that the issues raised in (i) and (ii) may be duplicated at a distance when precisely the same questions are asked about the relationship between living creatures in general and the cosmic significance of biological structures in the universe.

(i) A simple modal argument is sometimes of use in this argument; and if not of use, then carelessly neglected. If human beings are largely insignificant in the cosmos, then surely they are not necessary either. Krauss says as much explicitly. "You could get rid of us and all the galaxies and everything we see in the universe and it will be largely the same." But if human beings are not necessary to the universe, then it follows that the universe is not sufficient for human beings. If $\sim(\sim Q \supset \sim P)$ then $\sim(P \supset Q)$. If this is so, anything that might reasonably called a naturalistic explanation for the emergence of human life is beside the point. There could not be any such thing.

It cannot be said that physicists such as Krauss would welcome this inference.

(ii) Are human beings the only examples of conscious or highly intelligent life in the cosmos? This is a question that for the past fifty years (or slightly more) has been held in suspension between Fermi's paradox and the Drake equation. Considering the existence of aliens, Enrico Fermi asked a table of physicists where they might be if, in fact, they really existed; and considering the probability of their existence, Francis Drake argued that since that probability of intelligent life elsewhere in the universe converged rapidly to 1 the further the universe was scanned, there must be some very good reason for the fact that they have not yet appeared. Opinion among astronomers and physicists is strongly in favor of the conclusion that there is nothing so terribly unique about human beings that something similar should not be widely available throughout the cosmos. That all searches for something similar have been fruitless has not in the least diminished their enthusiasm—or, one might add, their need for additional funding.

The belief that human beings are alone in the universe because they are an accident in the universe is widely thought an acceptable, although disappointing, possibility.

The belief that human beings are alone in the universe because they are *unique* in the universe is now among the forbidden thoughts.

The geneticist Michael Denton has recently contributed a new point of view to this discussion.[11] Denton is very much a champion of Essentialism in evolutionary biology, very much the champion of species as real and enduring Platonic forms. There are features of the human species, he has argued, that are necessary to human beings if they are to be the kinds of creatures that in fact they are. He has drawn a markedly stronger conclusion. Those features of the human species that are necessary to the species are necessarily unique as well: If $\forall x\Box(Hx \supset Px)$ then $\forall x\Box(Px \supset Hx)$. If P is necessarily true of human beings then anything that is P is necessarily a human being. Although Denton is agnostic about the possibility of alien forms of life, he is quite certain that should they be discovered, then necessarily they will be indistinguishable from human beings as they now exist on earth.

The human species is real, permanent, enduring, and *unique*.

(iii) The revival in recent times of the thesis that human being exhibit, because they possess, something like an essential human nature has been made possible by the revival of modal logic and ancillary ideas of necessity and possibility. Essentialism, although still reviled by feminists, postmodernists, literary critics, and many historians, has enjoyed among analytic philosophers an enhancement in prestige. Very powerful ideas are involved. Some appear to lead to valid arguments, and even arguments that are sound. No one today can quite afford to take the identity theory of mind as seriously as it once was taken before its underlying modal structure was understood. Essentialism is of obvious relevance to issues of human nature and its properties, but much to everyone's surprise, Essentialism has played an important role in speculative theology as well. Anselm's ontological argument is now more than one thousand years old, and in the long history of religious thought, no one persuaded of its validity has remained long persuaded. Bertrand Russell is an example, his conviction that the argument was valid remaining vivid in his mind for the time it took for him to slap his forehead and exclaim *what was I thinking?* In 1970, Kurt Gödel expressed a version of the ontological argument in modal logic; it was this argument that he showed to Dana Scott, who, in turn, made it known to other modal logicians. It is today *still* little known.

More recently, Alvin Plantinga has created a version of the ontological argument in which from the premise that if there is a possible world **W** such that in **W** there exists an x, such that x exists necessarily, it follows that x exists. Plainly there exists such a world, **W**—our own, in fact. Plantinga modestly affirmed of his own argument that it was "victorious," but unlike the original ontological argument, which persuaded no one, Plantinga's argument has proven devilishly difficult to rebut, and philosophers have been left with the strange conclusion that the very ensemble of ideas that have made it possible again to discuss human nature may in the end have made it possible to establish a proof of the existence of God for the first time in human history.

7. Disgusting, No?

Although I am a fellow at the Discovery Institute, I have never supported the theory of intelligent design, criticizing it in print, and in podcasts, and over the open microphone whenever I get my hands on one.

I may have to change my mind. Nothing so commends the theory to my attention as efforts by the scientific establishment to suppress it.

They have, those efforts, been vigorous. Graduate students and untenured faculty quite understand that when it comes to Darwin, dissent is unwelcome.

Journalists now cringe with the best of them. When the linguist John McWhorter interviewed the biochemist Mike Behe on Bloggingheads, he was heard to mumble something in praise of Behe's work.

His words had hardly left his lips when the interview was cancelled.[1]

McWhorter issued an apology at once.[2]

What could he have been thinking?

He would never think it again.

In an orgy of mutual recrimination, Robert Wright, Bloggingheads's director, and George Johnson, a science journalist, lowered their foreheads to the floor. Each man invited the other to kick him, the results proving as satisfactory as a high colonic.

If thought control has in the past been vigorous, it is now shameless. Having signed a contract for the showing of the documentary *Darwin's Dilemma*, the Los Angeles Science Center cancelled the screening the moment they were reminded of what they had done. Officials cited the contract as an explanation. Darwinian bloggers at once lowered their heads in a display of common legal concern. In its press release, the

Discovery Institute referred to the Los Angeles Science Center as the Smithsonian Institute's affiliate. The definite article was in error. The Los Angeles Science Center is a Smithsonian affiliate. There are others.

So?

Does anyone believe that had the Discovery Institute proposed to show a film praising Darwin and his works, anyone anywhere would have objected?

The very thought is absurd. When it comes to Darwin, no form of adulation is extreme, and no form of dissent tolerable.

Cancelling the screening was an exercise in thought control. Like intellectual thugs the world over, officials at both the Smithsonian and the Los Angeles Science Center imagine that those who cannot see bad thoughts cannot conceive them. Because they are stupid as well as arrogant, they remain unaware that the most effective way to suggest that a position in thought is plausible is to attempt to suppress it.

Look at me. I may have to reexamine all my long-held beliefs about intelligent design.

Disgusting, no? And disgusting especially in virtue of the scientific community's solemn affirmation of the virtues of free speech and open inquiry. Don't take my word for it. Freedom of thought is widely considered a virtue by those proposing to deny it. The World Summit on the Information Society declared: "We reaffirm, as an essential foundation of the Information Society, and as outlined in Article 19 of the Universal Declaration of Human Rights, that everyone has the right to freedom of opinion and expression; that this right includes freedom to hold opinions without interference and to seek, receive and impart information and ideas through any media and regardless of frontiers."[3]

Such is theory. So far as the real scientific community is concerned, theory defers to practice, and practice, of course, to the imperative need to protect Darwin from his critics. Everyone has the right to freedom of opinion and its expression, the scientific community believes, but the right may be exercised just so long as the opinions expressed are those with which we agree.

This is hardly a novel doctrine.

Is it an exaggeration?

A reckless distortion of the truth?

Let us put the matter to the test. The Los Angeles Science Center has offered a clear-cut case of thought control in action. What is the likely reaction from the American scientific community?

I will venture a prediction. There will be no reaction whatsoever.

And what of the reaction of the Darwinian blogosphere, prepared as ever to swoon with indignation at any rebuke to Darwin's thought?

They will, to a blogger, applaud the cancellation. They will, in fact, discover an entirely new appreciation for subtleties in the law of contracts, citing Williston when possible, and one another when not.

And the reaction of the general public?

They will do nothing very extravagant—for now.

8. Majestic Ascent: *Darwin on Trial*

Richard Dawkins published *The Blind Watchmaker* in 1986.[1] The appearance of design in nature, Dawkins argued, is an illusion. Complex biological structures may be entirely explained by random variations and natural selection. Why biology should be quite so vested in illusions, Dawkins did not say. *The Blind Watchmaker* captured the public's imagination, but in securing the public's allegiance, very little was left to chance. Those critics who believed that living systems appear designed because they *are* designed underwent preemptive attack in the *New York Times*. "Such are the thought habits of uncultivated intellects," wrote the biologist Michael Ghiselin, "—children, savages and simpletons."

Comments such as these had the effect of raw meat dropped carelessly among carnivores. A scramble ensued to get the first bite. No one bothered to attack the preposterous Ghiselin. It was Richard Dawkins who had waggled his tempting rear end, and behind Dawkins, fesse à fesse, Charles Darwin. With the publication in 1991 of *Darwin on Trial*, Phil Johnson did what carnivores so often do: he took a bite.

Johnson was at the time a professor of law at the University of California at Berkeley, a man whose training had given him what great lawyers so often have, and that is a shrewd eye for the main chance. Darwin's theory, Johnson observed, is hardly in need of empirical support: it is its own best friend. "The prevailing assumption in evolutionary science," he wrote, "seems to be that speculative possibilities, without experimental confirmation, are all that is really necessary." This is wrong only to the extent that speculative possibilities without experimental confirmation are often all that is really *possible*.

Every paleontologist writing since Darwin published his masterpiece in 1859 has known that the fossil record does not support Darwin's theory. The theory predicted a continuum of biological forms, so much so that from the right perspective, species would themselves be seen as taxonomic artifacts, like the classification of certain sizes in men's suiting as *husky*. Questions about the *origin* of species were resolved in the best possible way: there are no species and so there is no problem. Inasmuch as the historical record suggested a *discrete* progression of fixed biological forms, it was fatal to Darwin's project. All the more reason, Darwin argued, to discount the evidence in favor of the theory. "I do not pretend," he wrote, "that I should ever have suspected how poor a record of the mutations of life, the best preserved geological section presented, had not the difficulty of our not discovering innumerable transitional links between the species which appeared at the commencement and close of each formation, pressed so hardly on my theory."[2]

This is, as Johnson noted, self-serving gibberish.

Few serious biologists are today willing to defend the position that Dawkins expressed in *The Blind Watchmaker.* The metaphor remains stunning and so the watchmaker remains blind, but he is now deaf and dumb as well. With a few more impediments, he may as well be dead.

The publication in 1983 of Motoo Kimura's *The Neutral Theory of Molecular Evolution* consolidated ideas that Kimura had introduced in the late 1960s. On the molecular level, evolution is entirely stochastic, and if it proceeds at all, it proceeds by drift along a leaves-and-current model. Kimura's theories left the emergence of complex biological structures an enigma, but they played an important role in the local economy of belief. They allowed biologists to affirm that they welcomed responsible criticism. "A critique of neo-Darwinism," the Dutch biologist Gert Korthof boasted, "*can* be incorporated into neo-Darwinism if there is evidence and a good theory, which contributes to the progress of science."[3]

By this standard, if the Archangel Gabriel were to accept personal responsibility for the Cambrian explosion, his views would be widely described as neo-Darwinian. In *Darwin on Trial*, Johnson ascended majestically above the usual point of skepticism. It was the great case of *Darwin et al. v. the Western Religious Tradition* that occupied his attention. The issue had been joined long before Johnson wrote. But the case had not been decided. It had not been *decisively* decided and like some terrifying cripple, it had continued to bang its crutches through all the lower courts of Hell and Dover, Pennsylvania.

A few nodding judges such as Stephen Jay Gould thought to settle the matter by splitting the difference between litigants. To science, Gould assigned everything of importance, and to religion, nothing. Such was his theory of non-overlapping magisteria, or NOMA, a term very much suggesting that Gould was endowing a new wing at the Museum of Modern Art. Serving two masters, Gould supposed that he would be served by them in turn. He was mistaken. In approaching Darwin's theory of evolution, theistic evolutionists acquired a posture of expectant veneration, imagining hopefully that their deference would allow them to lick the plates from various scientific tables. They were in short order assured that having settled for nothing, nothing is what they would get. From the likes of Richard Dawkins or Daniel Dennett, Gould got what *he* deserved.

And from Phillip Johnson too, but in a different way and with different ends in mind.

The scientific establishment had long believed that *in re Darwin et al. v. The Western Religious Tradition*, Darwin would prevail. They expected to be assigned governance over the ideology of a democratic society. Their palms had collectively commenced to itch. Newspapers hymned Darwin's praise, and television documentaries—breathless narrator, buggy jungle—celebrated his achievement. Museum curators rushed to construct Darwinian dioramas in which human beings were shown ascending, step by step, from some ancient simian conclave, one suspiciously like the faculty lounge at Harvard. A very considerable apparatus of propaganda and persuasion was put at the disposal of the Darwinian community.

And, yet, no matter the extent to which Darwin's theory was said to be beyond both reappraisal and reproach, the conviction remained current that it was not so, or if so, not entirely so.

"Why not consider," Johnson asked, "the possibility that life is what it so evidently seems to be, the product of creative intelligence?"

The question is entirely reasonable. It is the question that every thoughtful person is inclined to ask.

So why not ask it?

No standard by which science is justified as an institution rules it out. The ones commonly employed—naturalism, falsifiability, materialism, methodological naturalism—are useless as standards because transparent as dodges.

The geneticist Richard Lewontin—Harvard, oddly enough—provided an answer to Johnson's question that is a masterpiece of primitive simplicity. It surely deserves to be quoted at length and quoted in full:

> Our willingness to accept scientific claims that are against common sense is the key to an understanding of the real struggle between science and the supernatural. We take the side of science in spite of the patent absurdity of some of its constructs, in spite of its failure to fulfill many of its extravagant promises of health and life, in spite of the tolerance of the scientific community for unsubstantiated just-so stories, because we have a prior commitment, a commitment to materialism. It is not that the methods and institutions of science somehow compel us to accept a material explanation of the phenomenal world, but, on the contrary, that we are forced by our *a priori* adherence to material causes to create an apparatus of investigation and a set of concepts that produce material explanations, no matter how counter-intuitive, no matter how mystifying to the uninitiated. Moreover, that materialism is absolute, for we cannot allow a Divine Foot in the door. The eminent Kant scholar Lewis Beck used to say that anyone who could believe in God could believe in anything. To appeal to an omnipotent deity is to

allow that at any moment the regularities of nature may be ruptured, that miracles may happen.[4]

There is much in these remarks that is analytically defective. The "commitment to materialism" that Lewontin defends is hardly clear enough to merit rebuttal. The history of physics suggests the maxim that anything goes if something works. It is as useful a maxim in mathematical physics as it is in international finance.

Nonetheless, Lewontin, as Johnson understood, had properly grasped the dynamics of the Great Case, its inner meaning. What remains when materialism (or anything else) is subtracted from Lewontin's prior commitment is the prior commitment itself; and like all such commitments, it is a commitment *no matter what*. Had they read the *New York Review of Books*, mullahs in Afghanistan would have understood Lewontin perfectly. They would have scrupled only at the side he had chosen.

Darwin's theories are correspondingly less important for what they explain, which is very little, and more important for what they deny, which is roughly the plain evidence of our senses. "Darwin," Richard Dawkins noted amiably, "had made it possible to be an intellectually fulfilled atheist."[5]

But the Great Case, Johnson reminded his readers, has not yet been decided in the only court that counts, and that is the considered reflection of the human race. Efforts by one side to absent themselves from judgment are somewhat premature. Too much is at stake.

That much *is* at stake explains a good deal about the rhetoric of discussion in the United States, its vile tone. Biologists such as Jerry Coyne, Donald Prothero, Larry Moran, or P. Z. Myers are of the opinion that if they cannot win the argument, they had better not lose it, and what better way not to lose an argument than to abuse one's antagonist? If necessary, the biological establishment has been quite willing to demand of the Federal Courts that they do what it has been unable to do in the court of public opinion. If the law is unwilling to act on their behalf, they are quite prepared to ignore it. Having been spooked by some tedious Darwinian toady, the California Science Center cancelled with blithe unconcern a contract to show a film about the Cambrian explosion. Spooked by some other Darwinian toady, the Department of Physics at the University of Kentucky denied the astronomer Martin Gaskell an appointment in astrophysics that he plainly was due.

The California Science Center paid up.[6]

The University of Kentucky paid up.[7]

As Philip Johnson might well have reminded them, the law is a knife that cuts two ways.

At the Discovery Institute we often offer an inter-faith Prayer of Thanksgiving to the Almighty for the likes of P. Z. Myers, Larry Moran, Barbara Forrest, Rob Pennock and Jeffrey Shallit.

For Donald Prothero, we are prepared to sacrifice a ram.

And now? Both critics and defenders of Darwin's theory have been humbled by the evidence. We are the beneficiaries of twenty years of brilliant and penetrating laboratory work in molecular biology and biochemistry. Living systems are more complex than ever before imagined. They are strange in their organization and nature. No theory is remotely adequate to the facts.

There is some evidence that once again, the diapason of opinion is being changed. The claims of intelligent design are too insistent and too plausible to be frivolously dismissed and the inadequacies of any Darwinian theory too obvious to be tolerated frivolously. Time has confirmed what critics like Phil Johnson have always suspected. Darwin's theory is far less a scientific theory than the default position for a view in which the universe and everything in it assembles itself from itself in a never-ending magical procession. The religious tradition and with it, a sense for the mystery, terror, and grandeur of life, has always embodied insights that were never trivial.

The land is rising even as it sinks. And this, too, is a message that Phil Johnson was pleased to convey.

9. Memories of Ulaanbaatar

"So I'm curious. How did Ronald Reagan prove that if $(a + b) + n = a + (b + n)$ then $(a + b) + n + 1 = a + (b + n + 1)$. Can you share? Our side must have had a collective hemorrhoid when he got up."

"Hemorrhage, I think you mean."

"There's a difference?"

"Some people think so."

"Well, whatever. You want another one of those?"

"No, I'm good."

"The President didn't actually prove it. He did something better."

"Which was what?"

"He showed them how to prove it."

"Put me in the picture."

"Well, you've got to remember, they're all up there in Helsinki, snow everywhere, and everyone in shock over the thing with Tank."

"They ever find the bear, by the way?"

"No, I don't think so. But in any event, the President was in a giving mood. He could see the importance of the associative law. You've got to give the man credit. He got the big picture."

"For sure."

"The thing is, if $(a + b) + n = a + (b + n)$ then $(a + b) + n + 1 = a + (b + n + 1)$ is strictly hypothetical, if-then from the get-go."

"So?"

"It sets a lot of people off. Hell, it set the Russians off. They see that big staring *if* and they just shut down. You know what they're like, you spent, what, a couple of years in Moscow Station?"

"A couple of weeks, actually, but you're right. I know what they're like. But those new Russian blondes, my God, they were just coming on-line when I was there."

"I wouldn't know. I drew Ulaanbaatar, remember?"

"Terrible. I remember the plumbing. But anyway what's this hush-hush stuff the President gave away? I'll tell my grandkids."

"How are they, by the way? The little one make probation?"

"Not yet, but soon."

"That's great. But here's the deal. What the President told the Russians was that in order to prove the inductive hypothesis, you need to assume the antecedent and derive the consequent."

"He pulled that from where?"

"No idea. I couldn't make sense of the transcript. I studied French at Yale, don't forget. But you know, it's one of those things, I'm at the airport in Bucharest and I pick up a book that sets it all out. Hell of a thing. One minute it's Top Secret, the next, it's out in some potboiler in Bucharest."

"What's it called?"

"I forget, something about a tour. You need a refill?"

"No, I'm still good. I promised Marge I would go easy."

"I know how it is. Well anyway—here, let me just sketch it on the cocktail napkin. The first thing is you have an argument from premises, right?

The first premise: Brothers have the same surname.

The second: Richard and Stanley are brothers.

The third: Stanley has the surname Thompson.

The conclusion: Richard has the surname Thompson.

"And the second thing, you've got a hypothetical. If all brothers have the same surname, and if Richard and Stanley are brothers, and if Stanley has the surname Thompson, then Richard has the surname Thompson."

"So who are these Thompsons?"

"Something to do with submachine guns. I don't really know. But the point is that the two things are the same. That's what Ronnie gave away—the Delusion Theorem, the Deduction Theorem, something like that."

"What a name. What is it, I'm not following."

"The way that they're the same. If you go from premises to a conclusion, you can ball it all up in a hypothetical. It's the same thing."

"This the Russians didn't like?"

"This the Russians couldn't figure out."

"And you're telling me the Gipper could?"

"No, he was just handing this stuff off to Mack."

"Whatever happened to Mack?"

"I think he's in Butner Federal."

"Good man, Mack."

"The best."

"The thing that just put them out of the zone, the Russians, I mean, was this idea that you could prove a hypothetical by assuming its antecedent and then deriving its consequence."

"I can relate. It makes me want another drink too. What was I drinking? That's right, Cutty on the rocks. You good?"

"I'm good. I'm taking the Cessna up in about an hour. What the hell, I'll have another too. What can I hit up there?"

"The Attorney General?"

"You wish. But you see the point I'm getting at. The President gave it away, this idea that all you have to do to verify the inductive hypothesis is assume the antecedent."

"You mean that's all as in that's all?"

"Well, no, you have to derive the consequent too. So you start with the assumption that $(a + b) + n = a + (b + n)$ and then you derive $(a + b) + n + 1 = a + (b + n + 1)$. You do that, it's a done deal."

"This is something we could do?"

"But absolutely. The Israelis too. Now everyone can do it thanks to Sy."

"But the Russians didn't buy it?"

"Called it a provocation."

"So what happened in the end?"

"The usual food fights. Everyone went home with egg on their ties. Except for the Iranians, of course."

"The Iranians?"

"They were dying to prove it all along. We saved them, what, ten years."

10. Inn Keepers

A set is any collection that coheres as an object of thought. Once cohered, it is confined in the pen of parentheses: $\{1, 2, 3\}$ is the set comprising the numbers one, two, and three. There is only one relationship within set theory. An object belongs to a set, or it does not. Thus $1 \in \{1, 2, 3\}$ but $6 \notin \{1, 2, 3\}$. From the moment it was created by Georg Cantor at the end of the nineteenth century, set theory proved radically unstable, a sense of hysteria passing from Cantor to his own creation and back again, so that in the end, Cantor retired to a mental institution and set theory devolved into paradox.

But even without paradox, set theory, by its very nature, encompasses an aspect of the fantastic, so much so that David Hilbert saw in hotel management a way in which to convey the weirdness of the thing, its power to confound.

And why not? The mathematician with sets to fill and the inn keeper with rooms to let *do* have a common concern: Who gets to get in?

At Kronecker's Lodge—churches nearby—there are finitely many rooms and rather a meager breakfast buffet. Guests are turned away all the time, often by the proprietor, always with satisfaction.

Although there are only finitely many rooms, the Lodge is committed to a policy of commercial expansion. Rooms are being added all the time. *Potentially infinite,* the advertising brochure reads, and if this is small consolation to guests trusting in the word *infinite* but neglecting more carefully to consider the word *potentially,* they have, as Herr Kronecker remarks, only themselves to blame.

The Hilbert Hotel, on the other hand, is entirely more swank, if only because there are *infinitely* many rooms, and those infinitely many rooms are there all at once. No expansion is in prospect. Why on earth would it be needed? A policy of open admission prevails: anyone gets in because everyone gets in.

As it happens, the hotel is full, as an unobtrusive sign on the front desk somberly affirms. Owing to a convention, there is a natural number assigned to each room. But for all that, *no one* is turned away. Even though all of the hotel's infinitely many rooms are occupied by infinitely many guests, the hotel is prepared to accommodate infinitely many *new* guests.

That all of its infinitely many rooms are occupied, Inn Keeper Hilbert observes, is no reason, *natürlich,* to turn down turn-ups. By shuffling the number snoring in the first room to the second, and the second to the third, and the third to the fourth, and so on *ad infinitum,* a room is at once made available. And if one room, then many more, and if many more, then *infinitely* many more.

A hotel with an infinite number of guests in house *always* has an infinite number of rooms at hand, as inn keepers and mathematicians both observe, and observe at once.

The dispute in trade between Kronecker's Lodge and the Hilbert Hotel turns on the distinction between a potential and a completed infinity. Set theory is on the side of the Hilbert Hotel. Its infinite sets are all there all the time. Nothing could be more complete, the difference between *complet* and *complete* a matter merely of a dropped vowel.

The inclusion of an infinite set in the mathematical universe raised a number of eyebrows even before it raised a number of doubts. While the natural numbers go on and on to any *finite* extent, the *set* of the natural numbers has already gotten to where the natural numbers are going. It is complete, the progression of its numbers done. The idea of a completed infinity has always prompted mathematicians to ask what they could have been thinking? "I protest against the use of infinite magnitude," the great Gauss remarked, "as something completed," harrumphing thereafter that this "is never permissible in mathematics."

Following Gauss, there is the chronically harrumphing Leopold Kronecker, a one-man congregation of coughers, and all the voices of common sense, as well, saying with rare unanimity, but hardly any argument, that completed infinities are bad for trade. And not only for *trade*. What act of the human mind could possibly be adequate to a completed infinity? Theologians have always assigned to God the power to master infinity. His competence is an overflow of His confidence, His mind, not only vast but infinitely vast. In the encounter between God and set theory, one completed infinity is contemplating another. This is a comfort that mathematicians cannot enjoy.

In the end, concepts are not quite in conflict, and there is no paradox, but an air of mathematical mumbo-jumbo may perhaps be discerned, one striking enough to persuade at least one philosopher (William Lane Craig) of the existence of the Christian God.

III. Fall

11. The Social Set

Nicholas Christakis is the Sterling Professor of Social and Natural Science at Yale University, and, in his professional allegiances, both a physician and a sociologist. He has written about social networks, obesity, smoking, and happiness.[1] An achieved academic, Christakis is not a man inclined to leave a base uncovered. His *Blueprint*[2] is an engaging book, and if at 520 pages, it is too long for its argument, it carries the extra weight gracefully. Human beings, Christakis argues, are disposed to create morally refreshing societies. "A *scientific* understanding of human nature actually fosters the cause of justice by identifying the deep sources of our common humanity."[3] Those sources are deep because they are biological, and common because held in trust by the entire human race. "The thing about genes," Christakis writes, "is this: we all have them."[4] The correlative claim that our genetic heritage must act to foster the cause of justice follows as the triumph of hope over experience.

Blueprint's blueprint is a social suite comprising eight junior suites. They are, reducing things to their essentials, identity, love, friendship, cooperation, solidarity, dominance, learning, and social networks.[5] These are at the core of every human society, and they are expressed anew whenever societies are created.

Shipwrecks offer Christakis the occasion suavely to consider societies formed when half-drowned sailors discover the advantages of dry land. Some shipwrecks end passably or peacefully, the survivors dividing their labor while sharing their hardships. Ernest Shackleton's expedition to the Antarctic is an example. When the *Endurance* was crushed by ice, Shackleton secured the safety of his men on Elephant Island, and then sailed a small boat across seven hundred and fifty miles of open water to reach the wrong side of South Georgia. Crossing the island on foot, he sought and found help. His men remained disciplined, determined, and dutiful. No one was lost.

The sailors of H. M. S. Bounty were somewhat less creditable. Having given themselves over to what Captain Bligh called the allurements of dissipation on landing in Tahiti, they gave themselves over to the improvisations of debauchery on getting rid of Bligh. When they were not murdering one another, the women they had kidnapped were murdering them. Only two of the mutineers survived. Christakis is careful to insist that he is no genetic determinist.[6] The genes that he commends are serviceable but not domineering. They guide, shape, impel, dispose, induce, incline, or inveigle. In the case of the H. M. S. Bounty, they did rather less inveigling than one might have hoped.

Written history goes only so far, and then it gutters out. With a fine sense of the essentials, the Sumerians conveyed their tax rolls to posterity in the fourth millennium BC. What came before must be inferred from the detritus that pre-historic man left behind. Paleoanthropologists believe that modern human beings emerged roughly two or three hundred thousand years ago; human language, shortly thereafter. Before its emergence, human beings could not talk, and afterwards, they would not stop. If language was useful, it is odd that it was isolated, and if not, odd that it emerged.[7] By roughly forty to fifty thousand years ago, men had learned to decorate themselves, control fire, create primitive tools, and master representational art sufficiently to produce imperishable masterpieces on cave walls throughout Europe and southeast Asia. It is to those hunter-gatherers that Christakis assigns the genetic changes that allowed them to become sociable. When this happened, Christakis does not say, and how it happened, he does not know.

In his *Chronicon*, Eusebius recounts a story that he attributes to Berossus:

> In the very first year there appeared from the Red Sea... in an area bordering on Babylonia a frightening monster, named Oannes... It had the whole body of a fish, but underneath and attached to the head of

> the fish there was another head, human, and joined to the tail of the fish, feet, like those of a man, and it had a human voice. Berossus says that this monster spent its days with men, never eating anything, but teaching men the skills necessary for writing and for doing mathematics and for all sorts of knowledge: how to build cities, found temples, and make laws... In short, it taught men all those things conducive to a settled and civilized life.

"Since that time," Eusebius remarks regretfully, "nothing further has been discovered."[8]

The monster in this story is a matter of myth; not so its moral. Had Oannes addressed the fish, *they* would have continued placidly to gulp. Fish are fish, but men are men, and men, but not fish, have the power to acquire the arts of civilization. Why this should be so remains a mystery. Within evolutionary thought, mysteries require miracles. They are not frequently withheld. Language? A long-ago lucky break, Noam Chomsky has long argued, endowed a single human being with the capacity recursively to organize his thoughts.[9] One man, one mutation, and, thereafter, Ovid in his exile. It is a poignant image, but no more than that. The power to organize one's thoughts requires thoughts to be organized, and without them, recursion is as isolated as the capacity to dream in color.

Although Christakis is writing about society, there is very little sociology in this book. Love is an occasional feature of human life. Thousands have lived without it.[10] Bipedalism is universal. It is not clear why Christakis would think either a feature of *social* life. Personal identity receives a perfunctory treatment. A dog looking in a mirror sees another dog, a man, alas, sees himself. This Christakis accepts as evidence that we have some sense of personal identity denied the dogs. It cannot be said that this represents a stirring standard of success. Time and again, Christakis forgets that he is impelled by his commitments to study society, *its* classes, *its* structures, and *their* dynamics.

The blueprint is, in fact, a list of things found in society—*les choses trouvées*—and as long as his standards are lax, Christakis might have added language, abstract thought, bureaucracies, markets, art, architecture, civil engineering, music, mathematics, pointless pride, cooking, sanitation, racial rage, fashion, story-telling, dance, ritual, myth-making, poetry, science, taboos, philosophy, religion, gossip, envy, resentment, body adornment, a rich variety of perversions, politics, contracts, sport, taxes, and funeral orations. If love, why not gender? Every society before our own has divided human beings into just two genders, the distinction unvarying, inviolable, and irrefragable. If friendship and cooperation, why not enmity and conflict? If hierarchy, why not force? *The simple rule, the good old plan. He takes who has the power, he keeps who can.* If personal identity, why not original sin? "With respect to original sin," Dr. Johnson observed, "the inquiry is not necessary; for whatever is the cause of human corruption, men are evidently and confessedly so corrupt, that all the laws of heaven and earth are insufficient to restrain them from their crimes." If social networks, why not the law? If solidarity, why not factionalism, as when groups devolve into groupuscules and then groupies?

Whatever the plausibility of evolutionary sociology, it suffers the accidents characteristic of evolutionary psychology. Their skid-marks are the same, as forensic analysts say.[11] Does the experience of being in love feel overwhelming? Sometimes it does. Men tingle, women Twitter, and together they undertake the exercise that make the real world bake and shake. "There are biological reasons," Debra Soh writes, "that explain why the experience of being in love feels so overwhelming." It is love that "allows two people to bond in a way that increases the likelihood they'll procreate and maintain an environment in which the resulting offspring survive."[12] By this standard, central heating, indoor plumbing, Scotch whiskey, and old Frank Sinatra records may all be said to have a biological reason and so a biological explanation.

The male tiger copulates in what appears to be a spirit of snarling irritation, departing the next morning satisfied, solitary, indifferent, and aloof. Many men do as much. Or as little.[13] *The Shepherd in Virgil sought for love, and found him a native of the rocks.* But if love is not necessary for reproductive success, neither is it sufficient. *When love is over how little of love even the lover understands.*[14] It is marriage that plays a role in the complex economies of human life. Marriage is, after all, a social institution, one embedded in law, justified through custom, and sanctified by religion. Playing a biological role, does it have a biological *explanation?* Although research is, no doubt, continuing, it would seem unlikely that there is a gene governing pre-nuptial contracts. Between what is inscribed in the genome and what is observed in real life, there are, and must be, the reciprocating pistons of human will and action. Evolutionary psychology is surely correct in assigning to an amorous paroxysm some say-so in the scheme of things, but since this was never in doubt, it was never in need. Given the discontent that it frequently provokes, marriage *must* have had some strong compelling force in its favor.

Christakis is a sophisticated man and would, I expect, be pained to accept the evolutionary psychologists as *compagnons du devoir*. He is in their company anyway. His argument is unvarying and proceeds *from* some common feature of social life *to* the gene acting as its presumptive cause. The argument has no independent point of adhesion in molecular biology, and thus may be run equally in reverse, proceeding *from* the presumptive human genome *to* some common feature of social life.[15] If the human genome is everywhere the same, what explanation for human diversity? And if human behavior is everywhere the same, what explanation for genetic diversity?[16] When these equations are divided by their genes, the result has rather less to do with a scientific understanding of human nature than Christakis imagines.

If pigs cannot fly, neither are they ever born with wheels mounted on ball-bearings. Whether this is a fact of life or a law of nature is unclear.[17] The concept of a morphospace has, in this regard, come to play a stately role in evolutionary rituals. It is gorgeously attired, lavishly appointed, and disappointingly indolent. "Morphological spaces, or morphospaces," Phillip Mitteroecker and Simon Huttegger write, "are mathematical spaces describing and relating the phenotypic configuration of biological organisms."[18] Given the living pig, points in its morphospace represent the possible pigs, phenotypic variants. Those variants are described by a finite set of discrete parameters—wing length, for example. Although living pigs have wings of length zero, who is to say that in some corner of their morphospace, they may not be found with wings large enough to embarrass a condor? Who, on the other hand, is to say that pigs with wings are *pigs*? If not, what are they doing in a space devoted to pigs; and if so, why cannot pigs fly?

The requisite definitions of deviance are not obvious, as much a problem in zoology as in the law. Whatever the definitions, living creatures do not seem especially disposed to an equitable exploration of morphospace. The great museum of possibilities is, like the Uffizi, filled with empty rooms, closed corridors, whole suites blocked off, inaccessible.[19] The anthropologist Lee Cronk, in an exercise devoted to ethnographic hyperspace, has determined that there are 10^{53} possible human societies. Only a tiny fraction of them, Christakis remarks, "have ever been observed by anthropologists." This may well be true. Busy as they are said to be, anthropologists cannot look everywhere. But from the fact that almost all of the societies in Cronk's ethnographic hyperspace go unvisited, it hardly follows that those that remain are similar. All that one can say is that human beings seek one another out, and they seek one another out, to complete the inference, because they are human beings.

Qui se ressemble s'assemble and vice versa.

The conclusions that Christakis wishes to reach rarely survive a confrontation with cases. Friendship is an idea broad enough to encompass Mary O'Hara's *My Friend Flicka* and Johann Eckermann's *Gespräche mit Goethe*.[20] To say that Goethe and Eckermann were friends because each man had a gene for friendship is to say no more than that they were friends. Whatever the gene for friendship, it was not sufficient to prompt their friendship; and if it was necessary, in the sense that without it they could not have been friends, as much is true of their livers. Between those diffident genes, and what a man *does*, is something blank and unrevealing. A gene is, after all, a particular molecular configuration, and insofar as it codes for anything, it codes for the order of amino acids. *It* does nothing more. And *it* does not do that alone. The genetic apparatus is under enzymatic control, and so causally circular. It may be true that human friendship is linked to the human genome; it is a claim that requires the confinement of a causal connection.

This we do not have. For one thing, the details are missing. We can complete no connection between a particular gene and *any* phenotypic trait. For another thing, the conceptual coordination required is one urged between radically incommensurable domains. The gene is described in molecular biological or biochemical terms; human action and human nature are not. A different vocabulary is required, and once specified, it becomes plain that there is nothing tying the two together. Social life has its own distinctive character. Explanations involve a complicated give-and-take between observation and conjecture. Why do so many young women cover themselves in tattoos, looking in the end like Yakuza gangsters? Because they want to, is one answer. It is better than nothing, if only because it fits the facts. They are, after all, covered in tattoos. Those tattoos, in turn, dispel any doubt about what these women want. Just look at them.[21] These exchanges convey the impression of circularity, but a more appropriate metaphor might be an indeterminate equation in several variables in which the presumption of desire and its satisfaction in indigo represent one, but only one, possible solution—Token and Tattoo.

Body adornment is an ancient human obsession, pre-historic women, their remains suggest, as willing to adorn themselves as the ceremonial camels bound for Mecca.[22] The desire to make oneself sexually attractive is neat enough to fit plausibly into the scheme of evolutionary biology. Men are easily led, and as easily misled, and the woman determined to do both may well have had an evolutionary advantage denied her drab sisters. But the manifold of desire and decoration has a curious geometry all its own. A woman may, by progressive nakedness, pique a man's interest, and then his desires. Men in Victorian England, the fools, found an exposed ankle thrilling, while in the United States or Europe, only garments offering direct access to the main chance have a similar effect. These are circumstances that suggest that nakedness follows a simple linear relationship: less is better. The contrary is true. Clothing may proceed to the very threshold of the genitals, but nakedness is a universal source of shame—Token and *Taboo*.[23]

Blueprint is not a work of evolutionary biology, and it makes no claims otherwise. In justifying the premises to his argument, Christakis relies on the standard doctrine, now become the standard dogma. Both in *The Blind Watchmaker* and in *The Extended Phenotype*, Richard Dawkins very nicely set out the essentials. Random mutations and natural selection drive biological change. In a still lower gear, random variations and natural selection drive change beyond the margins of an organism. Maddened by the same reproductive urge, Bower Birds construct elaborate nests and men, elaborate cities.[24] If these ideas are now part of the Great Gabble, they remain well below the level of the serious sciences. They encompass neither the revolution in evolutionary thought introduced by Motoo Kimura's theory of neutral mutations, nor the criticism that an inherently random process cannot produce the complex structures characteristic of molecular biology, let alone human society. Men in the Kalahari find it profitable to go for days without water; in Silicon Valley, the advantage is lost. *Jedem Tierchen sein Pläsierchen*. Environments change, no doubt, for reasons of their own. If they are described at all, they must be described by a random variable. The product of two random variables is again a random variable, randomness going straight down to the bottom in Darwinian theories.[25]

Blueprint is a cheerful book. Like Steven Pinker, Nicholas Christakis is not a man to be worried overmuch by the charge of fatuous optimism. But it is a narrow book. It is narrow in its cheerfulness, and it is just this narrowness that suggests fatuity. "We do not...," Christakis writes, "find a functional society without love, friendship, cooperation or personal identity."[26]

Sure we do.[27]

In *Among the Believers*, V. S. Naipaul recounts a conversation in Jakarta with an Indonesian businessman, a Muslim, someone who "had the Indonesian feeling of things going wrong." He was, Naipaul observes, a man full of rage. "We have to kill a lot of people," the businessman remarked. "We have to kill one or two million of these Javanese." It had happened before in Indonesia, Naipaul adds, still in conversation:

> In 1965 the communists had been wiped out. A million people had been killed, he said, not half a million, as was now given out. And more should have been killed: there were two and a half million communists at the time. So a million and a half had escaped killing, and many of them were still around.
>
> I said, "If the killing starts, you may go yourself."
>
> "I might. I hope not. But I might."
>
> "I was told that in 1965 some people took out the gamelan when they went killing."
>
> "Of course. To add to the beauty."[28]

In Bali, Naipaul observed some pages earlier, "the killing was as fierce as anywhere else," and there, too, "to give a touch of ritual to the butchery, the village gangs took out the gamelan orchestra when they went killing."[29] The exquisitely mannered Balinese, heirs to an old culture, they, too, had crossed the *kala pani*—the black water.

Christakis is not wrong to think that human beings, and the societies that they create, are similar. He is wrong in finding this unequivocally a good thing.

Biology places the heavy hand of its constraints on human societies?[30] No one doubts that this is so. We do not know what those constraints are or how heavy the hand and so we cannot determine how widely societies meeting them may vary. But the twentieth century offers a sobering lesson in the grim power of diversity.

What cause in Nature for such hard hearts?

There is none.

Humani nihil a me alienum puto, Terence remarked. The idea is not foolish. But neither is it obvious. So many have seen it the other way around. *Nothing alien is human to me.* If the blueprint circumscribes the terrible societies of the twentieth century, it is too broad to be of interest, and if determined by the human genome, too narrow to be of hope.

We must look to other sources for our common humanity.

12. Godzooks

Craignez, Seigneur, craignez que le ciel rigoureux
Ne vous haïsse assez pour exercer vos vœux.
—Jean Racine, Phèdre[1]

Yuval Harari is a young Israeli historian. In his first book, *Sapiens: A Brief History of Humankind*, Harari surveyed the history of the human race;[2] in his second, *Homo Deus: A Brief History of Tomorrow*, he has written an account of its future.[3] Neither book is brief. *Sapiens* was a notable bestseller. Harari may not expect lightning to strike twice; he would not be inconvenienced if it did. In *Sapiens*, Harari expressed no very great use for the monotheistic religions of mankind, nor for the agricultural practices that, he supposed, made them possible. He commended stone age cultures with the enthusiasm of a man not required to live in any of them. For all that, *Sapiens* was very much a work of Whig history, an account of successive revolutions, each prefiguring the next. In *Homo Deus*, Harari argues that human beings are shortly to be improved. Greatly so. For a start, better genes, better neural circuits, better biochemistry. Thereafter, a variety of implantable contraptions: chips, stents, or shunts. Finally, a full promotion to the Pantheon, computer scientists, at last, inscribing intelligence in inorganic matter, the old-fashioned human body, declining into desuetude, replaced by the filaments and files of an alien form of life.

Our Colonial Master

V. S. Naipaul made popular, or, at least, well known, the idea that the West now commands a universal civilization, one whose principles extend as far as its power to convey them. "The wealth of the world has grown," he remarked, "power has grown, education has spread..." The universal civilization is dense, elusive, complex. "Simple charms alone cannot be acquired from it." "Other, difficult things," he writes, "come with it as well: ambition, endeavor, individuality." It is a civilization that imposes its own stern constraints on those who live within it, "unacknowledged, but all the more profound."[4]

These ideas are easily parodied. The Irish academic, Mark Humphrys, writes that in the "seventeenth and eighteenth centuries, the West invented science, democracy and capitalism." It was not a minute too soon. "After 5,000 years of ignorance, superstition, tyranny, war, genocide and poverty, the solutions to mankind's fundamental problems were at last discovered."[5]

If the solutions to superstition, tyranny, war, genocide, and poverty were discovered in the seventeenth and eighteenth centuries, they were, those solutions, well hidden in the twentieth.

The idea of a universal civilization—the very idea—is by no means new. In the second century CE, Aelius Aristides delivered a remarkable oration, a celebration of Roman greatness:

> If one considers the vast extent of your empire he must be amazed that so small a fraction of it rules the world, but when he beholds the city and its spaciousness it is not astonishing that all the habitable world is ruled by such a capital... Your possessions equal the sun's course... You do not rule within fixed boundaries, nor can anyone dictate the limits of your sway... Whatever any people produces can be found here, at all times and in abundance... Egypt, Sicily, and the civilized part of Africa are your farms; ships are continually coming and going.

The concluding words of this oration have a poignant irony that time has not effaced: "The whole world prays," Aristides said, "in unison that your empire may endure forever."[6]

A panegyric is the overflow in rhetoric of a system of belief. Our own is severely abstract, monotheistic in its single-mindedness, and fully accessible only to a scientific priesthood. "And we have removed from thee thy veil," the Koran remarks in verse 50:22, "and thy sight today is piercing." The veil removed, what is revealed is an edifice of great grandeur. It is in its form classical and austere. It appeals to a finite set of exact and fundamental theories. It is unique. What can be known must be known as a derivation from its theories.[7] But if it is unique, it is also incomplete. General Relativity and quantum mechanics are both true, but they are not true together. Physicists anticipate their incarnation in a single, finite, all-encompassing, and exact theory. The incarnation is the source of its greatness, the place from which power flows.

Past Imperfect

V. S. Naipaul wrote during the last decade of the twentieth century; he wrote to uphold the dignity of a universal civilization—that, and its difficulty. Writing almost twenty years later, Harari is concerned to document its dissolution. The liberal belief in individualism, Harari writes, is based on the assumption that every human being embodies a single, indivisible essence, something purely his own, free in its action, autonomous in its choices. Like words written on water, these ideas are destined to disappear. "Organisms are algorithms," Harari writes, and human beings "an assembly of many different algorithms lacking a single inner voice or a single self."[8] These algorithms are a part of the great wheel of being discerned by the sciences; and, no matter his private devotions, it is to the sciences that Harari bends his public knee.

Harari is a Whig historian, but he is not a Whig optimist. He is proud of himself as a man prepared to see things as they really are. Whether they really are as he sees them is rather less clear. *Homo Deus* is a work of speculation. Standards are looser than they might otherwise be. This is inevitable. In writing about the near future, Harari is guessing, and in writing about the far future, when human beings have long promoted themselves into the inorganic world, guessing again. For all that, *Homo Deus* is intended as a work of history, and the speculations in which Harari is engaged follow a familiar logical pattern. They are like initial value problems in physics. The future that Harari discerns must be projected from the historical present. The *historical* present. The day before yesterday is not good enough. Something more spacious is needed, some sense of the times in which we live.

"During the second half of the twentieth century," Harari writes, "[the] Law of the Jungle has finally been broken, if not rescinded."[9] By the Law of the Jungle, he means the state of civil society under conditions of war, famine, and disease. These are the conditions under which humanity has long lived and suffered. If they have not entirely disappeared, they are, at least, in abeyance.

Are they? Are they *really*? "Whereas in ancient agricultural societies," Harari writes, "human violence caused about fifteen percent of all deaths, during the twentieth century, violence caused only five percent of deaths, and in the early twenty-first century it is responsible for about one percent of global mortality."[10] Stone Age violence no longer commands anyone's moral interest, or indignation, and, in any case, Harari's assessment of pre-historic violence is, as Brian Ferguson observed, "utterly without empirical foundation."[11] Now well into the twenty-first century, we remain bound to the twentieth, haunted by its horrors. Harari's assertion that during the twentieth century violence caused *only* five percent of deaths world-wide is morally obtuse. The decline in violence is, most often, a statistical artifact of the growth in the world's population. Roughly six million Poles of Poland's pre-war population of thirty-five million died during the second world war—seventeen percent, or almost one in five. The world's population in 1939 was 2.3 billion. Point two percent of the world's population perished in Poland. Which number better expresses the horror: seventeen per cent or point two per cent? Would the horror have been less had the population of South America been greater? Neither murder nor genocide has in the twentieth century been randomly distributed. The world's population is an irrelevance.

"In most countries today," Harari writes, "overeating has become a far worse problem than famine." There are today famines taking place or about to take place in northern Nigeria, Somalia, Yemen, and the South Sudan. Some twenty million people, Secretary General António Guterres of the United Nations observed, are at risk.[12] They are not at risk because fat people are fat. They are at risk because they have no food.[13] If Chinese peasants are becoming obese, it has not been widely reported. Of the most terrible famines in history, many took place in the twentieth century. Persia suffered famine between 1917 and 1919. Eight to nine million died. A sixth of the population of Turkestan died of hunger between 1917 and 1921. Famine in Russia in 1921 caused five million deaths; famine in northern China between 1928 and 1930, three million. Famine in the Ukraine between 1931 and 1934 caused five million deaths; famine in China in 1936, five million. One million people died of famine in Leningrad during its wartime blockade by the German army. In 1942 and 1943, famines in China and in Bengal caused between three and five million deaths. Two and a half million Javanese died of hunger during the Japanese occupation. The little known Soviet famine of 1947 caused roughly one and one-half million deaths. Famine killed between fifteen and forty million Chinese between 1959 and 1961. One million people died of hunger during the Sahel drought between 1968 and 1972. Of *hunger,* note, and not obesity. The North Korean famine of 1996 was responsible for between 300,000 and 3.5 million deaths. No one knows its true extent—circumstances that, if they did not chill the blood, should have stayed the hand of historians writing about the disappearance of famine in the modern world. The second Congo war between 1998 and 2004 caused almost four million deaths from starvation. In 1998, three hundred thousand died in Somalia. They died because they had nothing to eat.[14]

The first half of the twentieth century was unparalleled in its violence. Violence declined in the second half of the twentieth century because European states were too exhausted, or too apprehensive, to repair again to warfare. If the second half of the century was less violent than the first, it was not peaceful. No one should take the decline as a sign of moral improvement. The Chinese Communist revolution, the partition of India, the Great Leap Forward, the ignominious Cultural Revolution, the suppression of Tibet, the Korean wars, the wars of Indochinese succession, the Egypt-Yemen war, the Franco-Algerian war, the genocidal

Pol Pot regime, the grotesque and sterile Iranian revolution, the Iran-Iraq war, ethnic cleansings in Rwanda, Burundi, and the former Yugoslavia, the farcical Russian and American invasions of Afghanistan, the American invasion of Iraq, and various massacres, sub-continental famines, squalid civil insurrections, bloodlettings, throat-slittings, death squads, theological infamies, and suicide bombings taking place from Latin America to East Timor are as yet unaccommodated. I have made these points before.[15]

> *Natürlich hab' Ich wieder recht*
>
> *Der Mensch ist dumm, die Welt ist schlecht.*

Derelict Doctrines

Harari's view of what is coming, or to come, is much influenced by what he calls "the new human agenda." Modern culture, he writes, "rejects [the] belief in a great cosmic plan. Life has no script, no playwright, no director, no producer—and no meaning."[16] This is hardly a view that is distinctly modern. It is as old as history. If what is familiar in this view is old, what is modern is false. Harari's sense that the life of man is less than might have been imagined, or expected, is the expression of his encounter with various derelict doctrines. "In recent decades," Harari writes,

> life scientists have demonstrated that emotions are not some mysterious spiritual phenomenon that is useful just for writing poetry and composing symphonies. Rather emotions are biochemical algorithms that are vital for the survival and reproduction of all animals.[17]

Biologists have demonstrated no such thing. What the life scientists are doing is anyone's guess. No one has ever supposed that emotions are useful just for writing poetry or composing symphonies. The concept of a biochemical algorithm occupies space without doing work. Some biochemical reactions may be described step by step, but this tells us nothing more than that some biochemical reactions may be described. Very many human emotions have nothing to do with survival or reproduction. There is peevishness, *déjà vu*, irritability, rapture, *Schadenfreude*, frustration, sloth, aesthetic bliss, and that ineffable sense of melancholy incompleteness known in Portuguese as *saudade*.

Emotions are not algorithms if the concept of an algorithm is made precise, and the claim is pointless if it is not. An algorithm may be transferred from one machine to another, but not an emotion or a sensation. You cannot feel my pain if I stub my toe; I cannot feel your jealousy if I steal your wife. On the contrary. That stubbed toe aside, I feel rather good about the whole business.

Anger is not inevitably felt "as a sensation of heat and tension in the body..."[18] A man may dissemble his anger, even from himself, and he may sustain a cold vindictive sense of fury for years without ever feeling flushed or even particularly hot-blooded. I am myself like that—implacable. Anger may come and go and it makes little sense to inquire whether it is the same emotion coming and going. Emotions have nothing like the clear-cut identity that is characteristic of an algorithm.

A great tribal chief may have a dozen squabbling wives, poor fool, and so a dozen conflicting obligations, but *not* a dozen competing angers. Like alimony, anger is burdensome, but not countable. Emotions may be controlled, guided, provoked, nudged, cultivated, refined, molded, or shaped, but not so algorithms or machines. There is no algorithmic structure controlling how emotions are felt. How they are felt is a matter of how they are *felt*. An algorithm may exist without ever being run, but an emotion that is never felt is like an idea that is never thought. Thoughts are not detachable objects; neither are emotions.[19]

Metaphysical Cake-Master

Homo Deus is not a work of philosophy, but its arguments turn often on philosophical or logical issues. Harari is persuaded that, no matter their convictions to the contrary, human beings are not free in their actions. As a debate in philosophy, freedom of the will is like *Jarndyce v. Jarndyce* in the law: it stretches its corrupt and unwholesome hand out to ensnare whoever is tempted by its arguments. The debate has retained its chief features since antiquity, and no philosopher or scientist has made the slightest contribution to enlarging it. Harari belongs to the ages. "To the best of our understanding," he writes, "determinism and randomness have divided the entire cake between them..."[20]

If human actions are determined, they are not free, and if random, not interesting. Freedom of the will must be an illusion.[21] Perhaps this is so. If freedom of the will is an illusion, then the illusion is both universal and inexpugnable. Every man is persuaded that something is within his power, and none that everything is beyond it. What explains the illusion? No less than in the paradoxes of perception, in which a wine glass reveals the sleek contours of a woman's silhouette, some account is needed.

The illusion goes too deep to be an accident. It is not random. On the contrary. Free will enters into every deliberation; it is the foundation on which every legal system is constructed; it controls every human exchange; it is the assumption that makes daily life coherent; and if Google, Facebook, Apple, and Microsoft are busy undermining consumer choice, they are busy only because, like the rest of us, they share in the illusion of free will, and are concerned to make the most of it. To do without the illusion is to live like the animals. *Considerate la vostra semenza fatti no foste a viver come bruti.*[22] An appeal to randomness is pointless. No deterministic account is remotely plausible. We are as little able to explain the illusion of free will as free will itself. If the illusion is not a part of the cake, the cake is not all that there is; and if it is a part of the cake, determinism and randomness do not divide it.[23]

Court in Session

What Yuval Harari does not believe about free will, he does not believe about God, the soul, or the human mind; but if he is skeptical about some things, he is credulous about others, and so reaches a point of equilibrium between believing too little and believing too much. "Scientists," he writes, "have subjected *homo sapiens* to tens of thousands of bizarre experiments, and looked into every nook in our hearts and every cranny in our brains."[24] *Je m'imagine cela.* There is no soul. Ten thousand more experiments may well have been devoted to finding the details of the Smoot-Hawley Tariff in the common bile duct—and with a similar standard of success.

If Harari is skeptical about freedom of the will or the human soul, in other respects he argues that the life of man is governed by a different imperative. Whatever is not forbidden by the laws of physics is possible. It is this dizzying sense of steadily expanding possibilities that allows Harari to accept with solemn credulity the promise that death is a soluble technological problem, or that, in time, human and machine intelligence, as Ray Kurzweil has predicted, will merge in the burst of a starlike singularity. Harari rejects a much older, darker view in which a life is bounded by irrefrangible limits—so far a man may go, but no further. Quite the contrary. So long as a scheme or suggestion is not physically impossible, Harari is content to accept as his own the epistemological maxim governing Silicon Valley—*anything goes*.

The appellate court is now in session. The possibilities that Harari sees winking on the great manifold of being? What about *them*? Determinism is a doctrine with philosophical bite only if it has some modal force. If it amounts to no more than the observation that generally one thing follows another, it is of no interest. An object dropped from a great height *must* fall toward the center of the earth. *It* has no say in the scheme of things, and *it* cannot do otherwise. Historical laws that determine which possibilities are realized and which not have the same force of command. *This* must happen; *that* is impossible.[25] If anything goes, then we are left with no deterministic explanations why some things went, and if they went for no reason at all, what, then, is the purpose of this book?

Future Imperfect

Human beings, Harari believes, are about to lose their social and economic usefulness as well as their souls.[26] Robots are coming, and, if not robots, then all-powerful algorithms. Having replaced chess champions and quiz show contestants, they are shortly to replace truck drivers, travel agents, accountants, lawyers, and doctors. Whether they are about to replace historians is a question that Harari wisely declines to discuss.

What makes their forthcoming domination inevitable, Harari believes, is the discovery that consciousness may be separated from intelligence. Computers are no more conscious today than they were in 1950, but they are very much more intelligent, and in the near future, they are certain to become even more intelligent. This is the information revolution that Harari has persuaded himself that he sees clearly. The Whig optimist now gives way to the Whig pessimist. The information revolution is likely to benefit the minority of those with the wit, or the money, to make use of it. "As algorithms push humans out of the job market," Harari writes, "wealth might be concentrated in the hands of a tiny elite that owns the all-powerful algorithms, creating unprecedented social inequality."[27] Algorithms might even become entities under the law, like corporations or trusts, Facebook's corporate algorithm showing Mark Zuckerberg the door in favor of itself.

Je pense, donc je commande.

I am as eager as the next man to see Mark Zuckerberg a victim of his own success, but I do not expect to see it any time soon. It is by no means clear that computers are in 2017 any more intelligent than they were in 1950; it is, for that matter, by no means clear that the Sunway TaihuLight super-computer is any more intelligent than the first Sumerian abacus. Both are incarnations of a Turing machine. The Sumerian abacus can do as much as a Turing machine, and the Sunway TaihuLight can do no more. Computers have become *faster*, to be sure, but an argument is required to show that by going faster, they are getting smarter.

An algorithm is a step-by-step affair, the residue in action of the antecedent concept of an effective calculation, a way of getting something done. In the 1930s, logicians precisely defined this old and informal idea: Kurt Gödel by means of the recursive functions; Alonzo Church, by the calculus of lambda conversion, and Alan Turing, by the Turing machine. The definitions coincided, leading Gödel to remark that the underlying concept was absolute. Effective calculability, Alonzo Church conjectured, could be completely expressed by the properties of a Turing machine. Although it cannot be demonstrated, this conjecture may be something like a law of nature, a part of the edifice.

These are ideas that, like do-it-yourself surgery, may easily go wrong. Stephen Wolfram offers an example. "The workings of the human brain," he writes, "or the evolution of weather systems can, in principle, compute the same things as a computer."[28] He refrains notably from endorsing the conclusion that the brain *is* a weather system. It is the next best thing: it is *like* a weather system. "Computation is therefore simply a question of translating inputs and outputs from one system to another." There are two assumptions in Wolfram's argument: that the human brain is nothing more than a computer; that the human mind is nothing more than the human brain. Are these assumptions true? Harari has no idea; Wolfram does not say. And no one else knows.

It is hardly beyond dispute that the human brain is a computer, except on the level of generality under which the human brain is like a weather system. It is difficult even to depict the simplest computational scheme in neurological terms. One neuron fires, and then another. Still a third neuron fires twice, as if it were adding the results. This is mere dumb-show. What is taking place on the neurological level lacks any coherent connection to addition, which is a recursive operation defined over the natural numbers. Michael Jordan offers a reasonable assessment:

> But it's true that with neuroscience, it's going to require decades or even hundreds of years to understand the deep principles. There is progress at the very lowest levels of neuroscience. But for issues of higher cognition—how we perceive, how we remember, how we act—we have no idea how neurons are storing information, how they are computing, what the rules are, what the algorithms are, what the representations are, and the like. So we are not yet in an era in which we can be using

an understanding of the brain to guide us in the construction of intelligent systems.[29]

It is possible to embed the rules of recursive arithmetic in a computer, but how might the embedding take place in the brain? If this question has no settled answer, then neither does the question whether the brain is a computer.

There remains the thesis that the human mind is identical to the human brain. Gödel's second incompleteness theorem demonstrated that no formal systems adequate to the description of the natural numbers could prove its own consistency. The proof turns on Gödel's ingenious re-description of consistency as a number-theoretic statement, a Diophantine equation. If the brain is a computer, it must be a formal system. Either it can demonstrate its own consistency, or it cannot. "So the following disjunctive conclusion is inevitable," Gödel writes, "Either mathematics is incompletable in this sense, that its evident axioms can never be comprised in a finite rule, that is to say, the human mind (even within the realm of pure mathematics) infinitely surpasses the powers of any finite machine, or else there exist absolutely unsolvable Diophantine problems of the type specified."[30]

This argument was endorsed both by John Lukas and Roger Penrose. Is it valid? I do not know.

But neither does Harari. And neither, for that matter, does Wolfram.

No discussion of these issues would be complete without some mention of consciousness. It is a topic on which it is possible to say anything without ever saying something. Zoltan Istvan is a trans-humanist, a student of life extension and digital immortality. That the first has not been achieved and the second is incoherent has been no impediment to his scholarship. "We have no idea how consciousness works," he remarks.[31] This is true only to the extent that we have no reason to think that consciousness *works*. Like the lilies of the field, it toils not and neither does it spin. "But the brain is still a machine," Istvan goes on to say, "so it's a matter of tinkering with it until we work it out." Istvan's faith in tinkering is not markedly inferior to my own; but judging from his enthusiasm, his successes would seem more considerable.

For his part, Harari is as baffled as everyone else. Consciousness? What is *it* doing *there*? David Chalmers referred to consciousness as the hard problem. That the problem is hard has become a part of the gabble. Everyone says that it is so. I am as worried as the next man. But quite before accepting consciousness as a hard problem, it would be useful to know what makes it hard and why it is a problem. It is not easy to say—one reason, I suppose, that the problem is hard. If I am not under anesthesia, asleep, or dead, I must be conscious. I am a busy man. When else could I be conscious? Yet in considering the remains of a day, I can hardly be expected to remember all of it, so I am largely unable to say anything about the apparently peculiar nature of my consciousness on those occasions, and when I do remember what I was doing, what I remember is chiefly what I was *doing*, and not anything especially about consciousness. At times, I am moved to comment on my consciousness, the more so when, with a murmured *glug*, I assure the dentist that I do not feel a thing, but then what is at issue is *self*-consciousness, a commentary on the real thing. Beyond observing that it is always hanging around, I have no idea what that real thing might be.

Mais je divague. If computers show no signs of consciousness, as Harari argues, this might suggest that, whatever else it might be, consciousness is not an algorithmic phenomenon—the perfect truth obviously. What then of Harari's grand claim that "every animal—including *Homo sapiens*—is an assemblage of organic algorithms shaped by natural selection over millions of years of evolution"?[32]

Big Data, Big Deal

It was just yesterday that any number of nervously shuffling TED-Talkers, cockroached microphones emerging from their ears, would, at various TED-talks, assure their audience that Big Data was a Big Deal. Harari is with them, an advocate of Dataism, an apostle:

> For scholars and intellectuals, Dataism promises to provide the scientific Holy Grail that has eluded us for centuries: a single overarching theory that unifies all the scientific disciplines from musicology through economics, all the way to biology. According to Dataism, Beethoven's Fifth Symphony, a stock-exchange bubble and the flu virus are just three patterns of dataflow that can be analyzed using the same basic concepts and tools. This idea is extremely attractive. It gives all scientists a common language, builds bridges over academic rifts and easily exports insights across disciplinary borders.[33]

Like phrenology, Dataism is easy to uphold, *look around*! serving as a compelling adjuration in both cases. Fat-heads *are* generally thick. But if data is everywhere, so is Fox News, evidence that being everywhere and meaning something are not quite the same thing. A "single overarching theory that unifies all the scientific disciplines"? Yes, but, *what* theory? The observation that there is a lot of data all over the place is not calculated to set the pulse racing.

A physical theory embodying Dataism must, at the very least, embody both special relativity and quantum mechanics. Physicists would sooner give up Harari than give them up. And so would I. It must embody, as well, a rigorously discrete structure, its elementary elements the natural and not the real numbers. It must abjure the old-fashioned but immensely powerful techniques of mathematical analysis; it must give up the continuum. All of this must go in favor of a physical scheme in which the physical universe is resolved into its discrete and computable elements.

Some physicists have found this idea attractive. Stephen Wolfram is an example. He is mad for universal computation and the vision of physics that it implies. "I even have increasing evidence," he writes, "that thinking in terms of simple programs will make it possible to construct a single truly fundamental theory of physics, from which space, time, quantum mechanics, and all the other known features of our universe will emerge."[34] Wolfram's scheme was rebutted by Scott Aronson. Either it violates Lorenz symmetry, and so special relativity, Aronson demonstrated, or it is not compatible with quantum mechanics.[35]

This is not a good augury, as my haruspex would say.

For all of Harari's assurances that data is the real deal, these of his reflections already suggest that he has jumped the shark, another way of saying that he has missed the boat. It is Deep Learning that has now commanded everyone's attention, a scheme of artificial intelligence that makes possible pleasantly obsequious digital assistants:

"Siri; Yo, Siri."

"Yes, Master."

Deep Learning is neither very deep, nor does it involve much learning.[36] The idea is more than fifty years old, and may be rolled back to Frank Rosenblatt's work on perceptrons.[37] The perceptron functioned as an artificial neuronal net, one neuron deep. What could it do? Marvin Minsky and Seymour Papert demonstrated that the correct answer was not very much.[38]

God tempered the wind to the shorn lamb. In the 1980s, a number of computer scientists demonstrated that by increasing the layers in a neural net, the thing could be trained by back propagation and convolution techniques to master a number of specific tasks. This was unquestionably an achievement, but in each case, the achievement was task-specific. The great goal of artificial intelligence has always been to develop a general learning algorithm, one that, like a three-year old child, could apply its intelligence across various domains. This has not been achieved. It is not even in sight. And no wonder. We have no theory that explains human or animal behavior. "The human mind," Istvan has remarked, "is virtually unexplored."[39]

Both chess and Go take place in confined spaces. The rules are plain; so, too, the goals of the game. After playing fifty million games of Go against itself, a computer easily defeated a human Go master. Whether it could have easily defeated fifty million Go masters playing against *it* is an interesting question. A kitten occupies a conceptual space bounded only by the limitations of its anatomy and its genetic endowment; but beyond that trite observation, we can generally do no better in explaining its behavior than remarking that Fluffy here generally does what she wishes to do. No record of its frisking will ever be anything more than a record of its frisking. Theories lie at a different level of analysis. Without them, there is no hope of constructing a general learning algorithm.

And these we do not have.

Like so much else in *Homo Deus,* Dataism serves chiefly to express Harari's great gullibility, his willingness to believe what some scientists say without wondering whether what they say is true. Dataism is not the Holy Grail; it is not a coherent theory; it is not about to unify anything. But, then, death is not a technological problem either, and the singularity is an infantile fantasy.

Men are not about to become like Gods.

Harari has been misinformed.

IV. Personalities

13. A Flower of Chivalry

Christopher Hitchens, 1949–2011

Christopher Hitchens's friends loved him without reservation, and at his death, they have praised him without restraint. I knew Hitchens only slightly. We had met over the course of four days in Birmingham, Alabama, where we participated in a debate. Hitchens was already gravely ill. I do not think he was yet in pain, but plainly he was suffering from the effects of chemotherapy. He walked slowly, and when he spoke in his rich plumy baritone, he spoke from a place far away.

The debate between us was far less a debate than a celebration of his determination again to appear in public. Before the debate, Hitchens found himself surrounded by well-known figures from New York and Washington, DC. He enjoyed their attention, and if he had on this occasion earned it by approaching the doors of death, I rather suspected that he thought earning it in this way was better than not having it at all.

Christopher Hitchens's reputation rests on his literary works, on his panache as a public speaker, and on his defiant atheism. He wrote on a very wide range of subjects, and his book reviews were often very fine. He liked to praise the writers and poets he loved: Oscar Wilde, Vladimir Nabokov, Evelyn Waugh, W. H. Auden, Wilfred Owen, James Fenton, many others. He read closely and he read well. As an essayist, Christopher Hitchens is often compared to George Orwell. The comparison is careless, and it is one that, in his final interview with Richard Dawkins, he rejected. Hitchens wrote fluently, Orwell, unforgettably. The difference is very considerable, but it is not to Hitchens's discredit. No man is obliged to be what he might have been.

Hitchens was an engaging public speaker, and he had the gift of gracefully holding an audience. His intimate interviews were often wonderful because, invariably, he was more elegant and far more articulate than his interlocutors. When faced with a rhetorical bruiser like George Galloway, his natural register failed him, and he did not have the dexterity to secure by means of an ironical divagation what he was otherwise unable to secure by matching bruise to bruise.

With the publication of *God Is Not Great,* Christopher Hitchens reached a mass audience. He became celebrated. When he discovered how well he had been received by the public, he tended to regard his own religious beliefs with the indulgence of a man who on discovering that he has been lucky in attracting admirers very naturally concludes that he has been justified in attracting them.

In conversation, he lapsed into agnosticism, arguing only for a theological variant of *who knows?* His inability to draw a sharp distinction between affirming that God does not exist and wondering whether he does was a source of discomfort, with Hitchens, in his debate with philosopher William Craig, at last taking refuge, and, I suppose, comfort, in the declaration that certain religious asseverations are so much "white noise."

His atheism nonetheless had a kind of shambling boisterousness that made Christopher Hitchens seem a Mirabeau to Richard Dawkins's Saint Just or Sam Harris's Robespierre. Hitchens was uninterested in subtle analysis. On the masthead of the Daily Hitchens, there is the legend: *What can be asserted without proof can be dismissed without proof.* The difficulty with this assertion is straightforward. If *it* has been asserted without proof, why should it be believed, and if not, where is the proof?

I asked Hitchens about this during a break in our debate. We had retreated to a forlorn hotel loading ramp in order to have a cigarette. "Well, yes," he said, "it's just a sentence."

What elicited Christopher Hitchens's indignation was no very refined sense of the inadequacy of theological arguments. He thought they were equally good, or equally bad, and never paid them any attention. But far more than Richard Dawkins, Sam Harris, or Daniel Dennett,

Christopher Hitchens had a vivid sense of the demands that religious belief *must* enforce. The Christian heaven he once dismissed as a celestial North Korea, and while this remark is flippant, it is not foolish. Christopher Hitchens found objectionable the very idea of a source of authority, and so of power, greater than his own. This has seemed to some of his readers all of the time, and all of his readers some of the time, both defiant and uplifting. The very same idea is at work in the terrible crimes of the twentieth century. It is inseparable from them.

Christopher Hitchens chose to greet death publicly. Had he thought of it, he might well have invited an orchestra. We signed books together after our appearance in Birmingham, and to admirers on his very long line inquiring after his health, Hitchens replied that he was dying. It was a response that inevitably took his interlocutor aback, the more so since it was true. I followed his interviews and read his essays about cancer and death. I found them moving. But they do not evoke the man. In his portrait of William Marshal,[1] *The Flower of Chivalry*,[2] Georges Duby describes William advancing "calmly toward death" in full public view, his friends and retainers at his side, "proud of having been the instrument of the final, the fugitive, the anachronistic triumph of honor."[3]

Having contracted a terrible illness in the twenty-first century, Christopher Hitchens returned to the thirteenth century in order to have it be seen to its end.

14. Giuseppe Peano

In 1900, European mathematicians held their Second International Congress in Paris. The first had been held in Zurich some years before. The mathematicians were meeting in the most beautiful city in Europe, but they were meeting in August, and as happens every summer, Parisians affirmed that they were surprised by the heat. Unfavorable comparisons were made with the Swiss efficiency that Congress organizers remembered but could not duplicate. The distinguished Prussian mathematician, David Hilbert, was scheduled to give the keynote address.

A scientific congress is a social as well as a scientific gathering. The Second International Congress was no exception. Mature mathematicians came to size one another up or down; younger mathematicians came to see and be sized. A mood of innocent intellectual optimism prevailed. "We hear within us the perpetual call," David Hilbert affirmed when at last he reached the podium: "There is the problem. Seek its solution. You can find it by pure reason."

In his autobiography, Bertrand Russell describes the Congress as "the turning point of my intellectual life because there I met Peano." Born in 1858 in Italy's Cuneo province, Giuseppe Peano was of peasant stock, and the only mathematician at the Congress who was not a member of the middle or upper European classes. Like Enrico Fermi, he had made his way through the Italian educational establishment by means of his talent. It could not have been easy. What attracted Russell's admiration in Peano's personality was an interesting combination of traits. "In discussions at the Congress," Russell writes, "I observed that he was always more precise than anyone else." And then Russell adds a remark that both amplifies his sentiments and compromises their nobility. Peano, he recounts, "invariably got the better of any argument on which he embarked."

Peano made decisive contributions to the theory of ordinary differential equations; he was a well-known and influential academic; and he was something of a passionate eccentric, committed to an international scientific language of his own devising that he called *sine flexione,* a kind of pidgin Latin in which case endings and inflections had all been dropped. The scheme embodied none of the merits, but all of the defects, of the Latin language. The late nineteenth century was an age of enthusiasm, and any number of scientists thought that if only they could persuade the scientific community to adopt a universal language, all would thereafter be well. It was in this environment that Esperanto was created. I do not think that any scientist of note ever bothered to learn Peano's *sine flexione,* and those who learned it never used it. Esperanto remains what it always was, and that is a language no one would think to use if not compelled to do so.

In 1889, Peano published a set of axioms for the natural numbers in a little book (no more than a pamphlet) entitled *Arithmetices principia, nova methodo exposita* (A New Exposition of Arithmetical Principles). Just why he chose to publish work of fundamental importance in classical Latin, its case endings and declensions intact, while discarding his own *sine flexione,* I do not know. The ideas that Peano advanced were remarkable, but they were not entirely original, very similar ideas having occurred to the German mathematician Richard Dedekind at roughly the same time. For reasons that remain unclear, Peano's work has become canonical in the sense that mathematicians everywhere refer to the *Peano* axioms, adding Dedekind's name only as an afterthought.

A few mathematicians have found it all too much. In an elegant little book entitled *Naïve Set Theory,* Paul Halmos remarked waspishly that "the Peano axioms *used* to be considered as the fountainhead of all mathematical knowledge." In the paragraph directly following, he shows why this is so: because they appear to be the fountainhead of all mathematical knowledge.

Thereafter, he declines conspicuously to reveal why this is no longer so.

Giuseppe Peano died on the 20th of April, 1932, and as his American biographer Hubert Kennedy remarks, "he lived too long." These are terrible words, a reproach that, although widely made of others, is almost never addressed to oneself.

Peano had made almost all of his great contributions to logic and arithmetic before the nineteenth century ended; and he had been rewarded. He had met the leading nineteenth-century mathematicians; he had sat sweltering as Hilbert delivered his magisterial address in Paris, and afterwards, he had taken his dinner at the Café Voltaire, returning later in the week to Turin on one of those elegant overnight wagon-lits that in 1900 allowed a distinguished academic to cross the Continent in perfect comfort. And he had profoundly impressed Bertrand Russell.

Thereafter something like a subtle dissolution of focus took hold of the man, one whose objective correlative, I suspect, was the increasing hoarseness that afflicted his voice, so that if he needed to strain to make himself heard, others needed to strain to hear what he had said. At some time in the early 1890s, he had conceived of a great mathematical project. "It would be very useful," he wrote, "to collect all the known propositions referring to certain parts of mathematics, and to publish these collections." When it came to arithmetic, he proposed to publish these propositions in the logical notation that he had himself devised. His goal, it would seem, was to reduce mathematics to a very considerable list, one in which each item was logically connected to the one that came before and led logically to the one that came afterward, a sense for the meaning of the list—or *formulario*—accessible to anyone who understood the underlying logical notation and was sufficiently perspicuous to see what Peano himself imagined that he had already seen.

The *formulario* was an exercise in intellectual self-deception, exciting the interest of no one beyond Peano's most immediate disciples, men who for one reason or another were persuaded that enthusiasm was in their best interests. Before 1900, the *formulario* was Peano's curiosity; and afterwards, it became his passion. The final edition of the *formulario* Peano published in his system of *sine flexione*, thus at one stroke embedding his ideas in two inaccessible symbolisms. Much to the consternation of other members of the faculty at the University of Turin, he insisted on presenting his own courses in the *formulario* style, his students quite properly complaining that they could not understand a word of what the hoarse, excitable old man was saying.

And thereafter, his life became a matter of waiting. The past came to reclaim him. He became increasingly fond of returning to his family farm in the Piedmontese countryside. He dressed simply. At mealtimes, he ate what he had as a child eaten. He did not lose the things that he had known as a sophisticated European mathematician, but he came to value them less. The seasons passed.

At the conclusion of *Il Gatopardo* (*The Leopard*), Lampedusa's elegy for his imagined ancestor, Don Fabizio, death at last arrives to claim the Prince of Salina in a stuffy hotel room. As an organ grinder spins out melodies in the street below, the Prince, Lampedusa writes, was "making up a general balance sheet of his whole life, trying to sort out of the immense ash-heap of liabilities the golden flecks of happy moments."

What remained golden was his affectionate regard for his nephew Tancredi, the memory of his dogs, his ancestral home, *Donnafugata*, "and why not?" he asks, "the public thrill of being given a medal at the Sorbonne."

In the growing dark he tried to count how much time he had really lived. His brain could not cope with the simple calculation anymore; three months, three weeks, a total of six months, six by eight, eight-four, forty-eight thousand, the square root of eight hundred and forty thousand...

And then nothing.

At his death, Don Fabrizio, the Leopard, was seventy-three; and so was Giuseppe Peano.

15. Sonja Kovalevsky

Sofya Vasilevna Kovalevskaya (Sonja Kovalevsky) was born in Moscow in 1850 and died in Stockholm in 1891. The city is mathematically unlucky, René Descartes having died there in 1650 of some dreadful bronchial infection. A woman of very considerable talents, both as a mathematician *and* as a writer, Sonja Kovalevsky lived within the confines of an impudent Russian melodrama, simultaneously its heroine and its victim.

Within that melodrama, there was wealth, privilege, and a luxurious estate; there was an overbearing father, a man whose moods could ruin the household's peace; there was a most musical *Mama*, the daughter of a famous Russian astronomer; there was an older sister, Anya, first-born and so best-loved, and a younger brother, Feyda, the household Prince and heir, Big Anya and Little Feyda attracting dangerously unstable elective affinities from their parents; there was a strict, prim, and humorless governess, mad for decorum and discipline (*of course* there was); and there was that staple of every Russian melodrama, an eccentric but fun-loving uncle, who, as she relates in her memoir, *A Russian Childhood*, told an eager unloved child fairy tales, arranged a chessboard to suit her pudgy fingers, and talked with great dreaminess about "squaring the circle, asymptotes, and other things that were unintelligible to me and yet seemed mysterious and at the same time deeply attractive."

As a child, Sonja Kovalevsky acquired the rudiments of nineteenth-century mathematics by studying a textbook written by yet another Russian figure scuttling in from the theater wings of time, a Professor Tyrtov, who just happened to be a landowner, a man of means, and a neighbor, his conviction that women were incapable of mastering mathematics dissolving in helpless admiration as the shy but determined Sonja Kovalevsky deftly sorted through the complicated formulae of his textbook and solved the problems that it presented. Having discovered her talent, Tyrtov persuaded her father that she must be allowed to continue her education, Sonja Kovalevsky becoming their communal ward, a little innocent being transferred from the care of one well-meaning wise guardian to another.

For all that, her father's assent required four years before it was fully forthcoming, but in the end, and with the sense that he had done a manful but difficult thing, he allowed Sonja Kovalevsky to study analytic geometry and the calculus in Saint Petersburg. She was tutored, of course, and chaperoned, and kept cozy, comfortable, and captive, the distance in her life from the ordinary world, in which men freely took up their studies in large, noisy, boisterous groups, serving only to inflame the intensity of her desires, her pitiful pained ardor.

No one doubted that Sonja Kovalevsky was remarkable—not her Russian tutors, at any rate. And no one doubted that she deserved a university education. But Russian universities were closed to women. If Sonja Kovalevsky could not study at home, she would have to study abroad. In nineteenth-century Russia, as in contemporary Islam, an unmarried woman's freedom to travel was almost as difficult to obtain as her freedom to study, if only because her latent erotic power was considered so dangerously unstable a force that any father would be made uneasy by the thought of *his* darling daughter reclining with easy indolence against the cushions of the international sleeper departing Saint Petersburg every evening, her decorously shielded limbs a provocation to plump Russian businessmen, military officers, card sharks, land-owners, bureaucrats, Swiss officials, and even the ministers of various tea and pastry wagons.

A woman sitting alone and—of all things!—reading a treatise on mathematics was widely regarded among even educated men as an invitation to debauchery. Anna Karenina had spent a good deal of time traveling alone on the night-sleeper from Saint Petersburg to Moscow, after all, and even though she was a married woman, no one could miss the associative clack of trains, travel, and treachery.

What Sonja Kovalevsky might have done abroad while living alone and doing as she pleased was an exercise in her family's already agitated erotic imagination. The solution was a masterpiece of contrivance: an arranged marriage to one Vladimir Kovalesky, a biologist by training, a paleontologist in prospect, and an ardent admirer of Charles Darwin. By surrendering her liberty, Sonja Kovalevsky gained her freedom. She decamped for Heidelberg, a beautiful university town in the nineteenth century, and today still lovely, graceful and gabled.

Her professors' glowing testimonials enabled her to meet Karl Weierstrass, one of the eminences of the German mathematical academy. Kindly, rumpled, and disheveled, Weierstrass challenged Sonja Kovalevsky with a set of problems he had prepared for his advanced students, and when she had solved them with a positively alarming degree of ease, determined generously that her "personality was [strong enough] to offer the necessary guarantees" for advanced training. To the uncles she had already acquired, Sonja Kovalevsky added a powerful new uncle, so that she appeared in European mathematical circles as the glowing star at the center of an avuncular galaxy.

Thereafter, her short life was consumed by her ardent nature. The contrived and pathetic marriage into which she had entered as a matter of convenience made demands of its own, and both she and Vladimir Kovalesky discovered to their surprise that an arrangement to which neither was committed became one in which both were consumed.

After four years in Heidelberg, the couple returned to Saint Petersburg, where Sonja Kovalevsky discovered almost at once that a society unwilling to allow her an education was equally unwilling to afford her a position. She gave birth to a daughter, whom she seemed equally to have adored and to have neglected. She wrote for various theatrical and literary publications; she started a novel. Persuaded like so many other talented women that her gifts were fungible, she and her husband embarked on a number of business schemes, each one a notable, even a spectacular, failure, disasters accumulating until their marriage dissolved under the strain.

Vladimir Kovalesky took his own life in 1883.

It can hardly be said that Sonja Kovalesky lived a life without honors—only that she lived it without luck. Decamping from Saint Petersburg for Paris, where her sister was already making the acquaintance of various revolutionary bohemians, men whose commitment to violence was offset by their indifference to work, she reentered the mathematical scene, and with that special gift she had for attracting uncles, caught the eye of Gösta Mittag-Leffler, a student of the great Weierstrass, and a powerful and determined mathematician in his own right. Mittag-Leffler became her last champion, in the end persuading the University of Stockholm to award her a probationary position, one of those awkward arrangements so familiar in academic life in which every requirement except decency is satisfied.

She continued to work; she achieved many notable results in the theory of ordinary and partial differential equations, and in 1888, she received the *Prix Bordin* from the French Academy of Science. Like the Russians, the French were prepared to honor achievement without ever making it possible. Her position in Stockholm was made permanent; and she was elected to the Russian Academy of Science. Her hope that as a member of the Academy she might be rewarded by an academic position was not fulfilled, circumstances that she met with a characteristic mixture of contempt and resignation. In 1891, she died quite suddenly after suffering from pneumonia, and now survives as a face engraved on a Russian postage stamp, and a name attached to a crater on the far side of the moon.

All this belongs, I suppose, to the universal history of sadness; but in her autobiography, *A Russian Childhood*, Sonja Kovalevsky recalls with some sense of wonder an early memory.

She was eleven. Her bedroom required wallpaper, and for reasons that even Sonja Kovalevsky cannot explain, the walls were covered with notes and scribbles from a calculus text owned by her military-minded father. Her uncle had already introduced her to mathematics, but not to higher mathematics or the formulas of the calculus.

"I noticed certain things," she wrote, "that I had already heard mentioned by uncle. It amused me to examine these sheets of hieroglyphics whose meaning escaped me completely but which, I felt, must signify something very wise and interesting."

But, really, isn't this is how we all are, much impressed by things we do not understand and hoping that they represent something very wise and interesting?

16. A Logician's Life

Pierre Abélard (Peter Abelard) was born in what is now Brittany in 1079. The most important logician of the twelfth century, he falls evenly between the two great eras in the history of logic, the first taking place in ancient Greece, and the second, in nineteenth- and twentieth-century Europe.

His family belonged to the minor nobility, and, as the eldest son, he was expected to become a soldier, a career that he rejected, he writes, because he preferred "the conflicts of disputations to the trophies of war."[1] Thereafter Abélard was introduced to late eleventh-century philosophy, chiefly by Jean Roscelin. With his education complete, Abélard wandered the Loire valley, "disputing," as he says, "like a true peripatetic philosopher, whenever I heard there was keen interest in the art of dialectic."

He was widely considered insufferable.

"At last I came to Paris." Abélard when. Then as now, the city radiated waves of glamour and prestige, and with those waves returned, drew in troubadours and poets, logicians and philosophers, architects, artisans, stone-masons, gold-smiths, windy prelates, money-men eager for cathedral contracts, and a remarkable number of prostitutes, drifters, low-lifes, spongers, wastrels, petty criminals, jugglers, necromancers, astrologers, minor clergy, dissipated aristocrats, heretics, and, of course, hunchbacks.

Having drawn the circle of his own wanderings to their center, Abélard wasted no time in denouncing the views of his rural master Roscelin. Not very much is known specifically of the doctrines that Roscelin had preached. A nominalist in name, Roscelin believed in words, and so became a minimalist in philosophy. Where Plato, and so many others, saw in universal terms such as red, good, brave, loyal, and hirsute the names of universals or Platonic forms, Roscelin stopped at the water's edge, seeing nothing in words beyond words. Condemned for heresy in 1093, he was exiled to England, the Catholic Church having correctly noticed that once a man is disposed to doubt the existence of universals, his doubts about the Trinity cannot be far behind. Abélard's own criticisms followed the long boat or skiff that carried Roscelin across the choppy waters of the English Channel, the man's sense of indignation mounting as he faced the English coast, with Abélard's criticisms stinging at his buttocks.

"If you had savored only a little bit of the sweetness of the Christian religion," Roscelin would later write, and there followed the usual complaints of a teacher making the pained discovery that teachers always make, namely that their students are no longer sufficiently mindful of the "great benefits" that they have received from their instruction.

No universities—not yet. No degrees. No committees. No chairs. No tenure. Teachers themselves established schools. They clambered onto hillsides and with their students arrayed before them, talked into the wind. Abélard considered his contemporaries perfect fools. "I began," he writes, "to think of myself as the only philosopher in the world, with nothing to fear from anyone."

His reputation owed much to a contrived encounter with an older, more established philosopher, William of Champeaux, "the supreme master of the subject," as Abélard observes. William was the arch-deacon of Paris and head of the Cloister School at Notre Dame, a big, bruising, well-known figure, much crippled by his unenviable ability to express a philosophical position adroitly without in the least being able to defend it intelligibly. If Roscelin had dismissed universals from the world, William called them back, insisting with a slow, measured shake of his tonsured head that justice, humanity, goodness, whiteness, or beauty are as real as Socrates or Aristotle, the proposition that Socrates is a man denoting Socrates and designating his humanity.

A nervous cough-like harrumph erupts from the back of the lecture room. Abélard shambles to his feet. If Socrates is a man and Aristotle is a man, he asks, then is the same humanity in both men?

Having no real idea what to say, William says finally that "in the common existence of universals, the whole species [is] essentially the same in each of its individuals."

And thereupon Abélard pushes poor baffled William, his wattles now wobbling indignantly, from one absurdity to another, concluding finally that on William's view, it follows inexorably that Socrates is identical to a donkey.

"Although he [William] welcomed me at first," Abélard writes, "he soon took a violent dislike to me because I set out to refute some of his arguments and frequently reasoned against him."

As his contemporaries observed, Abélard was everywhere in Paris in the first two decades of the twelfth century, talking, writing, lecturing, and in general jabbing his tense index finger into a great many withdrawing and affronted chests, his logical skills now so sharp that, by means of endlessly divided distinctions, he seemed able to slice up the very air he breathed. It would seem that on hearing Abélard's lecture, Anselm of Laon became "wildly jealous," circumstances that Abélard assigned to every conceivable cause except the one that he had set in motion.

"Since the beginning of the human race," Abélard observed with some asperity in his autobiography, *Historia Calamitatum* (*A History of My Misfortunes*), women have "brought the noblest men to ruin."

"There was in Paris at the time," Abélard writes, "a young girl named Héloïse."

Born in 1100, Héloïse grew up somewhere outside Paris, and was educated at the abbey of Notre-Dame at Argenteuil, the child she must have been disappearing into the soft folds of womanly flesh she became, just as the man Abélard was emerging from the irritable adolescent he was—double pupation, I suppose, and so something that conforms entirely to Aristotle's idea of a chance event when those liberated butterflies meet in mid-flight.

I could have seen the two of them from my window, Héloïse passing in quick tripping steps in one direction, even as brown and baggy Abélard, his cassock flapping, lumbers toward her from the other, she tripping on, he executing the proverbial full-stop and double-take of a man whose senses are violently suffused.

He was at once "all on fire with desire for this girl."

Héloïse lived with her uncle, the Canon Fulbert, in a house on the Quai. The original has been largely destroyed, save for a few sturdy medieval timbers, but a sign commemorates the great romantic drama that took place there long ago. The seduction proceeded by means of a series of steps meant to promote Abélard from logician to lover. "I had," he writes, "youth and exceptional good looks as well as my great reputation to commend me." Mutual friends were invoked. They adverted to Abélard's great reputation as a teacher and his uncompromising continence.

"We were united," Abélard writes, "first under one roof, and then in heart, and so with our lessons as a pretext, we abandoned ourselves entirely to love."

Uncle Fulbert, although having never been commended for his intelligence, must at some point have noticed the moans and distracted mutters coming from *le grenier* above, with its straw pallet, sooty walls, and those small windows overlooking the brown river just below. He was apparently rather slow on the uptake. Quoting Saint Jerome with satisfaction, Abélard writes that "we are always the last to learn of evil in our own home." But if Fulbert could not smell smoke, he was eventually persuaded to see fire, largely because, as Abélard remarks, none too delicately but with a certain stubborn pride, he and Héloïse were "caught in the act."

"We shall both be destroyed," Héloïse remarked quite lucidly, in words that Abélard quotes. "All that is left for us is suffering as great as our love has been."

She was quite right. The passion that had consumed them then consumed them. Abélard and Héloïse were separated and re-united. Their stories and evasions grew elaborate; and through it all, Uncle Fulbert, baffled by events and powerless to control them, fumed and steamed and plotted and schemed, until suffocating with fury, he set in motion by means of a gang of ruffians the events that would lead to Abélard's dreadful mutilation.

Thereafter, both Abélard and Héloïse entered religious life, Abélard because he was unable to conceive another plan, and Héloïse because she was forced to do so by Abélard. She took her monastic vows most unwillingly. She quite knew they would bind her for life, and they did.

It is their story that remains, imperishable after eight hundred years, the logician in conflict with the lover in Abélard.

In everyone.

Did I mention that the house in which Abélard and Héloïse consummated their affair was a few steps from my own apartment?

Or that nothing remains of the original medieval structure but a few interior beams?

I think I did.

17. Chronicle of a Death Foretold

Traveling from Santiago to Buenos Aires, Don Pedro de Los Angeles carried with him a blue and gold parrot, a monkey with a ribbon tail, and a locked steamer trunk. His wife, the beautiful Senõra Sabrina, whose green eyes were as deep as the sea, greeted the parrot and the monkey with cries of joy, but when she asked what was in the trunk, Don Pedro said nothing, shaking his head, and then giving orders to the servants to carry the trunk to a closet behind his study on the third floor. Days and years passed. Don Pedro's full black beard turned white and cataracts shrouded his eyes. He walked slowly with the aid of a cane whose hand grip was shaped like an eagle's head. The beautiful Senõra Sabrina became stout, her flesh quivering as she walked, and the low lovely voice with which she had once sung songs of love grew hoarse with age. One day, Don Pedro became ill with the ague, and sensing that his end was near, he withdrew to his bedchamber on the third floor of the white villa with the turquoise shutters. He suffered for four days, but on the fifth day, his mind was clear. After the servants had left, his wife approached his bed.

"Don Pedro," she said, "I have never asked anything of you but the love to which I was entitled, but I wish now to ask a favor."

Don Pedro said nothing.

"Don Pedro, for forty years, I have wished to know what was in the trunk you brought with you from Santiago. Satisfy my curiosity, for you know that I will never look inside that trunk without your permission."

"Senõra Sabrina," said Don Pedro, "there is a manuscript within the trunk. It is bound in vellum. The words are written on parchment. It is very old, older than the dawn of time. A copy of the manuscript survived the great fire that lit the skies of Egypt and consumed the libraries of Alexandria."

"A manuscript?" Senõra Sabrina asked in astonishment. "All these years you have clutched a manuscript to your heart?"

"Yes," said Don Pedro.

"Does it contain secrets, Don Pedro?"

"I do not know. I have not read it. It is foretold that all who read it will go blind."

Senõra Sabrina looked at her husband's sightless eyes without saying anything.

"But you must know something of this manuscript," Senõra Sabrina cried out in vexation, a trickle of perspiration falling between her breasts like water sliding between two mountains.

"Mere possession of the manuscript is a blessing," said Don Pedro.

"That is all very well, but what does it say?"

"The manuscript contains a series of numbered propositions, written in a very careful hand. Each proposition is said to have the unique ability to express and to exhibit the truth, so that by reading them, a man would know where the jaguar goes at dawn, and what will be the date of his death, and why the whale cries in the sea at night."

"And do you know the date of your death, Don Pedro?"

"Yes."

That night, Don Pedro died peacefully in his sleep. Senõra Sabrina sat for two days by his body, as is the custom, and on the third day, she withdrew the key to the steamer trunk from the mahogany box on Don Pedro's writing desk. Carrying a candle, for the closet had no windows, she bent stiffly, blew the dust of years from the trunk's lid, and with trembling fingers, turned the lock. A dark, rich smell emerged. Senõra Sabrina brought the flickering candle close and peered inside.

There was nothing there.

V. Language

18. The Recovery of Case

David Berlinski and Juan Uriagereka

It was April 1977. Noam Chomsky and Howard Lasnik were about to publish an important essay in linguistics titled "Filters and Control."[1] Having seen and studied the preprint of the article, Jean-Roger Vergnaud wrote to its authors.[2] Vergnaud had "some ideas to communicate." Chomsky and Lasnik were unable to incorporate those ideas in their essay. Time was short; the mail, slow. They did something better. They incorporated Vergnaud's ideas into their work.

Vergnaud's letter has become famous among linguists, outlasting, if not outliving, its author.

Jean-Roger Vergnaud died in Los Angeles in 2011.

Sight Unseen

Most readers are not likely to have seen this sentence before:

1. The dung ate the slug's tail on the sum of 2 + 2.

It is not a sentence that suggests very much, but it *is* a grammatical English sentence.

This is something that English speakers recognize at once, and recognize without effort. Sentences such as 1 may be embedded in still other sentences:

1a. Solomon says that [the dung ate the slug's tail on the sum of 2 + 2].
1b. I heard [him say [that the dung ate the slug's tail on the sum of 2 + 2]].
1c. Readers realize [that I heard [him say [that...]]].

If c is a grammatical English sentence, then why not

1d. Ralph believes that [readers realize [that I heard [him say [that...]]]],

and so on ad infinitum? An allusion to infinity suggests an obvious question: How could infinitely many sentences be encompassed by the human brain, which, like the human liver, is blunt in its boundaries? In the first half of the twentieth century, Alonzo Church, Kurt Gödel, Emil Post, and Alan Turing created in the theory of recursive functions a mathematical scheme commensurate with the question's intellectual dignity. The theory is one of the glories of twentieth-century mathematics.[3] The factorial function $n!$, to take a simple example, is defined over the numbers $n = 0, 1, 2, 3, \ldots$. Its domain and range are infinite. Two clauses are required to subordinate the infinite to finite control. The base case is defined outright: $0! = 1$; and, thereafter, $(n + 1)! = (n + 1)n!$ If the functions inherent in a natural language are recursive, the language that contains them comprises infinitely many sentences.

Sentences used in the ordinary give-and-take of things are, of course, limited in their length. Henry James could not have constructed a thousand-word sentence without writing it down or suffering a stroke. Nor is recursion needed to convey the shock of the new. Four plain-spoken words are quite enough: *Please welcome President Trump*. Prefacing 1d, on the other hand, with yet another iteration of *Ralph believes*, is no improvement on the original. Quite the contrary. It is a deprovement, like one hundred rounds of "For He's a Jolly Good Fellow." If sentences in English can be new without recursion, they can also be recursive without being new. The rules of grammar establish only that natural languages are infinite. Why they are as they are, no one knows. The same displacement of attention is at work in arithmetic. For anyone unaccountably persuaded that thirty-eight is the largest natural number, the rules of arithmetic say otherwise. The *rules*, note. The argument needs no further steps.

Native Speakers Speak

For years, American psychologists affirmed, on the basis of no evidence whatsoever, that children acquire their native language by an arduous process of discipline and training. B. F. Skinner had taught pigeons some simple skills and saw no reason that the same principles of stimulus conditioning could not explain how Chinese children acquired Mandarin.

He was mistaken.[4]

Children acquire their native language without training, and what training they do receive is haphazard, degenerate, incomplete, or fragmentary.[5]

Consider 2a and 2b:

> 2a. You are happy.
> 2b. Are you happy?

There is only one verb in a. It goes to the left in b. It is just possible to imagine that a child, having mastered a, could be brought to master b by reinforcement of some sort—a series of electrical shocks, perhaps.

But consider

> 3a. Anyone who is interested can see me later.
> 3b. *Is anyone who interested can see me later?

The strategy employed at 2b results in the verbal hash of 3b, a point marked by a Cyclopean asterisk. The correct question is

> 3c. Can anyone who is interested see me later?

Children otherwise confused by the exigencies of the spoon never make the mistake in 3b. "Knowledge of language," Chomsky and Lasnik remarked, "extends far beyond available experience."[6] On the level of the niceties, experts may prevail, as when the French Academy bans *le week-end* or *le snack* as Anglophone abominations; but a language belongs to its speakers, and it is their intuitions that determine what it can say and how it can say it.

Where else to turn; who else would know?

Chomsky has always been interested in the most elementary forms of grammar, and so in what is obvious enough to be overlooked.

> 4a. *(I) love *(Lucy).
> 4b. (Yo) amo *(a Lucy).
> 4c. (Nik) maite dut (Lucy)

In English (a), one cannot drop subjects or objects; in Spanish (b), one can drop subjects but not objects; in Basque (c), one can drop them equally and good riddance to them both. The morphology of *Nik*, the Basque I, and *Lucy*, the American *comedienne*, remain encoded in the verb *maite dut*. In English, the only possible order of constituents is *I love Lucy*. In Basque, all permutations are possible. Every speaker of English, Spanish, or Basque knows such facts. Asking native speakers for their judgment is an imperative of research. For generative grammarians, it would appear to be the only imperative. Field work? "That is a complete waste of your time and the government's money," the linguist Robert Lees wrote to some grant-seeking schnorrer. "You are a native speaker of English; in ten minutes you can produce more illustrations of any point in English grammar than you will find in many millions of words of random text."[7]

Native speakers retain their authority about native speech even if their judgments are less than categorical. *He met his wife in Italy*, natives say. *He met in Italy his wife* is off, although *he met in Italy his wife of three days* goes down better. In *Lolita*, Vladimir Nabokov may sometimes be seen seated on the sofa of these solecisms. Then again, if native speakers flag *he met in Italy his wife*, it is not as decisively as they flog *in wife he Italy met*. Some linguistic intuitions are all or nothing; others not.

With doctors, it is the same thing.

The cholesterol level of yours? Not so bad. Not so good either.

Great Goals of Fire

In his masterpiece of 1964, *Aspects of the Theory of Syntax*, Chomsky set three goals for linguistic theory.[8] Two of them are trite. A linguistic theory must be observationally adequate, ruling out 3b and ruling in 3a. And it must be descriptively adequate, accounting for the properties of English or Japanese in terms of their grammars—the device that "gives a correct account of the linguistic intuition of the native speaker...." That native speaker is, *au fait*, no off the street knock-off. On the contrary. Chomsky's native speaker is a one-man Platonic form. He is, Chomsky affirmed,

> an ideal speaker-listener, in a completely homogeneous speech community, who knows a language perfectly and is unaffected by such grammatically irrelevant conditions as memory limitations, distractions, shifts of attention and interest, and errors in applying his knowledge of the language to actual performance.[9]

Observational and descriptive adequacy, generously understood, have long been counted as goals of traditional linguistics. Vouchsafed the chance to read a preprint of Chomsky's *Syntactic Structures* in the fourth century BC, the Sanskrit grammarian Pānini would have felt right at home. But the third goal of linguistic theory, explanatory adequacy, is otherwise. The grammar of Greek is intended to explain Greek to the Greeks, even if, in the end, it is all Greek to those Greeks. Universal Grammar (UG) is intended to specify the most general principles of human language. It must provide an explanation for the extraordinary fact that a Japanese child raised in Paris will acquire French, but not Japanese, and a French child raised in Tokyo, Japanese, but not French. Either child may acquire both French and Japanese, of course, but neither will fail to acquire French *or* Japanese. Linguists and philosophers may have known this in antiquity; they did not say so with any great conviction, and they may not have said so at all. It was left to Chomsky to remark with the full force of his genius that every human language can be acquired by any human being. Universal Grammar, Chomsky concluded, must be a species-specific characteristic of the human race, biologically encoded, genetically transmitted.

In & Out

A DESCRIPTIVE GRAMMAR ADEQUATE to the demands of a particular language comprises a hideously complicated system of rules. *A Grammar of Contemporary English*, by Randolph Quirk, Sidney Greenbaum, Geoffrey Leech, and Jan Svartvik, runs to more than one thousand pages; and even at that length, readers may well conclude that the indefatigable Quirk, Greenbaum, Leech, and Svartvik were just warming up.[10] By the 1970s, it was becoming clear that no system of compromises could completely reconcile the rules of Japanese or Hungarian with the aims and claims of Universal Grammar. "There is a certain tension," Chomsky and Lasnik wrote with some understatement, between these pursuits.

> To attain explanatory adequacy, it is in general necessary to restrict the class of possible grammars, whereas the pursuit of descriptive adequacy often seems to require elaborating the mechanisms available and thus extending the class of possible grammars.[11]

It makes no sense to assign to Universal Grammar the complex and often rebarbative grammatical rules of *every* human language. No one is born knowing the grammar of Mingrelian. The grammatical distinctions between even closely related languages are almost always sharp as swords. Both English and French are prepared to have Ernest get rid of some poor schlub named Bill, but in English, there is the simple sane syntax of

5. Ernest wants Bill to go,

while in French, the subjunctive is needed, as in

6. *Ernest veut que Bill s'en aille*,

or

7. *Ernest veut que Bill parte.*

A word-by-word translation of 5 yields only

8. **Ernest veut Bill aller*,

which, although comprehensible, is *pourri jusqu'à la moëlle*, as fastidious French snoots might say. It is bad to the bone. (Google translates 5 as *Ernest veut le projet de loi pour aller*, thus suggesting that, Stephen Hawking and Elon Musk notwithstanding, anxieties about artificial intelligence are somewhat premature.) Children learning English acquire 5; learning French, they acquire 6 and 7. An *acquisition* suggests something they might have just picked up, but not knowing the grammar of either language, just how did they pick up anything at all?

"The history of transformational generative grammar," Mark Baltin observed, "can be divided into two periods, which can be called expansion and retrenchment."[12] This has given contemporary linguistics a very characteristic breathing-in and breathing-out structure. "During the early expansion period, a primary concern was the description of grammatical phenomena."[13]

Breathing in.

Explanatory theory "was correspondingly loose..."

Breathing out.

> During the retrenchment period... the focus of attention shifted from the construction of relatively complex... statements to the construction of a general theory of grammar, restricted as to the devices it employed, which could be ascribed to universal grammar.[14]

Breathing in.

Whatever the balance between complicated and quite specific rule systems and Universal Grammar, it was clear by the 1970s that one of them would have to take precedence over the other.

The Courtiers Gather

In 1975, Massimo Piattelli-Palmarini organized an encounter between Jean Piaget and Noam Chomsky at the Royaumont Abbey, some twenty miles or so north of Paris. In an essay entitled "Encounter at Royaumont," Howard Gardner recalled the ingathering of courtiers at what was formerly an austere Cistercian monastery.[15] The grace of God prevented Piattelli-Palmarini from organizing the conference at a *Carthusian* monastery, where vows of silence would have prevailed. In attendance, Gardner wrote, were

> Nobel laureates in biology, leading figures in philosophy and mathematics, and several of the most prominent behavior scientists... It was almost as if two of the great figures of the seventeenth century—Descartes and Locke, say—could have defied time and space to engage in a joint meeting of the Royal Society and the *Académie Française*.[16]

On s'imagine cela. Piaget had long been eager to participate in such a discussion; Chomsky, less so. But in the end, "he accepted the invitation proffered by the late Jacques Monod."[17] Gardner emphasized how the meeting influenced "the future awarding of research funds, the interests of the brightest young scholars, and, indeed, the course of subsequent investigations of human cognition."[18]

Events followed a familiar academic trajectory:

> Piaget noted "all the essential points in this about which I think I agree with Chomsky." And Chomsky acknowledged "Piaget's interesting remarks." As the discussion proceeded and became increasingly heated, the tone became distinctly less friendly. Piaget criticized the nativist position as "weak" and "useless," even as Chomsky described certain Piagetian assertions as "false," "inconceivable," and (in a mathematical sense) "trivial."[19]

By common consent Chomsky impressed biologists otherwise well-disposed to Piaget with the force of his arguments and the precision and pertinence of his examples. When he wearied of combat, Chomsky ceded the floor to his Minister of War, Jerry Fodor, who succeeded in further flabbergasting the biologists by insisting that his most trivial remarks had the structure of a logical proof.

In fact, Gardner added, the keynote for the conference at Royaumont was set by the cybernetician, Guy Cellérier, who compared the development of the mind to climbing a hill. Cellérier did not need to add that by climbing a hill, he meant climbing *up* the hill, an interesting example of the tacit knowledge to which ordinary speakers appeal the minute they open their mouths.

And the Paradigm Shifts

Royaumont was notable in marking the beginning of what Chomsky would later call the bio-linguistic paradigm. Long before Royaumont, Chomsky had argued that the acquisition of a language in childhood represents nothing less than the maturation of a biological system; long after Royaumont, he argued that he had been right long before Royaumont. "Assuming that language has general properties of other biological systems," Chomsky wrote in 2007, "We should be seeking three factors that enter into its growth in the individual: (i) genetic factors, the topic of UG, (ii) experience, which permits variation within a fairly narrow range, and (iii) principles not specific to language. The third factor includes principles of efficient computation, which would be expected to be of particular significance for systems such as language."[20]

These are, in their largest aspects, principles that govern the development of the visual system or the maturational progression into puberty. No one learns to see in three dimensions or to interpret an arrow in flight as a figure moving against an unchanging background. Children see what they see and grow as they do, and at the age of thirteen or so, the boys, at least, lose their elfin graces and enter into the semi-adult world of bullfrog-like voices and ripe pustules.

Some biologists welcomed Chomsky's discovery that he was, deep down, a biologist with a marked lack of enthusiasm. Skinner had long insisted that behaviorism was nothing more than a local form of Darwinian evolution; he concluded that behaviorism must be correct in virtue of its reflected glory. That the argument might go in reverse, like leverage in the commodities market, did not occur to him. In his famous review of Skinner's *Verbal Behavior*, Chomsky emptied Skinner's reputation of its brimming content, and on those occasions in which he had talked or written about the evolution of the language faculty, he seemed to suggest that since nothing was known, anything could be said. This came perilously close to a kind of contemptuous indifference to Darwinian doctrinal affiliations.

However far it might have been from biology itself, the bio-linguistic perspective did suggest a strategy by which universal and particular grammars could be seen as aspects of a single system. The principles of Universal Grammar were assigned a regulatory role in the governance of every human language. Some were so obvious as to have gone unmentioned for thousands of years. Latin grammarians certainly knew that Latin is constructed from a finite number of words. It has a distinctive atomic structure. So does every human language. The grammarians failed only to observe, or to remark, that there is no obvious reason why this should be so. Other topologies are possible. Giraud's Theorem describes an association between a first-order theory and a Grothendieck topos, one that goes from the austerities of the theory's logical structure to its meaning.[21]

No natural language goes there or does that.

The atomic structure of language belongs to the familiar category of facts that seem to have been well known without ever having been widely remarked. The A over A principle is otherwise. It was not known at all until Chomsky presented it to an audience of uncomprehending linguists in 1962.[22] They had never heard of such a thing. If a rule ambiguously applies to some element A in a structure of the form $\ldots [_A \ldots [_A \ldots]]$, the rule must apply to the largest (or the longest) bracketed A-like constituent *before* it applies to A. Thus $[_A \ldots [_A \ldots]]$ *over* $[_A \ldots]$.

There are two relevant noun phrases (NP) in

> 9. I won't forget $[_{NP}$ my promise to $[_{NP}$ that idiot Washburn]],

but the rule governing which of them may be extracted stops

10. *That idiot Washburn, I won't forget my promise to,

dead in its tracks, while waving a white baton at

11. My promise to that idiot Washburn, I won't forget.

Whatever the principles of UG, counting, curiously enough, is not among them. Human linguistic and arithmetic abilities seem to belong to systems maintaining only the most distant of diplomatic relations. In a Chinese fragment from 200 BC, a student asks his teacher whether he should spend more time learning speech or numbers. His teacher replies: "If my good sir cannot fathom both at once, then abandon speech and fathom numbers, [for] numbers can speak, [but] speech cannot number."[23] No grammatical rule involves counting words, because no grammatical rule involves counting *anything*. Even the linear order of a natural language, in which one word comes after another, is a concession to the limitations imposed on speech by a single channel of communication. Were human beings able simultaneously to speak through their mouths and snort through their noses, the demands of linearity might well be relaxed.

Hear, Hear

Throughout the 1960s, many working linguists paid lip service to UG, but when it came to making sense of the devilishly complicated structure of the English language, their proposals were tame to the point of triteness. More rules, better rules, language-specific rules, rules without limit, and so rules without end. Robert Lees's dissertation, *The Grammar of English Nominalizations*, was published in 1960, and under his tense pre-wordprocessing thumbs, English nominalizations appeared to be governed by as many rules as the *Halakha*.[24]

At some time in the 1970s, it became clear to linguists that *more rules*, like *more gravy*, was an injunction subject to the law of diminishing marginal utility. In their paper about filters and control, Chomsky and

Lasnik codified with increasing confidence a radically disjunctive view of linguistic theory. Beyond its universal principles, UG contained a system of open binary parameters. The universal principles were true of all languages; but "an actual language," Chomsky and Lasnik wrote, "is determined by fixing the parameters of [the] core grammar."[25]

This idea was very much in the air. So many things are. A line of influence ran from microbiology to generative grammar. Chomsky had been deeply impressed by the operon model of the bacterial cell—the work of Jacques Monod and François Jacob. In his Nobel Prize address, Jacob provided a long look back:

> We can therefore envision the activity of the genome of *E. coli* as follows. The expression of the genetic material requires a continuous flow of unstable messengers which dictate to the ribosomal machinery the specificity of the proteins to be made. The genetic material consists of operons containing one or more genes, each operon giving rise to one messenger. The production of messenger by the operon is, in one way or another, inhibited by regulatory loops composed of three elements: regulatory gene, repressor, operator. Specific metabolites intervene at the level of these loops to play their role as signals: in inducible systems, to inactivate the repressor and hence allow production of messenger and ultimately of proteins; in repressible systems, to activate the repressor, and hence inhibit production of messenger and of proteins. *According to this scheme, only a fraction of the genes of the cell can be expressed at any moment, while the others remain repressed.* [emphasis added] The network of specific, genetically determined circuits selects at any given time the segments of DNA that are to be transcribed into messenger and consequently translated into proteins, as a function of the chemical signals coming from the cytoplasm and from the environment.[26]

The success of these ideas in prokaryotic populations prompted both Monod and Jacob to generalize them to encompass the eukaryotes. "What accounts for the difference between a butterfly and a lion, a chicken and a fly, or a worm and a whale," Jacob declared, "is not their chemical components, but varying distributions of these components."[27] The claim has become famous. Whether it is true is another matter entirely. One could with equal justice say that what accounts for the difference between the Great Pyramid at Giza and the Large Hadron Collider in Lausanne is a matter merely of the varying distribution of their components.

For all that, it is possible to see in Jacob's remarks the emerging outlines of the principles and parameters approach to linguistic theory. English is a heads-up language. *The picture is hanging on the wall.* In Japanese, it is the other way around. *E wa kabe ni kakatte imasu. (The) picture wall on is hanging.* Japanese is a heads-down language. Once a parameter has been set, its influence ramifies throughout the grammar of the set-upon language.[28]

The question how human languages can be fundamentally the same if they are so very different invites the peremptory, but premature, response that *if* they are so very different, they could not be fundamentally the same. Not so. Two languages may be alike because both languages respect the principles of UG, *and* unalike because they vary across a finite number of binary parameters. Languages as far apart as Mohawk and English, Mark Baker argued in *The Atoms of Language*, are separated by only a handful of parameters.[29] When the parameters of Mohawk are changed in favor of their English-language settings, it becomes clear that Mohawk speakers intended to speak English all along. And vice versa, of course. Anthropologists have made similar arguments about human nature. It is everywhere the same except in matters of sexual discretion, taste, fashion, coloring, clothing, and the way in which to greet the rising or the setting sun. It was on encountering the Nambikwara that Claude Lévi-Strauss realized that this was so, and assigned an improvement in his humility to the experience. The handful of differential parameters by which men are separated are more noticeable than the great universal principles by which men come to recognize one another as men—but they are less important.

Languages, too. It is the same.

As all stars shrivel in the single sun, the words are many, but The Word is one.[30]

Straight outta COMPton

INTRODUCED IN 1967 BY the linguist Peter Rosenbaum, a complementizer, or **COMP**, is, on generative principles, a part of speech, and like **NOUN**, or **VERB**, entitled to the majestic upsweep of capitalization, the brand mark of boldface.[31] Before tensed sentences, **COMP** appears as *that*:

12. Trottweiller believes *that* silence is golden;

but before infinitives, it appears as *for*:

13. Trottweiler prefers *for* Agnes to keep quiet.

Whether, if, whither, and *whereupon* are among the **COMPS**; and **COMP** as a category may be empty, too; *that* and *for* have both disappeared from 14:

14. I think Trottweiler prefers Agnes to keep quiet.

In her MIT PhD dissertation, "Theory of Complementation in English Syntax," Joan Bresnan argued that **COMP** should get its own category, Ś.[32] Generative grammarians had until that very moment thought of S (Sentence) as the highest of categories (*größte Kategorie aller Zeit,* as German linguists like to say). Unlike traditional grammarians and schoolteachers, who had diagrammed sentences in terms of subjects, verbs, and objects, generative grammarians argued that sentences were strictly two-man jobs:

15. S → NP + VP,

where NP is a noun phrase, and VP a verb phrase. But whether S is a two- or a three-man outfit, on Bresnan's view, it has a back-up in Ś:

16. Ś → **COMP** S.

Although **COMP** is a category comprising the most ordinary of words—*that, for, if,* after all—it has played an outsized role in the ongoing drama of generative grammar.

Anarchy & Order

WELL BEFORE CHOMSKY, LEONARD Bloomfield had argued that "the lexicon of a natural language is basically an appendix of its grammar, a list of its basic irregularities."[33] This distinction between the orderliness of a grammar and the anarchy of its lexicon, generative grammarians carried over intact. They were happy to do so. The lexicon of a natural language is not really a dictionary. It does not define a cow as *Animal quadrupes ruminans cornutum,* as Samuel Johnson remarked in observing that definitions often make things darker.[34] A lexicon is closer to a chrestomathy—of words and idioms, obviously, but of morphemes, too, when necessary. Lexical items are identified by their features, the lexical "dog" listed as [+ N], [+ ˈdɒg], [+ count], [+ animate], [– artifact], [– stative], [+ slobbering] ... It is in the lexicon that one sees naked the primitive connection between sound and meaning. There is *a dog* in the English lexicon, *un chien* in the French, and *ein Hund* in the German, and there is no better reason that this should be so beyond the fact that it is so.

Grammatical rules do not reach down to touch the anarchy of such facts. This is entirely compatible with the hypothesis that, morphological differences aside, human beings share a single lexicon, so that words, like electrons in quantum field theory, are all essentially identical.

The classification of lexical items in terms of their binary features carries over to grammatical categories. Languages have nouns, verbs, adjectives, and prepositions. Chomsky presented an analysis of these distinctions in terms of two binary features: +/- **N** and +/- **V**. A noun is all **N** and no **V**. A verb is all **V** and no **N**. An adjective is both + **N** and + **V**; but a preposition is neither and so figures as a grammatical eunuch. "We might just as well eliminate the distinction between feature and category," Chomsky remarked, "and regard all symbols of the grammar as sets of features."[35]

A four-fold scheme is the result:

	+ N	– N
+ V	Adjective	Verb
– V	Noun	Preposition

The old-fashioned analytical apparatus, by which nouns were regarded as the names of persons, places, or things, and verbs were thought somehow to designate actions, has been given up for good. Nothing much is left of the ancient Aristotelian categories either. A similar movement has taken place in biology, as evolutionary biologists have come to realize that, like the parts of speech in generative grammar, species are nothing more than ever-shifting sets of features. Willi Hennig published his masterpiece, *Grundzüge einer Theorie der phylogenetischen Systematik* (*The Foundations of a Theory of Phylogenetic Systematics*), just seven years before Noam Chomsky published *Syntactic Structures*. It took biologists twenty years, or more, to understand what he had done.[36]

The irregularity of a natural language having been reduced, and confined, to its lexicon, its orderliness is expressed by its rules. In "Filters and Control," Chomsky and Lasnik expressed themselves satisfied with what linguists had come to call the Extended Standard Theory, or EST. Most rules are context-free. They have in $\alpha \rightarrow \ldots \beta \ldots$ a common form. To the left of this scheme, a single symbol, α; in the middle, an arrow indicating that the single symbol must be rewritten; and to the right, the rewritten result, the insulating down of three dots serving to show that rewriting conveys one symbol to any number of them.

The EST contains an obvious rule by which a sentence may be rewritten as a noun phrase and a verb phrase:

17. S → NP + VP.

But a verb phrase, the EST at once sings out, may also be rewritten as a verb together with a complementizer:

18. VP → V + Ś.

This introduces a recursive loop

19. Ś → **COMP** S,

the initial S in 17 now reappearing in 19.

Phrase structure rules give rise to base phrase markers, 19 leaving a structural residue in 20:

20. $[_S$ NP $[_V$ V $[_{PP}$ P $[_{NP}$ D N]]]].

After lexical insertion, 20, but not poor Luca, comes vividly to life in

21. Luca Brasi sleeps with the fishes.

Recursion serves to promote 21 to

22. Tessio said that Luca Brasi sleeps with the fishes,

a process *sine fine*, as Latin rhetoricians would say, an incidental question from an inattentive mobster—

What did Clemenza just ask?

—sooner or later encompassing all of the Corleones.

23. Clemenza asked whether Tessio said that Luca Brasi sleeps with the fishes.

But phrase structure rules do only so much. The EST required still other grammatical operations to accommodate an undertaking so simple as asking a question.

The conveyance *from*

24. Luca Brasi is sleeping with the fishes

to

25. Who is Luca Brasi sleeping with?

or even—in the case of a gangster with a taste for fancy diction—

26. With whom is Luca Brasi sleeping?

cannot be achieved by phrase structure rules without a loss of generality. This was the burden of Chomsky's *Syntactic Structures*.[37] Some linguists and philosophers were skeptical. Surely it *is* possible to come up with rules yielding simple phrase-markers for 25 or 26? A certain amount of effort was devoted to constructing transformational grammars without transformations, an undertaking that, in retrospect, suggests the correlative ambition to construct airplanes without lift. The problem lies in the phrasal descent from [*sleeping with the fishes*] to [*sleeping with*] to [*sleeping*]. The meaning of the verb does not change as each question is being asked. It is the very same verb throughout—*sleeping with x*. What is variable is only which *x* anyone is sleeping with, an observation commonly made about domestic affairs as well as grammar. This is just what those cascading phrase markers fail to reveal.

The generation of a question involves a complex mapping between phrase structures. Transformations are required and this is a context-sensitive process. Functioning rather like hash functions, transformations take complex arrays into complex arrays and so elaborate phrasal contexts into elaborate phrasal contexts:

(Luca Brasi is sleeping with the fishes) → (With whom is Luca Brasi sleeping)?

Ah yes, the fishes.

COMP Constructions

In her influential PhD dissertation, Joan Bresnan had noticed that **COMP** constructions are remarkably labile in English. Before standalone sentences, **COMP** deletion is obligatory.

27. *That Rome was not built in a day

hangs in midair, a **COMP** deletion away from the trite thought that Rome was not built in a day. So does

28. *Whether Stearasil starves pimples,

another uneasy mid-air survivor of a pending **COMP** deletion.

Before stand-aside sentences, on the other hand, **COMP** deletion goes either way.

COMP contraction reduces

29. I don't think that Stearasil starves pimples

to

30. I don't think Stearasil starves pimples.

But in still other sentences, **COMP** deletion goes bad at once.

31. *Trottweiler is a lunatic was obvious from his speech,

is no good as anything more than a spastic sputter; but

32. That Trottweiler is a lunatic was obvious from his speech,

is a fine, manly objurgation.

On encountering some tedious privilege-checker,

33. for you to keep checking your privilege is becoming tiresome

is both satisfying as a rebuke and correct as a sentence; but not so

34. *You to keep checking your privilege is becoming tiresome.

Simply restoring **COMP** to 31 and 34 returns them to sentential dignity.

Given the many occasions in which it might be useful to get rid of **COMP**, Chomsky and Lasnik needed to address the question whether to delete **COMP** constructions across the board, or to take on the job one **COMP** at a time. "The conditions under which such deletion rules could apply," Henk van Riemsdijk remarked,

> were, of course, originally stated in the structural descriptions of each individual deletion transformation. But here as well, a generalized theory was felt to be preferable. Ideally, such a theory would amount to the claim that there is one generalized deletion rule, "delete α," which would be subject to a set of powerful constraints that would prevent massive over-generation and ensure proper application in specific languages. Chomsky and Lasnik (1977) was an important step in that direction. *That*-deletion, *for*-deletion, and *wh-* deletion were abandoned and replaced by a rule of free deletion in **COMP**.[38]

A principle of free **COMP** deletion, Chomsky and Lasnik decided, should be one of the rules of core grammar.

> 35. In the domain **COMP**, delete [α φ],

where α is an arbitrary category and φ an arbitrary structure.

Get rid of **COMP** *ad libitum*, as physicians say, often to their regret.

Linguists, too.

The Modern Conveniences

THE RULE OF FREE **COMP** deletion has in its favor the fact that the alternative is worse. Without free **COMP** deletions, rules would require ordering. If there are two rules in the grammar's core such that one must be applied before the other, there are, all at once, three rules, a nuisance for linguist and language learner alike—the original two rules, and the rule stating which one of them comes first. This sort of thing can quickly get out of hand, especially when imperative and reflexive constructions are mutually engaged. If *wash yourself* represents the reflexive and imperative rules by which *you wash you* goes over to *you wash yourself*, and thereafter to *wash yourself*, the other way around would have the imperative apply directly to *you wash you*, yielding **wash you!* Once the subject is obliterated by the imperative, the reflexive rule lacks a correct structural description to which it can apply.[39]

How *screw you* emerged from various competing grammatical claims is not well-understood.

In Chomsky's Master's thesis on modern Hebrew morphophonemics, rule ordering went down to the twenty-fifth level. By the time that Chomsky and Lasnik came to write about filters, they realized that children learning English, having mastered the edifice of English grammatical rules, would also have had to master their proper order of application.

An orthodox Jew, it is often observed, has no time to be anything other than an orthodox Jew.

Native English speakers under a regime of rule ordering did not seem much better off.

Free **COMP** deletion thus has in its favor all of the modern conveniences. On the other side of this particular ledger, there is the fact that, just as Robert Lees suggested, English speakers can come up with a dozen challenges to free **COMP** deletion:

36a. It bothers me *(for) [Bill to win].
36b. It is illegal *(for) [Bill to take part].
36c. It is preferred *(for) [Bill to take part].
36d. I want very much *(for) [Bill to win].
36e. He argued passionately *(for) [Bill to be given a chance].
36f. There is someone at the door *(for) [you to play with].
36g. I received a book on Tuesday *(for) [you to read].
36h. *(For) [John to take the job] would be preferred.
36i. *(For) [John to be successful] would be unlikely.

In each of these examples, **COMP** deletion has overshot its intended mark.[40] *I want very much Bill to win* is, for example, a mistake typically made by non-native Mandarin speakers of English.

"We hope to preserve the very simple and general rule," Chomsky and Lasnik wrote, "that elements in **COMP** may freely delete, as a rule of core grammar."[41]

No one could object to the hope.

Filters

Within the context of "Filters and Control," it is the filters that are intended to choke off the gibberish that the drain of free **COMP** deletion would otherwise let through. The idea had its origin in Dave Perlmutter's 1968 dissertation, published in 1971 as *Deep and Surface Structure Constraints in Syntax*.[42] Chomsky and Lasnik promoted filters to theoretical status. The filters, they argued, "will have to bear the burden of accounting for constraints which, in the earlier and far richer theory, were expressed in statements of ordering and obligatoriness, as well as contextual dependencies that cannot be formulated in the narrower framework of core grammar."[43]

There were eleven filters in all. The [*for-to*] filter excluded

37. *The Cardinal was planning for to go to Rome,

but left open the possibility that

38. Bobby Joe was planning for to marry his sister

might be an Ozark dialect. Other filters ruled out double **COMP** constructions in which two comped elements appear side by side:

39. *Lothario is the man who that came,

a construction, as Dutch linguists promptly observed, that appears quite naturally in Dutch.

Constructions in which a lexical noun phrase finds itself directly attached to an infinitive—these were of special concern. *Samson to bring down the house*; or, more generally, [α **NP** *to* **VP**]. Linguists had long known that the English infinitive is often in conflict with its ostensible subject.

40. *It is unclear what the late Slobodan Milošević to do

is a sentence that only the late Slobodan Milošević could have loved, even though only two letters separate 40 from the unoffending

41. It is unclear what the late Slobodan Milošević *is* to do.

Given the conflicted concourse between noun phrases and their ancillary infinitives, the [α **NP** *to* **VP**] filter was intended for disciplined regulatory work:

42. *[$_{\alpha}$ **NP** *to* **VP**], unless α is adjacent to and in the domain of Verb or *for.*

Although permitted by the rule of free **COMP** deletion in core grammar, unwanted examples are flagged down later, when, like the rest of the core constructions, they come up to the surface. For all that, 42 has an undeserved air of terminological mystery, and at a first reading, it might seem that the asterisk marking unacceptability and the word "unless" are somehow in conflict, like two lifeguards determined to rescue one victim. The confusion is needless. The Chomsky-Lasnik filter resembles the declaration, seen often in old-fashioned burlesque houses and movie theaters, that no minors are allowed *unless* accompanied by an adult. A trip of three steps is involved.

43. I want very much for Bill to win

is sanctioned in core grammar by the grammar's phrase structure rules.

44. I want very much Bill to win

is, in turn, justified by the rule of free **COMP** deletion. By the time that 44 makes it to the surface, ready either to be spoken out loud or handed over to the logical system, the Chomsky-Lasnik filter restores it to the common decencies of a grammatical sentence by blocking **COMP** deletion:

45. I want very much for Bill to win.

On the other hand,

46. John believes Mary to be brilliant,

and

47. For Mary to be so brilliant, she had to work hard at it,

sail right through. "Mary" and the verb "believes" are side by side in 46; and "Mary" comes right after "for" in 47.

The argument has now acquired a distinctive four-part shape. The rules of the grammar's core sanction indifferently any combination of a lexical noun phrase and an infinitive: [**NP** *to* **VP**]. They sanction as well any embedding of [**NP** *to* **VP**] into a still larger **COMP** context: [comp NP to VP]. They permit, in the third place, the free deletion of **COMP** in this context—any **COMP**, any time. And, finally, filters are provided to handle the overflow into ungrammaticality; the representations that make it through the filters make it through them as grammatical sentences.

Vergnaud's Letter

No one would think to say that the EST was wonderfully elegant. It might even seem—not to *us*, of course—as if the system's filters were an adventitious afterthought, something that grammarians added to the system to tie up a few loose ends. A superficial look at a modern internal combustion engine often conveys the same impression.

Well, what you got, you got lifter tick on account of the fact that you got a bent push rod. Which one of you figures he's Juan Fangio, by the way?

Grammatical filters were destined to do useful work; and, like hydraulic lifter rods, they appeared ineluctable. A grammatical theory cannot easily do without the first; and the internal combustion engine could not easily do without the second. What gave pause to the EST was not what the theory contained, but what it lacked. The Chomsky-Lasnik [$_\alpha$ **NP** *to* **VP**] filter served the ends of descriptive adequacy; it served those ends by abbreviating any number of anomalies of the sort in evidence at 36. There was no particular need to example them on a case-by-case basis. The filter served to execute a full sweep. Bent on marriage, Bobby Joe remains where the [*for-to*] filter left him: midway between violating a rule of grammar and outraging a taboo. Double **COMP** constructions were left to the Dutch. What remained unaccommodated by the Chomsky-Lasnik filters was the demand for explanatory adequacy. What deep concept tied them together and served to show that the prohibitions that they enforced—no to *I want very much Bill to win,* no to *the late Slobodan Milošević to do,* no, in thunder, to *Bobby Joe*—were a part of a unified system of prohibitions, a system arrayed against things that were contrary to law, *malum per se?*

It was this need that Vergnaud's letter met. Vergnaud's letter had some of the effect commonly assigned to heat lightning. It lit up the scene. There should be a name for events of this sort. Heat lightning, with its intimation of a clutch of ghastly Grant Wood cows huddled underneath some spider-branched oak, is too American-Gothic for our taste. Perhaps the German *Gedankenblitz* will do.

In 1956, Francis Crick discovered transfer RNA by what amounted to a transcendental deduction. Given the chemical discrepancy between the nucleic acids and the proteins, something *must* mediate between them. He was entirely correct. He had been guided to this conclusion by nothing more than his uncanny intuition.[44]

Gedankenblitz.

In the same year, Kurt Gödel wrote a now-famous letter to John von Neumann, in which, after sensitively wishing the stricken von Neumann an improvement in his health, Gödel posed the question whether P = NP?[45]

Gedankenblitz again.

Vergnaud's recovery of Case belongs in this distinguished class. Whether case is morphologically specified, as in Latin, or abstract, as in English—Case Majeure, as linguists say—are matters on the surface of things, where language is largely froth. Deep down, Case is compelling because linguistics has become a part of the Galilean undertaking, a way of explaining what is visible by an appeal to what is not. Chomsky and

Lasnik knew that this would become so; but in Vergnaud's letter, they could see that it was becoming so.

This is no small thing.

The Recovery of Case

PUER PUELLAM AMAT. THE boy loves the girl. But equally *Puellam puer amat*, which is again the boy loves the girl. Latin nouns and pronouns are all entombed in the closed coffin of their case. There are seven cases in the singular: nominative, accusative, dative, genitive, ablative, vocative, and locative. They are all morphologically marked, something that Latin-speaking children once picked up with ease, and later little Latinists picked up only by memorizing those grim endings, one after the other. The Latin plural requires seven additional endings. Beyond a few case-like relics—*who, whom*—English is not inflected for case.

Yet Jean-Roger Vergnaud, in his letter to Chomsky and Lasnik, saw a way of simplifying their system on the assumption that English, too, had a form of case. "Here's what I have in mind," he began. "I believe that this filter [the $[_{\alpha}$ **NP** *to* **VP**] filter] could be replaced by a filter that governs the distribution of certain kinds of NPs."[46] To accommodate this idea, Vergnaud proposed that the English language, against all appearances to the contrary, possessed a three-part case structure:

The subject case is the case of subjects in tensed clauses. The sentence that the subject case is the case of subjects in tensed clauses illustrates itself.

The genitive case is the case of *Mary's book, hers, yours, mine*, the honorary genitive, *etc.*

The governed case is the case of verbal and prepositional complements, as in *Mary saw him, Mary gave him a book, Mary talked to him, a book by him.*[47]

If three English cases are now on the mortician's table, they are certainly not anywhere much in evidence in what a native English speaker might say. "Case inflectional morphology," Vergnaud cheerfully admitted, "is quite poor, of course."[48] Cases do linger in the English system of pronouns: *I, me, mine, you, yours,* and all the rest of the stand-alones, shut-ins, and stand-ins, but in comparison to the fantastic abundance of Latin inflections, the English pronouns represent only the shrunk shank of a morphological system that was case-heavy more than eight hundred years ago.

The English cases to which Vergnaud appealed are theoretical entities; and since they are invisible, they must be inferred. Physicists understand inferences of this sort at once. Why else would they talk of spin with respect to entities that do not spin and are not entities? Or countenance those exquisite Faddeev-Popov ghosts that flit into existence and then flit out again—as do we all?

"A characteristic property of infinitival constructions," Vergnaud argued, "is that, in such constructions, the subject is in the Governed Case."[49] This is a fine insight, and not one that Latin linguists would have made. They were persuaded that the nominative *must* betoken the subject. Not so. A noun phrase can be displaced in Latin, as in *Caesar occiditur,* where "Caesar" is in the nominative despite the fact that it is the logical object of the verb. *He* was murdered, after all.

English has something similar. Witness Vergnaud's examples,

> 48a. We'd prefer for *him* to leave.
> 48b. It is illegal for *him* to leave.
> 48c. We found a man for *him* to speak to.
> 48d. For *him* to leave would be unfortunate,

all of them brilliantly chosen because, in the *he-him* distinction, English retains an ancient morphological case marker. The noun phrase is in the governed, or even the accusative case, but the noun phrase carrying the case is serving as the subject of the infinitive that follows.

Assumptions now begin to multiply, but with exhilarating force. "Well, I shall hypothesize," Vergnaud wrote, "that the distribution of infinitival constructions of the form *NP to VP* follows from the distribution of NPs in the Governed Case." An otherwise invisible case is now given control of an otherwise problematic construction.

"Specifically," Vergnaud continued, "let's posit the following filter":[50]

> 49. "A structure of the form ...[α...NP...]..., where NP is in the Governed Case and α is the first branching node above NP, is ungrammatical unless (i) α is the domain of [– N] or (ii) α is adjacent to and in the domain of [– N]."

Two years later, Chomsky expressed 49 as a principle:

> 50. *NP if NP has phonetic content and has no Case.[51]

There are three points that are not immediately obvious in 49 and 50.

The first: that [– N] may have attributes of a verb or a preposition, and either may sanction Case in its domain. In its negative incarnation, [– N] functions as a Case assigner; made positive as a noun or adjective, as a Case receiver.

The second: that whatever the noun phrase, if it is speakable then it *must* have Case.

The third: that infinitives must have a subject; and if no speakable subject may be found, then the otherwise silent **PRO** must go where lexical NPs dare not tread. The grammatically impeccable

> 51. Susan tried to solve the problem,

represents the phonetic residue in real life of

> 52. Susan tried [**PRO** to solve the problem],[52]

and not anything like

> 53. *Susan tried [John to solve the problem].[53]

John is clueless in 53 because *tried* has left him caseless. Without a case-marked noun phrase, the infinitive has no subject, and simply hangs in midair—whence the demand that the Case filter encompass noun phrases with a voice of their own.

The burden of Vergnaud's elegant argument is that case is obligatory, even in English. If English cases are not directly reflected in their morphology, as plainly they are not, their assignment is surely not arbitrary. The accusative case assigned *Caesar* in *Caesar to cross the Rubicon* is determined either by some antecedent verb or by some locally loitering preposition. "That is to say," as Jonathan David Bobaljik and Susi Wurmbrand observe, "verbs and prepositions have the distinctive characteristic of being (accusative) case assigners, and thus the disjunctive environment stipulated in Vergnaud's 'unless' clause is none other than the domain of accusative case assignment."[54]

While verbs and prepositions perform this function, *how* they perform it is rather less clear. Some barely sensed prohibition of action at a distance is at work throughout. Case assignment is a local operation, one constituent influencing another more or less directly. The world would have been a relatively simpler place if elements in [– N] assigned Case only to sisterly constituents. This does happen: there is *cross him at your peril* or *go easy on him*. But it is easy to see that a comped preposition is generally not the sisterly constituent of the subject to which it assigns Case. In

54. For [John to solve the problem], ...

the **COMP** *for* is a sister to the entire sentence.

If Case is not assigned under simple sisterhood, or at an arbitrary distance, what are the structural conditions under which it *is* applied? This is no easy question. Having relieved Samson of his hair along with his manhood, there is no grammatical sense in which

55. *Delilah decided Samson to bring down the house.

The verb *decide* cannot cross the non-finite clause [Samson to bring down the house] to assign *Samson* any case at all. But

56. Delilah believed Samson to be better off bald

makes perfect grammatical sense, evidence that while "decide" remains stuck at non-finite frontiers, "believes" crosses over them with no passport at all.

"The Case Filter provides an account of this contrast," Bobaljik and Wurmbrand remark, "*if* [emphasis added] what is special about the *believe* class is that they permit Case assignment across a non-finite clause boundary."[55]

Little if, big if, native Mohawk speakers say.

Case in Point

VERGNAUD'S CASE FILTER REPRESENTED an impressive achievement in unification, bringing Chomsky and Lasnik's various and vagrant filters under the umbrella of a single governing concept. No matter the dialect current in the Ozarks, [*for-to*] constructions are stricken from the *official* record by case considerations, and so are double **COMP** constructions. The anomalies at 36, once handled by the Chomsky-Lasnik [**NP** *to* **VP**] filter, are now handled redemptively by Vergnaud's case filter. After this has been seen, it is easy enough to see.

These are local triumphs. A global triumph follows. Case is the great instance of a principle *and* a parameter, and so a vindication of the very methodology of the principles and parameters approach to language. Finnish, German, and Latin are case-heavy; Chinese, English, and French, case-lite. Case is in these contexts a matter of how words are marked. Abstract Case lies beyond the reach of morphology. It is an aspect of UG itself, a part of its principles. Whether cases are destined to appear marked for dear life in one language like Finnish, or destined to disappear without much of a trace in another language like Chinese, reflects nothing more than parametric variations among languages. Noun phrases require abstract Case in *all* languages. Chinese was long thought caseless, even by Chinese linguists, and was widely regarded as a language with no inflections whatsoever. This is true only to the extent that Chinese fails to reflect its cases in its morphology, one reason that classical Chinese poetry is so very difficult to translate into English. It was Audrey Li who demonstrated the persistence of Chinese Case in his brilliant dissertation, *Abstract Case in Mandarin Chinese*.[56] Until Li's work, few linguists believed that case figured in Chinese; after it, few linguists doubted it. In Basque, Japanese, or Latin, on the other hand, case enters directly into their morphologies. These differences ramify throughout their grammars. Languages like Latin with their rich inflectional systems typically permit marked noun phrases to appear in displaced sites. This is not true of languages like English.

The parameters of a natural language are rather like the iridescent lights of a large neon sign that, with certain bulbs dimmed or illuminated, spell out over the squawking metropolis of a child's initial exposure to language, English, Hungarian, or Japanese. The Case parameter is by default off. If it is not there, no positive evidence is required to see that it is not there. On hearing Finnish in the ambient atmosphere, the Finnish child sees in his mind's eye the Case parameter winking on. One expects toddlers, not having yet mastered the case morphology of their native language, to start practicing relatively fixed phrasal orders, even in an otherwise flexible but inflected language.

They do not have a minute to lose.

The concept of Case has now become entrenched within modern linguistic theory, so much so that various displacement operations could not be stated without it. The construction of the passive voice is triggered by Case considerations.

When the Bible reports that *Cain killed Abel*, it places *Cain* in the nominative and *Abel* in the accusative case. If *Cain killed Abel*, then obviously, *Abel was killed by Cain*. With this analysis, traditional grammarians may be observed leaving the room well-satisfied. Modern theories are otherwise. The introduction of the past participle, with its distinctive morphology, triggers a series of subtle grammatical twitches in core grammar. The past participle *killed* requires a noun phrase on its right.

That Cain Abel killed is not English. Abel must stand where he was, in English, and, alas, in life. The first prodromal shiver leading to the passive occurs when *was killed* is assigned both its object in Abel and some undetermined subject:

57. Something was killed Abel,

or

58. *e* was killed Abel,

where *e* designates an empty category.

Under ordinary circumstances, verbs have the power to assign Case. In

59. Cain killed Abel,

the verb *killed* assigns to *Abel* grammatical standing in the morphologically unmarked accusative case.

But in 58, *was killed* has lost its animating powers of case assignment. This is the decisive feature of the passive voice. But if *Abel* cannot be assigned case, the Case Filter rules the sentences ungrammatical. Questions of case now lead to a dilemma: either the passive voice is ungrammatical or case considerations must force the errant noun phrase *Abel* to scoot over the sentence to the only slot in which it can receive case at all. That is the slot marked by the empty category *e*.

Whereupon there is

60. Abel was killed.

This analysis has remained virtually unchanged within the minimalist program, where case plays a central role in terms of activation conditions for transformations: a noun phrase whose case is checked via an agreement process (obvious in many Romance languages) becomes inaccessible to further transformations.[57] Case comes to the fore within the theory of transformations in a way that Vergnaud did not anticipate and could not have seen.

No one thinking about the passive voice would very easily conjecture that the necessary movements by which it is made possible have anything obvious to do with case.

Yet it is so.

If case as a concept is both a principle and a parameter, the Vergnaud filter by which it is expressed, Vergnaud argued, is not one filter among others. It "looks very much like a principle of UG." In the apparently moribund structure of the English case, Vergnaud had encountered a principle of Universal Grammar. The idea is remarkable in its daring. Case morphology is patent in Basque, Finnish, or Latin, but not in English or in French. After admitting as much, Vergnaud argued in defiance of the facts that an abstract form of case is relevant in every language. Vergnaud had only his taste to indicate that his filter "looks very much like a principle of UG."[58]

His reasoning was exquisite because, in so many respects, it was not reasoning at all.

Progress in linguistics should not be assigned the aspect of an intellectual deliverance. Beyond the expanding circumference of light, there remains the enveloping area of darkness. Vergnaud understood that two fundamental issues of language remain unexplained: how children acquire languages rapidly and without effort, and how human beings in general acquired the species-specific characteristic of the human race. These problems are inferior in difficulty only to questions about the origins of life. Some progress has been made in explaining how children acquire their native language. They do so in virtue of their universal inheritance. When Chomsky first advanced this idea in the 1960s, philosophers responded both that the very idea was absurd and that they had known it all along. It now seems inevitable. But if human beings are notable in their possession of UG, what explains the acquisition of Universal Grammar by the human species?

This is a far more difficult problem.

Jean-Roger Vergnaud's letter now belongs to the perpetual inventory of remembered things. The master dies with the matter. Linguistic theory has changed profoundly in forty years. Vergnaud's letter remains a deeply moving document, the expression of his desire to see beneath the infernal arbitrariness of description to the place where unity prevails.

VI. Place

19. Prague, 1998

"We reserfed for you room," my host had assured me when I had called from Hamburg.

Now I am at the train station, not the Hauptbannhof, but a way station in Holesovice, a dingy district north and east of the city center.

The taxi driver stares at the address I have been given, baffled; an exchange with a colleague follows in Czech. They stand there rooted: two stolid unshaven men. A smile finally creases my driver's face.

"Far away?" I ask, spreading my hands apart. "*Weit?*"

"*Nikt so weit,*" he answers vaguely.

The hotel turns out to be very *weit* indeed: across the city and into a Stalinist suburb on the other side of Prague. We drive for more than twenty minutes. There are scruffy lots everywhere, waste-filled muddy lawns, a few crumbling tract apartment houses, and then the University Hotel itself, a shabby cinder-block building of perhaps six stories, with bars on the windows and graffiti on every wall, the whole place evil-looking, like a blister.

The taxi driver walks up to the front door, which is closed. There is no one about. He peers into the building, his hand shading his eyes, and looks at a sign affixed to the door. "*Geschlossen,*" he says when he returns to the Skoda. Closed. He shrugs his heavy shoulders. "Iss possible you call?" He pantomimes the dialing of a telephone, his thick index finger twirling the air. It is Sunday morning. I have no idea where to reach my hosts.

My driver understands: "*Alles kaput,*" he says.

We drive to the center of Prague, where I am deposited at the Hotel Jalta.

Is there a room? There is. One hundred and twenty-five dollars a night. Dollars. Not kroners.

"*Sind Sie sicher?*" I ask. Are you sure?

"*Ganz sicher,*" says the girl behind the counter. "*Ganz, ganz sicher.*"

She switches to English: "We are all now capitalismus," she says meaningfully.

I mount the stairs, the bell boy lumbering in my wake. Two clean narrow beds, a locked mini-bar, a tiny Russian-made television, a guide to the nightlife of Prague. Heavy curtains. A hissing radiator. It is very warm.

I point to the mini-bar. The bell boy shakes his head to indicate that the thing defies comprehension. "*Geschlossen,*" he finally says. It is apparently the one German word that every Czech knows. I ask him how much I should tip. He shrugs his shoulders and looks irresolute. "Must piple, no tip," he finally says.

Blockhead.

I shave and shower and walk to the Stare Mesto, the old city. I watch the ornate clock turn the hour; I look at the gorgeous Baroque architecture, remarking to myself how much like a wedding cake ornament some of this stuff looks like. I wander over to the ancient Jewish quarter, where tours of the cemetery are being sold for a few kroner. I watch a pair of young men press brass coins on an old-fashioned coin stamping machine.

Prague at dusk, and then early evening, a full moon over the Karluv Most, the Charles Bridge, the river glossy below, swans paddling slowly, Hradcany Castle and the gentle stone buildings of the Mala Strana in the background.

The main streets are lined with hulking blonde women. One comes up to me. "You vant business sex," she asks? I say no.

"Vy not?" she says peevishly, drawing her thick eyebrows together.

Breakfast the next morning is fearfully expensive by Czech standards. A buffet has been advertised. A number of stainless steel trays are arranged on a long table. They are filled with pickles or variations of the pickle: Cucumber slices, sour pickles, sliced pickles, pickles with toothpicks, gherkins. Stale bread is on the table, the rolls crumbing to the touch. There are also three or four steam trays. I lift the cover of the first. Nothing. Only boiling water. Ditto for the second and the third.

I point to the steam trays and look inquisitively at the waiter. He shrugs. "Maybe tomorrow," he says.

Later that morning, the secretary from the Center for Theoretical Study rings me up at the hotel. She is enormously put out that I thought to make my own accommodations. She tells me to go to a street that sounds like *Clapnada*. I ask her to spell it. *C-a-l-a-d-s-t-a*, she intones. On the map, the only street that sounds anything like Clapnada or Caladsta is *Celestna*. I decide that this must be right, if only because the word has a Latin root.

My room turns out to be a suite in an old building belonging to the university. The quarters are palatial—a living room, separate bedroom, bathroom and foyer. The ceilings are at least fifteen feet high and timbered, the huge wooden beams decorated in what looks like pastels. The effect is an unnerving contrast between the solidity of the timber and the fragility of the colors. Later, someone tells me that these apartments were reserved for the day-time use of high party officials. I imagine a pretty woman sitting in this apartment, braiding her hair, waiting.

Three keys are necessary to enter the building: one for the front door, one for the hall door, and one for my apartment. There is a sign above the hall door:

> Do not forget to lock door with seinem schlussel. Otherwise foreigners come into your room in the night unwillingly.

That afternoon I walk over to the Center to meet with the director, Ivan Havel. He is a small, energetic, merry man, with gray hair worn in thick curls, gray eyes, and a trim, compact body. He is dressed in a well-cut English suit and wears a shirt with French cuffs. He speaks English, which he has acquired at Berkeley, with a considerable Czech accent, and lisps as he talks, spraying saliva in every direction; at lunch he is a menace.

He wants to get to the bottom of the business of the University Hotel. His slow-moving, tall blonde secretary makes a number of calls in Czech in order to determine how it was that the University Hotel was closed on Sunday. Each call trails off inconclusively. I sense somehow that both Havel and his secretary believe that the hotel was in fact open and that *I* turned the place down. They are embarrassed and indignant.

After a while, Havel loses interest in the University Hotel. He tells me about some of the other visitors to the Center. The philosopher John Searle had come in May. Havel rolls up his eyes. "I vas prepared for his arroganz," he says, "but ozers ver not."

Then he talks about consciousness, suggesting broadly that analytic philosophers are making a considerable mistake by denying its existence. There is an old-fashioned Continental style to his speech and thought. I find myself agreeing with whatever he says. Finally he asks whether consciousness is an emergent phenomenon. I have no idea.

Presently Sir Arnold Bergen enters the room. He is an immensely distinguished British pharmacologist, in Prague to deliver a lecture to the Academy of Science. He is perhaps in his mid-sixties, lean, vulpine, his hair covering the top of his head in strands drawn up from one ear; he has a large powerful nose, the thing like a flugelhorn.

We go out to lunch at a club said to be frequented by Czech reporters. The food is mystifying. I order dumplings and Bergen, carp. Steins of foaming Pilsner all around.

I ask Sir Arthur whether it might not be possible to design a perfect drug. He looks at me shrewdly and lifts his beer glass.

Havel says that no one knows what to do now; he talks of a mood of demoralization. I listen attentively; he is, after all, the President's brother. Havel himself does not appear demoralized about anything.

Bergen says that England is a different country as the result of immigration. We agree that the movement of peoples across borders is going to be a terrible problem in the new Europe.

After lunch, walking along one of the main streets, I see a sign: Dr. -- ; there follows a complicated Czech name; the man is a specialist in Calanetics, an American weight loss system having something to do, I remember, with cellulite. I think of an exercise room in which a number of lardy Czech women dutifully are lifting their meaty thighs. "Vun, two, and up, ladies," says the Czech Calaneticist.

The one store in the central district that is up to date and always crowded is the health food store. It is American, of course. "We are working to get you the foods you need and want," says one sign, "please be patient." I wonder aloud to Bergen why dietary anxiety should be so common now in eastern Europe.

"Because these people now have enough to eat," he roars, very satisfied with his answer.

At the cinema, Madonna's *Blonde Ambition* is playing. I suggest to Sir Arthur that we might collaborate on a handbook of all that is objectionable in the modern world. We agree on rock music and Madonna. "Oh yes, Madonna," Sir Arthur says enthusiastically. I am warming up to the project, outlining in detail the sections on Jesse Jackson, cable television, Arnold Schwarzenegger, feminism, and the like; Sir Arthur wishes to add to the list the modern biography. He explains how disappointed he was to learn of the sordid details in the life of John F. Kennedy. I go along with him on this, but I see that our project is going to be more difficult than I first thought. I rather enjoyed those sordid details.

By and by, we come upon a pastry shop. There are only three trays on the shelves and the pastry is waxy and abhorrent. Nonetheless, there is a long line. One woman waits by the cash register staring into space and making change with enormous deliberation; another stands behind the counter and takes orders, writing things down laboriously on a square of oilpaper. Of a sudden she drops what she is doing and scuttles to the back of the shop. After a few minutes she emerges with a new pastry tray containing things that look like purple crumpets. She begins leisurely to rearrange the items on the shelves, first taking out one tray of pastries, and then the other. Business comes to a halt.

I stomp out of the store, pastryless, fuming with inexpressible indignation. I see a huge yellow sign advertising what looks to be a pile of grapefruits. Cubafruits, it says. Can I really have come to Prague, only recently liberated by the sheer exercise of its moral will, prepared to be indignant because the shops are less full than they might be in Paris?

It would appear so.

Later that afternoon, walking once again toward the river, I am struck by what are obviously very old large globes covering the street lamps. They have been segmented by black wire or paint in order to form a series of interlocking pentagrams. The effect is of unusual artistic interest, the globes of a sudden appearing faintly fleshlike and swollen, the contrast to the geometrical severity of the design striking and elegant.

Then I stop at the Kafka exhibit. There are pictures on the wall and generous excerpts from the novels. I did not know that Kafka spoke, read, and wrote Czech. I look at all the exhibits. There are many interesting pamphlets for sale and a number of books about Kafka and Prague. I approach the young woman at the counter and ask for something *by* Kafka. She shrugs her plump shoulders. "Iss sorry," she says. "*Für diesen Bücher müssen Sie nach Deutschland.*" For that you must go to Germany.

On the Karluv Most, I am struck once again by the extraordinary light, in which blue, blue gray, and gray are offset by a kind of smokiness; I wonder if it might be pollution; but there are few cars in Prague and almost none in the central quarter. I finally come to the conclusion that the smokiness is the atmospheric effect of the decomposition of the sandstone that has gone into the construction of the bridge itself, an interesting example of an artistic entity making possible the unique conditions under which it may best be appreciated.

At the far end of the bridge, an American couple are singing songs from the sixties. *Michael Row Your Boat Ashore* seems to be especially popular. They are singing the song enthusiastically, strumming their guitars with great thrashing strokes. I wonder what impels these young people to leave Burbank or Pasadena in order to sing along the Karluv Most. I know the answer myself: almost every European city offers the illusion of finely segmenting the manifold of experience, so that to an American sensibility Prague appears as dense with possibilities as it is physically reticulated by small streets, urban alleys, footpaths, little walkways.

At the other end of the bridge, two Czechs are playing old Slavonic folk tunes, one on the oboe, the other on the guitar. They are fine musicians both, the oboe and the guitar making for an unusually successful combination. The melodies probably go back in racial memory to the Middle Ages. No one has to ask what the songs are about. As I am listening, I turn and look upstream at the Vltava. A thin, elegantly long cruise ship has just emerged from underneath the bridge and is gliding upstream, its lights subdued and carefully modulated, the very opposite to the garish Parisian *Bateaux mouches* on the Seine; and as it glides noiselessly along, a sinuous trolley consisting of three linked cars begins to cross the heavier industrial bridge upstream from the Karluv Most, the sound it makes entirely muffled by distance, so those two enchanted objects, the ship and the tram, appear to be moving silently toward an imaginary point of intersection where their separate worlds of light will merge fantastically into a luminous and limpid starburst.

My lecture is scheduled to begin at eleven. Sometime after ten, Ivan Havel and Sir Arnold Bergen and I set off by metro for the mathematics faculty. We arrive at a shabby brown building. Ivan Havel announces regretfully that there are no elevators. We will have to walk up four flights of stairs. Havel makes a deliberate attempt to mount the stairs slowly, as if he were used ordinarily to bound up them vigorously, like the undergraduates, and Sir Arnold mounts them manfully, surreptitiously taking deep shuddering breaths. I am tremendously pleased that I am less winded than either of them when we finally get to the top.

I am introduced to Professor Schweik, who is an internationally known mathematician, and Professor Swoboda, who is a philosopher. Both men appear to me to be in late middle age, perhaps sixty or so. They have very similar round, almost globular heads, thinning hair, very sallow skin, and shockingly bad teeth. They are dressed in shabby suits and their bodies have a defensive weariness.

Schweik is extraordinarily intelligent. He speaks English in an odd way, appearing to fetch each word he utters from a great distance. Nonetheless, his grasp of English grammar is perfect, and very often he expresses himself not only with precision but with an eerie economy of effect. Talking of Thom's classification theorem, he says: "It is certainly true that the biologist need not know that there are precisely seven stable unfoldings, but it is important that he realize that there is more than one."

A fine observation.

I give my talk in a room with a strange glass blackboard. When I am introduced, Havel says that I am a writer as well as a scientist. This elicits a murmur of approval. There are twenty or so people in the audience. The room quickly grows stuffy but everyone listens intently.

At one point, I say: "The miracle of the calculus, after all, is that the real world may be understood in terms of the real numbers."

Schweik immediately interrupts: "*That* is precisely what one should expect in virtue of Tychonoff's theorem."

I am taken aback and say something inane. I make a note to re-think these remarks of mine about space, time, and the real numbers.

Afterwards, Havel announces that he and Bergen have something important to do. I expect that Havel will be the first man in Prague to acquire a cellular telephone.

Schweik, Swoboda, and I set off for lunch. As we walk, Schweik says of the neighborhood: "It is like Brooklyn, overwhelming in its ugliness but so large that there cannot help but be some interesting things to look at."

The first restaurant we come to is divided into two rooms. One is completely full, the other completely empty. Schweik asks whether we might sit in the empty room. He is told no by the waiter. He shrugs his heavy shoulders and we walk out. On the street he says that everything is still like that. "You see, no one has any connection with the institutions in which they work."

I say good-by to Schweik and Swoboda at the Metro station. I watch for a moment as they trudge down the street. Their tread is heavy and tired; I notice that they barely lift their feet from the ground.

At dinner that evening, I am unceremoniously joined at my table by a middle-aged German couple. The woman proceeds to light a cigarette, blowing smoke in my face. The waiter comes over and tells the woman that smoking is forbidden. It is his first effective act. The couple get up from the table in a great huff.

Afterwards, their place is taken by a Czech lesbian, with a freckled oval face, and her prey, an addled young English girl. The lesbian is talking intently in a low seductive voice. "First the conzert," she says, "zen ze sauna, yes?"

The English girl looks around nervously. "Well, yes," she says.

At the table next to mine, three elderly French women are waiting in frosty indignation for the cheese. Each time the waiter passes, their leader raises a bony forefinger and sings out: "*Mais le fromage.*" The waiter registers their request with a dip of his chin, but when he returns from the kitchen, he is inevitably *sans le fromage*. Finally, the Frenchwoman summons another older waiter to the table. He returns with the cheese. Perhaps they were expecting *Brie* or *Camembert.* What appears on their plate looks to me like several slices of rolled Muenster, the oilpaper still sticking to the cheese. The ladies nonetheless tuck into the horrible stuff gratefully, trying unsuccessfully to smear the cheese on the sharp stale little baguettes served with dinner.

When my meal comes, it consists of two dingy grey slices of cutlet over a mound of french fries. It is designed to be *medaillons* of *bifteck,* my waiter explains, over *champignons.*

Yes, well, where are those *champignons?*

My waiter looks down at the plate and pokes at the meat with his finger. "*Nikt da,*" he says mournfully after finally turning my cutlet over.

Afterward, I walk around Wenceslaw Square, following for a few meters a pretty young blonde girl of no more than ten or so, walking with her elder sister, I imagine, or a fond aunt, who has somehow been allowed to shave her skull so that her blonde hair now quite literally starts to fall from a point on her head level with the top of her ears. The effect is one of atrocious ugliness.

Later that evening, the concierge at my university lodgings stops me to talk. He is a mild, inoffensive, middle-aged man; he spends most of his time watching television.

"You lif in California, *tak?*" he asks.

"*Tak.*"

He opens his ledger and begins to rifle through the pages.

"Ve had here in April zomvon else from Californi. Here is. Professor Jacobson. You know?"

It was no one that I knew.

"*Tak,* here he go out in morning, come back for lunch."

The next day, I set off for Dresden.

My train departs from the Hauptbannhof. The railway station is itself a fine example of iron architecture, dating, I would guess, from the end of the nineteenth century. In the main hall, three hundred or so people are staring at the information board expectantly. Six international trains are scheduled to depart within the hour. They are all listed on the board, but no track information is posted. I endeavor to ask someone what is happening, using pantomime and the little Czech I have managed to acquire. Nothing.

Finally I walk to the tracks. A Czech commuter train has just pulled in; I ask the trim female conductor about the train to Berlin. She jerks her head toward the adjacent track and taps her watch significantly.

I race down the steps. The corridor is absolutely jammed with people moving sluggishly in the wrong direction.

"Out of my way, you dumb Czech shits," I shout.

Dresden is already a part of the West. On the drive from the railway station to the hotel I notice with a shudder that every tree along the avenue seems to be precisely the same height and consequently the same age.

At breakfast the next morning, there is a buffet spread out. This is the real thing, not the Prague business of the empty steam tables. The Germans go to it with great deliberation. I follow one man's progress. Bread is taken by the kilo; then butter, cheese, salami, three kinds of jam in little pots, his plate heaped perilously. He sets the food down by his table setting and fetches another plate from the rack. He loads the second plate with fruits, more cheese, dumplings, bacon, little sausages, two kinds of raisin cake. This, too, is brought over to the table. Then he sits in his chair, knees apart, and raps his spoon imperiously against his coffee cup. "*Bitte*," he sings out to the waitress. Please.

"*Ja, ja*," she says briskly, "*kommt*."

After the coffee is poured, he begins to eat with enormous deliberation.

Three Frenchwomen are sitting at a nearby table. I recognize them. They are the women who had forlornly demanded cheese in Prague. They are taking nothing but coffee and a croissant. They look at the German. One of the Frenchwomen lifts her nose fractionally.

Comme il bouffe, she says. How he stuffs himself.

20. Old Hose

Whatever it might have been in the larger scheme of things, the university had by the third week of class acquired a novel incarnation for me as Old Hose, the hose emerging in part from the Spanish *José*, as in *Hey José, you see them knockers, man?* and in part from the general down-at-the-heels way the place held itself together, the buildings resisting somehow the temptation to sag, the fountain in the center of the campus, its water turned off, staring upward like an indolent eye. I had arrived three years earlier; I left three years later, the dark cloud of my own discomfort a lunatic contrast to the southern sunshine that seemed to *spill* over the place, lighting up even the restrooms with a lurid Latin light. I thought I might write about things; I made a few false starts, the usual literary divagations (*mais, je divague*)—symptoms, I now realize, of a subject that insolently refused to be sustained as an object of thought; the place—Old Hose, I mean—existed in a realm *beyond* the powers of parody.

I had a faculty ID card with my picture, and a wooden pigeonhole for letters in the department office; I had keys to the room in which coffee was kept percolating, the stuff inky by the end of the day; I had been introduced to my colleagues. The men were in their late middle age, with spider-webbed noses, stooped shoulders, concave cheeks. The women were atrociously ugly. Many were lesbians. Their hair was cut short and frosted orange. They used no make-up and wore leather jackets with silver zippers. Some had tattoos. They refused to shake hands with me. Or with any other man.

I had been hired to teach critical thinking by the chairman of the department. She sat opposite me now; we had met in the library. She was short and enormously stout and talked in a hissed breathy whisper, rings of yellow fat, I imagined, closing about her trachea. She was a cousin hidden away in a dark cellar, a comical cognate, to those Ubangi women who stretch their shapely necks by means of a series of concentric teak and ivory rings. She suggested that I call her Doctor Lulu. I endeavored to look earnest and intent. *Eh, what's up Doc?* I had taught logic before, of course. If all men love some women do some women love all men? *Yo Waldburger.* A sudden start, like a pigeon fluttering: Waldburger composing himself: Waldburger composed: *I dunno man.* Not in prospect, such exercises, Dr. Lulu assured me. This is a course in critical *thinking*, she said, not logic. "Here look." She pawed over some papers on her desk and after shuffling things up considerably passed a yellow-covered, stapled sheaf of notes to me. "This is our interactive cultural module." I turned to the first page. There were diacritical marks above each word. The thing was written in Vietnamese. I looked up. Dr. Lulu shrugged her massive shoulders. She waved a pudgy hand as if to insist that her stoutness placed her above detail. I liked her. Teach whatever you want, she seemed to say.

My office was in a new faculty-designed building, Alice Walker Hall; it had been the only structure on campus to suffer significant damage from the Loma Prieta earthquake, whole slabs of extravagant marble crashing to the walkway with a dusty roar, windows shattering, foundations cracking, cracked, the Dean, a sour Irishman, nodding on the telephone in his office a week later as the damage was explained to him in lugubrious financial detail, saying I *knew* those farts had their heads up their ass.

I shared quarters with a poet, a linguist, and the department's new professor of creative writing, a full-blooded Cherokee, a fabulous ethnic acquisition, the affirmative action equivalent of four blacks or thirty-two women. Tonto I saw rarely and when I did he was generally drunk, weaving into the office late in the afternoon and furiously demanding to know where he had deposited his keys or his pen or a paper left by some adoring student. Later in the year it was discovered that the books he had published he had not written. No one thought the less of him. The poet, Winfred Blatski, was on the telephone a good deal. The receiver grew out of his ear like an extravagant organ. He was forever conducting urgent, whispered conversations in which large sums of money figured; poetry was evidently a more forthcoming financial enterprise than I had been given to understand.

When Blatski was not on the telephone, he was everywhere else in the little office, hanging his tweed jacket on the room's only hanger, disgusting damp stains underneath the arm holes, standing with one hip braced against his chair arm, or sitting in pudgy perplexity at his desk, scribbling out expense reports, or standing on his toes to fetch a book from the top shelf of the bookcase, and, of course, causing an entire row of books to topple over.

It was Blatski's responsibility to bring a number of younger poets to the campus as a part of a forum funded by a retired Santa Cruz plumbing contractor named Leonard Glauber. Blatski would walk diffidently to the center of the stage and at the podium hawk to the back of his closed fist and announce that Ms. Antipode *uh* here is going to read *uh* from her new, her new—a pause to consult the coffee-smeared notes that he was clutching—sonestina, *Learning to Love my Lover's Lips*. There would be a dry rustle of applause, a few coughs. Ms. Antipode would herself cough once or twice, adjust the microphone ceremonially, tapping the bulb with her finger tip, and then announce defiantly that her poem was dedicated to her lover: *I cannot lick my lips my lover's like, she bends her head, her knees trembling as my arched tongue travels backward across her thighs...* In the audience were members of the English department, now nodding absently: Wiggsy Riddlepest, prepared to lend an ear (or anything else) to her Sapphic sisters, a few undergraduates, and Leonard Glauber, wearing a red blazer over a *Glauber Works* t-shirt, his hands folded serenely across his ample belly.

George Nercessian, the room's other occupant, was conspicuous chiefly by his absence; he affected the office like an ectoplasm, leaving behind only tantalizing traces of himself—a copy of Chomsky's *Managua* lectures, a handbook on Burmese phonology, a guide to the grammar of Polish, an orange cut neatly into sections and left standing on the desk like a dwarfed Aztec suppliant. When one day I opened the door, I was surprised to see the phantom sitting in his chair, leaning forward, a young woman in front of him, his hand on her knee.

"Yes?" he asked with perfect composure, as if I were somehow an interloper in my own office.

"I'm David Berlinski."

"The Mysterious Other," said this Nercessian with maddening insouciance, suggesting somehow that it was I who had been absent from the office for so many weeks while he himself had been implacably at work.

We would hold office hours between eleven and twelve. At noon, we would rise, the two of us, walk past the Bloods in the hall, exiles from the now closed Afro-American Center, which had been housed on the earthquake-devastated fifth floor of the building, and exit into the warm sunlight. Leaving Alice Walker Hall was always like passing from darkness into light. "Yes," said George Nercessian gravely when I remarked on the beauty of the day. A number of booths and tables had been set up on the walkway that bisected the campus. At one, a group of morose Koreans was tending a charcoal brazier, endeavoring by means of a palm frond, which their leader waved solemnly, to stir the coals into glowing life. Another table was given over to Moslem literature. Its proprietor looked very much like Malcolm X and stood in the sun talking intently to the open air, his index finger stabbing at the sparkles. "De white man," he was saying, "has not told you de truf. No, no, no, he has not. Dat debil, he has not told you de truf."

Dat Debil.

As we sauntered along, George nodded discreetly toward a number of undergraduates: a large-breasted girl with long dirty blonde hair, a slim-hipped young brunette in boots and jeans carrying a backpack in a loping stride. He indicated the objects of his attention by means of a delicate nod of his head, a tilt, a curiously civilized gesture. These were students with whom he had conducted affairs. "I'm here for the pussy," he said suavely. He preferred very young women and regarded a position as a high-school track coach as a distant, dreamy, utterly unobtainable ideal. His conquests carried no grudges. "How do you do it?" I asked. We had reached the end of the walkway and were about to leave the campus. George fluttered his fingers in the air as a sign of his delicacy. "It's all very simple."

"I don't understand."

"Of course. *You* couldn't even bag a Filipina."

I liked them, my students. They gave off heat, but not light. One muscular young man, with untroubled eyes and a clear complexion, was painfully nervous about speaking aloud, his smooth face mottling with blood whenever I called upon him. By and by, he relaxed. He was a member of the California Highway Patrol. He told us stories of the road, all delivered in that rich police vocabulary, full of *perps* and *peds* and accounts of how one day chasing a *perp* at speeds in excess of *one hunerd miles an hour easy* this *ped* he just walked in front of the vehicle and it wasn't even a *bam*, you know, more like a *splat* and yeah, you get used to it; when I asked him why he had not volunteered for the motorcycle patrol, given his love of speed and danger, he replied solemnly that *my Mom she won't let me, she'd just freak out.*

There were California lower-class natives in my class, monstrous boys with ripe pustules and bleached blonde hair, an earring in one ear, or young women with thick legs and a kind of low-slung Edsel-like pelvis, or the statistically inevitable one-in-a-thousand raven-haired beauty, eyes glowing, lips cheery cherry red, as tart as tart could be. They lived at home, these teenagers, with their parents, rootless themselves those parents, a grandmother yet living in Idaho, in a house by a field where the wind blows off the plains, the screen door banging fitfully, someone calling *Rachel* over and over again. They ate Cheese Whiz, Big Macs, Doritos, mayonnaise on white bread, Velveeta, macaroni and cheese, fudge pies; they aspired to police work or accounting or business management or *I dunno get a job, something, I guess;* they worked part time, and took care of their baby brother, their mothers not entirely diligent about birth control, leaving the diaphragm in the medicine chest and prone thus to pregnancies in their forties; they did not read and could not write and they were touching and earnest and good-natured, curiously old-fashioned, devoted to those mothers of theirs whom they referred to as mom —*I think my mom she's so neat.*

In the fall, I taught critical thinking, in the spring, the calculus and differential equations. The department of mathematics was home to a number of enormously satisfied incompetents, men who taught their lovely, limpid subject by drilling students over and over again in a few problem sets and who regarded their own monstrous ignorance as nothing more than a majestic whim. There was even a distracted lunatic somewhere who spent his time writing science fiction novels in which strangely voluptuous women would find themselves chained to the thirteenth dimension in their underwear.

A few Russian immigrants had come to Old Hose by means of fantastic journeys, inconceivably difficult stratagems. Igor Pninofsky was no more than five feet tall; he had an unhealthy look, evoked as much by a life of fear as by a bad diet; he spoke English with an ineradicable, almost opaque Russian accent and regarded his colleagues and students, now that he had miraculously been awarded tenure, with barely disguised contempt. His courses were of fearful difficulty. "Iss nofink," he would say when it was observed that he had again failed almost all of the students reckless enough to study the calculus with him. "In Moscou, *ch*all fail." The Chairman of the department, Vergil Smith, a plump perfectly bald computer scientist, endeavored to interpose himself between the implacable Pninofsky and his enraged students. "Now look, Igor," he would whine placatingly, "you have to remember that this isn't MIT."

"Iss not possible forget," Pninofsky would rumble.

And there matters would stand so that in the end Pninofsky had no students whatsoever and remained free to devote himself entirely to his research in partial differential equations. He had lost eight years altogether. When he had applied for permission to emigrate, Russian authorities had stripped him promptly of his position at the University of Moscow; he simply sat at home in his tiny apartment. "No books," he said, "no paper. Nofink." Four years had been swallowed up learning his own brand of barely serviceable English. Now that he had put teaching behind him, he worked furiously to catch up. "Vary difficult," he said. "So much *ch*eppens." We tried often to talk mathematics, but he remained utterly uninterested in differential topology and vaguely contemptuous of anything that did not involve hard analysis.

Most of my students were Asian. I had learned a few words of Vietnamese from an old French grammar book, *Leçons Vietnamienne,* intended no doubt for black-eyed foreign legion troops stationed in southeast Asia. *Chow an,* I said one day, with a grotesquely incorrect accent; this provoked a furious burst of tittering from the gaggle of short-waisted girls who with perfect impunity began to whisper to one another behind their closed-tight little hands; but afterward, one of the boys in my class, a serious, smooth-skinned Vietnamese named Nguyen, came up to me and said *Chow an* correctly; and when later I asked this Nguyen a few polite questions about his background—Where are you from? What have you done?—I heard in response only a confused, barely articulated story: the open ocean, the South China Sea, the staring sky, Mother, brother, chop, chop.

Sometime in the spring, Jarred Blockkopf died at his house in the Berkeley hills; I had seen him shuffling down the corridors of Toni Morrison Hall dressed in a chartreuse shirt and an absurd plaid jacket, a colostomy bag tucked discretely behind the waistband of his pleated slacks; he would advance the halls with a series of fierce snorts, more or less dragging his stroke-crippled leg behind him, and my natural sense of sympathy for his shambling was offset entirely by my anxiety that he would fix me with his one good eye, the other, being glass, having a tendency to wander irresolutely, lay one of those veiny hands on my shoulder, and with a moist exhalation of foul denture breath ask solemnly how I was doing.

Vergil Smith asked me to prepare the notice. I could think of nothing to say. Blockkopf had done nothing, influenced no one. He rarely published and what he had published was either incorrect or trivial. He had no hobbies, no passions. I asked Michael Twipt for advice. Twipt was a logician who had conceived the thesis that sixteen truth values (true, almost true, almost almost true, and so on to finally finally false) were required to explain ordinary inference. He had spent years on his research and produced finally a paper setting out his main result. A journal in New Zealand had accepted it for publication. He was very proud. "What do you think, Mike," I asked? "About Blockkopf, I mean." It was dangerous to afford Twipt a conversational opening. He was like the Ancient Mariner. Twipt folded his forehead upward in concentration. He had a small face and a large mustache. A minute went by. "He was always on time," he finally said.

"Colleagues will remember with a feeling of real loss," I wrote, "Jarred Blockkopf's sense—his *outstanding* sense—of punctuality."

In late spring, I attended a conference sponsored by Pepsi-Cola; it was devoted to the university in a multicultural context. The San Jose Hilton had been given over to the proceedings; a gay sign on the marquee carried the legend *Welcome Multiculturalists* in red block letters. A table had been set up in the Gold room with literature by a number of Third World authors, one in particular, T'shumba A'laka, having actually materialized from a pile of red books, all of them copies of his own work, an enterprise in which he demonstrated that whatever was of value in the Western tradition (the spoon, tribal masks, flint) was of African origin.

An open luncheon preceded the afternoon session. The salad bar at the hospitality lounge was the bleak shrine toward which the sad great tubby women attending the conference migrated like lumbering caribou and before which they stood in waddling indecision, heaping their plates finally with radishes, lettuce, garbanzo beans, cucumbers, sprouts, bacon bits, and Green Goddess dressing, the whole awful concoction to be eaten slowly, thoughtfully.

The afternoon session of the conference met around an elliptical table. Joseph Loman sat at the head, in the chairperson's seat. He was a philosopher of legendary taciturnity, his conversation a series of subdued grunts. He was tall and thin and ran fifteen miles every day. His contribution to philosophy was an unfinished paper in which he argued that time moves in four directions. He welcomed us to the proceedings by saying "uh welcome" in a low voice, his palms upturned. The President of the university, a woman of preternatural stupidity, had taped an address. After some fumbling, Loman managed to get the tape recorder to work. "There is a mine field that lies between freedom of expression—among our most precious civil liberties—and freedom from racial or sexual harassment—among our most basic civil rights," said the President.

Afterward, Priscilla Fishbein was the first to speak. She was a professor of Leisure Studies. She sat primly at her spot, knees clenched.

"You know, something has always like bothered me. I'm Anglo and I'm really into getting in touch with my Anglo and Celtic roots and all. I'm interested in growing spiritually, becoming a more spiritual person."

George McGeorge, the university's affirmative action officer, had discovered an ingrown hair below his chin and was endeavoring to stretch his neck in order to extirpate the offender; he was well known on campus for having physically attacked a copy of Alan Bloom's *The Closing of the American Mind* at a conference on literacy held some weeks before. He had ripped the pages of the book from its spine and thrown them on the floor; afterward, he stamped angrily on the debris. I remembered that he had little feet.

Priscilla Fishbein recommenced her drone.

"And anyway," she said, "it's not my fault that I was birthed here. I mean I didn't have any say over where my parents decided to birth me and anyhow I do feel a spiritual community with this country, and the trees and all, even though it is very hemogestic ..."

"Hegemonistic," murmured Wiggsy Riddlepest, who had been listening attentively.

"Hemogestic and all and what I really am asking is I feel so *attracted* to certain Native American traditions, I want to know whether like it's all right for me even though I'm Anglo to use those traditions in my own spiritual quest. I mean so many times you people seem to feel that it's wrong to do that. I just want to know how you feel about that?"

Ann Two Tree nodded. She had been born Annabel Damplowitz, her association with the Nez Perce a family rumor that her great grandmother had been raped by a savage on the journey from St. Louis to San Francisco in the late 1870s. A tendency to blush violently had reintroduced her to her ethnic roots.

"Uh yes," she said. "You know I'd like to critique your remark about *you people*. I thought that showed insensitivity."

Rita Oxenblöt nodded vigorously, shaking her jowls like a poodle. She was married to a Negro, a politically successful union of which she was inordinately proud, her pleasure marred only by the fact that her husband beat her with gong-like regularity. In other respects, her organs of indignation were unusually well developed.

Priscilla Fishbein shrank in her chair and mouthed the word *sorry*.

"But I think," Ann Two Tree continued, "that, you know, what's really important is respect, respect for other people's traditions and way of life. Even though I'm Nez Perce on my mother's side, I wouldn't like do a Nez Perce chant unless, you know, it was all right, I was asked to do the chant, or I felt I had permission from the tribal elders to do the chant, you know what I mean? Otherwise I would feel I was not demonstrating the respect I should."

I tried to imagine Ann Two Tree doing a Nez Perce chant, perhaps by the salad bar in the hospitality lounge.

"But I feel so *attracted* to Native American spirituality," Priscilla Fishbein whined.

"Well, that's part of reality, isn't it?" said Ann Two Tree happily, "we're all attracted to things we can't or shouldn't have,"—she gave Wiggsy a heavy, meaningful look—"other people's possessions, or their wives, or husbands, or lovers."

George McGeorge lowered his chin and said: "Let's not have a catfight here."

Ann Two Tree and Wiggsy Riddlepest slitted their eyes and turned to look at him simultaneously.

"That is a derogatory sexist term," said Wiggsy.

"It indicates bias," Ann Two Tree added. "It's demeaning and stereotypifying."

"Hey," said George McGeorge, "I'm just here to dialogue with you ladies."

Frank Harebal returned the conversation to the point at issue: "Are you saying, then," he said, "that it's *always* wrong for Native American traditions and spiritual practices to be used by Anglos?"

Harebal was a philosopher flamboyantly committed to affirmative action. Just recently he had argued in the campus newspaper that Native Americans of the seventeenth century possessed a legal culture superior to that of contemporary Great Britain. He suffered from an aggressively nauseating body odor whose existence he denied. "I do *not* eat garlic," he said with florid indignation when Rita Oxenblöt, his office mate, inquired diffidently about the matter.

"I'm saying that it's part of the respect we should have for people of color that we just don't *take* their traditions," said Ann Two Tree.

A silence enveloped the room. Wiggsy Riddlepest looked hopefully at the beeper on her webbed belt. She was the campus rape crisis counselor. Often her beeper summoned her at odd hours. Students and colleagues were accustomed to seeing her burst explosively from the lecture hall *en route* to the bedside of a date rape victim. Today the beeper was silent.

Joseph Loman looked about. "Uh," he said.

Frank Harebal pushed his chair back from the table with a scraping sound.

A few motes of dust rose in the air above the oiled and polished conference table and spun in the sunlight that streamed through the windows of the room.

I was dying of hatred and boredom.

I never went back, except once, to recover a pair of expensive Reeboks I had left in a filing cabinet in my office. A woman named Stuntvesel was sitting at my desk. She looked at me with fierce glittering eyes as I rummaged for my sneakers. I made my apologies and left. Outside, the campus was squatting in the harsh thrilling sunlight. The department of Leisure Studies had erected a huge red banner above the campus walkway. It said: *Leisure: The Balance in Life*. A picture of an enormous balance scale illustrated the legend.

Old Hose! It was beyond being beyond even.

21. Vienna, 1981

During the year that I lived on the Oberedonaustrasse, everyone in Vienna fell in love with the Palmer's model. Dressed in a shimmering satin slip, she sat facing the camera, leg crossed, her lovely languorous face unsmiling, lips parted, a cloudy unfocused expression in her gray eyes. *Weiss lieb Ich,* the caption ran, which means I love white and meant nothing whatsoever. For a time, her picture stood on every kiosk in the city, and when the poster was taken down, to be replaced by a photograph of some rangy Amazon wearing bikini briefs, the general sense was that nothing would ever bring back the moment of initial glory.

In the early evening, I liked to sit on the terrace of the Café Landtman, the air sooty, a kind of ambient vagueness, tuxedoed waiters looking out into the world with hooded waiters' eyes. One I asked for a glass of water in French—index finger raised, *un verre d'eau, s'il vous plait.*

"*Oui Monsieur,*" said the waiter, who had started from his trance to glide over to the table. "*Vous avez choisi?*" he asked, his head tilted toward me. I had left the menu closed. He had tense, black eyebrows.

"*Hier wird ein ausgezeichnetes Französich gesprochen,*" I said.

"I speak every language," he answered in musically accented English.

He was amused by my admiration, and grave.

I liked the great Hapsburg monuments, the things filling the various public spaces with a grand, gaudy, somewhat myopic air, as if they were wondering where everything and everyone had gone.

And I liked the statue of Prince Eugene in the Heldenplatz, the Hofburg behind him, his horse rearing from a parking lot, a nice touch that; at the far end of the lot, where unofficial parking, it was said, is *streng verboten,* there were always a row of somber Mercedes—taxi-cabs, actually—the drivers standing beside their cars, shifting their weight from one foot to another, smoking, and behind the taxi-cabs, a lime-green Lamborghini.

Late afternoon, early fall, the hazy, mazy, hot and humid Viennese summer. There are apples from the countryside in all the stores in the first district, and sausages from Hungary hanging in great ropey strands in the windows of A. Meindel's delicatessen, and enormous wheels of rye bread, and bunches of dried flowers, great platters of cheese. In the streets that run into the Kaernterstrasse, roasted potatoes are stacked in a contraption that looks like an organ grinder's music box. They are entirely Viennese, those potatoes, and served in a greasy translucent paper cone with an alarming tendency to tip over when filled, the pigeons looking things over from their ancient roosts with a red-eyed sense of expectation.

I walked through the first district that day with nothing at all in mind. Everyone in Vienna still smokes, eats greasy food, and drinks, the men entering middle age with immense clubbed fingers and red pouched eyes. When I inquire of my neighbors in the pastry shop whether my smoking will bother them—*Darf Ich hier rachen?*—I am generally regarded as an idiot, as if I were asking permission to breathe or eat my pastry. No one exercises except for the solemn stalwarts who gather in the health clubs on the Unterdonaustrasse to pass the medicine ball around and get themselves pummeled by a masseur. The thing is actually quite cheap. I went once. When I had finished with the steam bath, and the obligatory dainty dip into the cold clean communal pool, I took a massage with someone named Fritzi. His strokes were indescribably painful. I grunted.

"*Zu hart?*" he asked, smirking.

"*Aber nein,*" I said.

It was a matter of honor.

The second district, I was advised by friends, was the late night haunt of prostitutes and drug dealers. "Unsafe," my hostess said with thrilled dismay. I headed there anyway. By and by, after ambling through the streets of the second district, which look rather like upper Manhattan, I found myself in the Prater. The leaves on the great deciduous trees had started to turn from dark green to a mottled yellow, finally falling of a sudden as if it were all too much to bear. Swedish *au pair* girls, judging things by their copper-colored hair and a sing-song lilt to their German, sauntered through the park, hand in hand, their bullet-headed charges lagging behind. "*Nah, komm schon, Rudi*," one of them sang out over her buttery brown shoulder toward Rudi, who was sitting placidly in the walkway, the look of contentment on his face suggesting gorgeously filled diapers.

"Attaboy, Rudi," I said as I passed, "make them carry you."

I crossed the imaginary line that separated roly-poly Rudi from his Swedish monitors, and headed back to the Donau Kanal along the Praterstrasse, where elegantly dressed elderly gentlemen were walking petulant white poodles, urging them on, the poodles looking up at me with their beady, malevolent brown-red eyes.

It was almost dusk now, the traffic beginning to hoot softly in the streets. Somewhere in the city, serious men dressed in *lederhosen* were serving boar in cranberry sauce for an early dinner, or pheasant, or stag, banging immense platters on the table, while in the corner of the restaurant a congregation of Austrians in very fashionable peasant dress grew progressively more tipsy and were about to launch into the third stanza of an interminable medieval drinking song.

Dusk falling, fallen, a Viennese Saturday, late in the year.

In curious concern with Einstein's theory of relativity, clocks run slower in Vienna than they do in Paris. Grim gray Zurich, I suppose, remains the absolute measure of time. Whatever the Viennese may say to one another, Vienna is a city in which work is regarded with bluff amusement. Energy is short-lived. The Viennese are short-lunged, the whole city like a group of men drinking late in a *stuberl* and determined to get organized and even organizing themselves in brief fitful bursts only to settle down again for another round—beer, perhaps, or a Schwartz Katz, a Rheinriesling, the sort of local wine that produces a fierce headache the morning after and leaves the tongue coated.

I remarked on this peculiar Viennese time-tolerance—a kind of moral indolence, really—to my friend Selinde, a tall, very striking, brillo-haired brunette, with cat-green eyes, a wonderful high forehead, and a trick of holding her head at an odd angle so that she seemed always to be looking down on things, men especially. We had walked down the Kaernerstrasse from the Burg Ring to the Stephansdomplatz, looking in all the stores for a special kind of brooch. Now we were in the Café Europa. I was applying myself to a Mokka and a sticky pastry in which sugar and almond paste had been soaked in rum and covered with a smooth purple frosting—*punchkrapftorte*—and getting a good deal of the stuff on my tie. Selinde was sipping chastely at a *Weisweingespritz,* looking at me fondly as if to say she knew I couldn't manage to eat the thing without making a mess. I wondered how they did it, she and her husband. Get by, I mean. Despite years spent in Vienna, he had managed only the rudiments of German (*Ich möchte etwas kaufen,* and so on), and tended when the going got tough to lapse back into French. When he was not on assignment in the Sudan or filming penguins in the Antarctic, the two films destined to be artistically resolved into a single intense *document,* he spent most of his time in the coffee houses, chiefly the Hawelka, or the Raimond on the Volksgartenstrasse, or even the Landtman, if someone needed to be touched for money. Selinde spoke five languages, or fifty, all of them well, and managed to invest even French with a certain sly and lazy suggestiveness. She, too, had something to do with cinema. Every six months or so she would disappear into the Far East (Bali, I think) and then return like a starburst loaded with exotic fabrics that she sold to all the better fashion houses and stores. They seemed, the two of them, to have discovered a way of life in which luxuries appeared as public goods, like air or water. Vienna was full of people to whom things simply came.

We both ordered coffee.

"I have no intention," Selinde said to me firmly, blotting her small shapely lips with a paper napkin, "of ruining my life with work."

Me either. I had left Paris and come to Vienna largely in order to have left Paris. I worked at the International Institute for Applied Systems Analysis (IIASA), a rootless, somewhat shady institution occupying in Baroque splendor a set of three palaces. Created during the palmy days of détente, Brezhnev and Nixon smirking as they signed the accords, the thing was supposed to serve both East and West in a spirit of tolerant neutrality, and until someone or other was caught passing secrets or semiconductors to the other side, the Institute was regarded as a model of international cooperation. There is a park behind the castles, and a very elegant square in front of them, and a row of charming town houses in the village, and an air throughout of considerable and careless luxury. The conviction is strong among scholars that all this is somehow a very good deal.

The director of the whole place, a good-natured imbecile, collected his thoughts in a suite with frescoed walls and immensely tall ceilings in which plaster cherubim had been molded; the thing was larger than a football field. He sat, I recall, at an Empire desk, his plump posterior wedged into an oiled and gleaming walnut chair. A dainty porcelain stove before which Maria Theresa herself was said to have warmed her feet stood in the corner of the room. Every year from this office I received urgent requests for financial assistance. But then, IIASA is the larger Viennese world in miniature. Nothing is quite what it seems, not even the eastern Europeans. One afternoon, I was handed a written request to meet with the head of the systems science section, a swarthy, chain-smoking, no-necked Pole known at the Institute for his phlegmatic stolidity. He was like a moose. The note was marked confidential. We met at the *stuberl*. He got right down to business.

"You are filospher, yes?"

"Well, yes."

"The Mind of God," he asked urgently, his voice thrilled, "infinite or no?"

"Infinite," I said. "Absolutely."

"It *ch*annot be," he answered, his expression earnest, sincere, his voice rumbling. "I haff proof." He fished his worn leather briefcase from the floor, withdrew a dogged manuscript from the thing, and set it on the table. "In first place," he began, prepared evidently to read the whole thing to me at a single sitting. I stopped him by holding up my hands.

"Andrei, Andrei, Andrei," I said.

On the anniversary of the October Revolution, the Russian delegation was in the habit of throwing a lavish party, and although the Russians were not known for their conviviality, the party had become famous in international circles for its caviar, brought in by diplomatic pouch, and iced vodka. That year, the party was held in a suite in the Blue Palace. The reception was scheduled to commence at four in the afternoon, but by three o'clock all of the Institute's workmen were lined up at the table, standing patiently in their workclothes, the Russian delegation surveying with bleak indignation the center table, as workman after workman would, with a solemn grunt of satisfaction, help himself to a stupendous scoop of caviar, almost as if the stuff were egg salad, while at the back of the line, Institute officials shifted from foot to foot in an agony of impatience, craning their necks to see whether anything would actually be left after these louts had finished.

Double vision: then and now—a peculiarly Viennese perspective. I asked my physician once where he would live if he had the choice. "Oh, California, absolutely," he said, with that inflected Viennese lilt that he took to be the expression of his own very personal brand of English.

He closed his eyes and smiled a dreamy, self-absorbed smile, his rather stern features softening. "Can you imagine," he said, "the Chief of Cardiology in Santa Barbara made his rounds in shorts."

Could *I* imagine?

The features of his face reassembled themselves into their habitual tense configuration.

"But you couldn't leave Vienna forever?"

"No, I suppose not. There is all this." He waved his hand in a little arc, the *all this* taking in everything without words: the music, the coffee houses, whipped cream on Sunday afternoon, the Crown Prince Rudolf yet slipping off in his fiacre, his coachman Bratfisch whistling an especially soft and rustling melody—*wo bleibt die alte Zeit?*—while somewhere to the east of the city, in a country castle, his mistress, sloe-eyed, peach-lipped, waits, a single rose pinned to her auburn hair.

"All that is nonsense, of course, *quatsch*," he said. "But we stood when a professor entered the room."

So does everyone in Vienna. Or did.

Once the last living member of the royal Hapsburg family—the widow of Charles I, actually—paid a visit to the city. For days, the papers talked reverently of little else. I wandered to the square in front of the Stephanskirche just before she was to arrive. The usual curious and indifferent crowd was there, of course, but toward the center of the square I could see that the spectators were older, dressed impeccably. They stood waiting patiently, the men with their chests puffed out, wearing Austrian hunting hats with feathers, the women frail, like mannequins, and tidy. An honor guard decked out in red and gray Hapsburg uniforms was at attention. A drum roll began. And then, inching its way along, a coach drawn by six splendid horses passed alongside of the crowd and came to a halt. At the back of the square, where teenagers clustered, red rubble on their cheeks, or wispy beards, there was an aching sense of expectant tenderness, until the coach door opened, and a tiny, wizened, terribly old woman, dressed somberly in black, descended from the coach, helped by four enormous footmen, stood erect in the square, and with glittering, glaring eyes looked out at the crowd and for a moment smiled, her ancient lips wrinkling.

In central Europe, nothing is ever given up for good or lost forever. On the Seitenstettengasse, guards with small submachine guns stand watch over the city's ancient synagogue. They look thoroughly unprofessional, like so many Austrians, as if great crimes might be committed as they stared vacantly into space. The great crimes have already been committed. The guards are there for show. The apartment buildings on the street are very old, one that I stayed in briefly having been built in the fifteenth century. In a few of these buildings, the street level apartments have been converted to cabarets, the separate cabarets, like the many arms of Vishnu, representing one essential club. By eleven, they are filled with young businessmen in heavy suits (Viennese men have no patience with Italian fashion; they cling to woolens and worsteds, which they purchase at Willi Sibernagel) and pretty smiling women sitting in pairs or triplets, giggling to themselves or talking in the brush-soft, singsong Viennese dialect. The whole thing is puppyish and pat, a breezy informality prevailing, the music out-of-date and very loud.

In the Reiss Bar or the Queen Anne Pub or the Galerie Bar, outsiders are not greeted warmly. The faded-flower, crushed-violet aristocracy come here to drink, the men bobbing and nodding to one another, the women coy, constrained, their German altogether elegant now, and precise. These are people who in spring or autumn yet attend the great formal balls. They know how to ride and where to purchase a saddle and how to bow and how to curtsey and how to dance the mazurka and how to shoot and how to use six forks at dinner. Not my skills, precisely. Eyes narrowed, lips pinched, woolen jacket with leather cuffs at the sleeves, a barside companion surveyed me with an expression suggesting that, after all, there really is a difference between us, you and me, and, of course, there was.

Fashionable restaurants come to life of a sudden and then fade quickly away. One at the end of the Seitenstettengasse—the Salzamt—is so very secure in its system of allegiances that it does not carry a sign with its name on the door or at the windows. There is a small bar at the head of the restaurant, the central corridor is painted a Maria Theresa yellow, the food is a racial babble, classic Austrian dishes alongside pasta and a variety of French confections. No music. A delicate diffident restaurant, where young, elegant, very Austrian women appear alone at twilight, and like heroines in a novel by F. Scott Fitzgerald, seem always to be waiting for some soft and secret signal.

"*Ja, ja*," remarked my friend, Dr. Bernard Ludwig. "Vienna, is *fantastisch* what is happening."

"*Fantastisch* how?"

We had left the Salzamt after a drink—it was too crowded for dinner—and were walking through the first, along the Hohermarkt.

He stopped for a moment to collect his thoughts.

"*Wie sagt Mann dass?*" he asked. The word he was looking for was "trendy." He resumed his drumbeat-determined stride.

"It's so California," he finally said. My poor Ludwig. He had spent a week in Los Angeles.

And now a few snapshots. Here is the Kaerntnerstrasse at twilight, just before the elegant empty stores close, a saleswoman tenderly fingering her strand of pearls at the entrance to Cartier's, the horses nodding peaceably by their carriages in the Stephansdomplatz, the drivers in top hats talking to one another in Viennese slang. Or the *würstl* stand on the Francis Joseph Kai at four in the morning, the only one open, the late-night drifters lined up patiently, everyone ordering bread, sausage—*geschnitten, ja?*—mustard, and beer, the sausages hissing on the black and greasy grill. Or the Mariahilferstrasse, the Iranian proprietor of a small store (rugs, chiefly) speaking execrable pained German, a formal portrait of the Shah on the wall. Or the long stretch of the Gurtel from the seedy

Westbannhof to the Allgemeinen Krankenhaus and over to the Donau Kanal, the streetwalkers gabbling to themselves. Or a taxi-driver in his fantastically organized Mercedes, compartments and built-in devices for everything, maps, lotions, even a mini-bar in the back, whipping the huge machine through traffic, and when I asked how he had learned to drive so expertly, told me that he spent twenty years driving a Yellow cab in New York. Or the Statsoper on a Friday evening, the Vienna Philharmonic, Bernstein conducting, the audience dressed extravagantly, men in formal wear, women in long gowns, flaunting themselves, and in the orchestra or by the bar during intermissions, a tourist dressed in a Slave-of-Passion t-shirt and a schlumpy vest, fingering his neck in embarrassment. Or the Konzerthaus on the Lothingerstrasse, Benetto Michelangeli scheduled to appear, everyone tense—the man is known to cancel concerts because of a pimple—and then a great wave of applause, the seats made of iron, uncomfortable, no one moving. Afterwards, a late supper at the Hotel Sacher, still arch, still very formal, Michelangeli entering the room dressed in a black cape, everyone tapping their menus in applause, the snooty headwaiter bowing low, reverential. Or the Burgtheater on the Karl Lüger Ring, Schnitzler tonight, or Nestroy, or Lessing, or even Shakespeare in translation, Hamlet saying, of all things, *Sein oder nicht zu sein*. Or the Kunsthistorische Museum, the Breughels on the third floor, peeling in the humidity, and, in a corner, a single throat-catching Vermeer, the art of painting. Or the gardens by the university on the ring, with their outdoor café, the service, please note, impossibly slow, the linden trees heavy, fragrant. Or the long narrow park by the Donau Kanal, everyone on skateboards. Or the Heurigen in Grinzing, row after row of wooden tables, the tops splintery, a sign commemorating the fact that once Beethoven slept here or that Schubert contracted syphilis in the rooms of the charming inn just above the tavern.

Although everyone in Vienna speaks some English, the German language covers the city like a cloud, the inflected language giving rise to an inflected life. Once I was asked to deliver a lecture at the University of Vienna. "German or English," I asked my host, a mathematician who prided himself on his cosmopolitan command of the language of James Fenimore Cooper. "Oh, English, of course," he said. "We are all very sophisticated here."

Very well, English.

At eight, the university had pretty much shut down. The lecture room had the empty, somewhat spooky feeling of a large space put to little use. My friends were there, and a handful of mathematicians from the university—serious men, with soft white hair and delicate hands locked in suspension underneath their chins, and a poet I had met at a party, whose poetry, I remember, tended to short spastic bursts—*Warum?! Wie so:; Nein! Darf Ich?*—in which stray snatches of this and that were modulated by a good deal of bizarre punctuation.

I began my lecture and realized promptly from the vacant expression on the faces in the audience that no one understood a word of what I was saying.

Afterwards the poet came up, the froth of remonstration about to form on his lips.

"I know," I said, "better in German."

"Ten years ago, everyone would have understood you in English. Now everything is different."

"How so?"

A soft hand-waggle.

"There is a center now," he said, all the old ghosts sitting up suddenly and like penguins applauding decorously.

Soft focus please, and, perhaps, Vaseline on the lens. Has it been properly remarked how pretty Viennese women really are? They are bigger somehow, the Viennese women, with round shoulders and full bosoms, and a lovely languid carriage, but long-limbed, too. I am talking of a full-blown drowsy prettiness.

In the fall, the Viennese light acquires a rufous satiny sheen, especially at twilight, the deep velvet blue of the Donau Kanal, which I can see from my bedroom window, merging mysteriously with the red flashes of the enormous neon sign on the roof of the office building on the far side of the canal, the one that spells *Versicherung*.

For a time, the two local newspapers carried a collection of erotic advertisements in which specialties would be arranged by categories. These were sordid affairs, *entre nous soit dit*, but irresistible anyway. *Nur in Wien* was the general theme. Mothers and daughters advertised together; twins were said to be available for the man with a passion for secret symmetries; and there were look-alikes ranging from Marilyn Monroe to long-forgotten Viennese actresses. One notice that especially caught my eye and that I shall always treasure—*immer, immer, immer*—ran for weeks, and was obviously placed in the newspaper by some hopeless, but enthusiastic, amateur. *Macht alles*! it said. And there followed a telephone number.

Everyone read these notices and there was a real sense of disappointment in the coffee houses and at IIASA when both newspapers decided to end them.

Here are my notes. The Rottenturm on the Rottenturmstrasse is within sight of the cathedral and very elegant. There are pictures of beautiful women on the wall and on a marquee near the door. The women are all very young and look as if they live in Arizona. As, indeed, they do. The pictures are all from *Playboy*. The women inside the bar do not look as if they had a longing for desert landscapes. The Eden is rather a dump, *malheureusement*, and the Opium Den has spots on the carpeted floor and the most questionable of sanitary arrangements. At the Renz, the strippers give way from time to time to magicians, acrobats, or Polish folksingers doing their best to interest the boys at the bar in higher things.

Crushed violets: imagine the smell. And the woods at sunset. In Bucharest, I am told, before the war, the infinitely elegant, multi-lingual manager of the better hotels, dressed in a creamy cut-a-away and striped trousers, would ask each newly arrived guest, his well-barbered head held at an angle as he put the question, whether one pillow was required or two. Two, yes, by all means two. And there would be in bed that evening an oblation from the hotel itself, a very special kind of bon-bon, her black hair spread against two pink pillows.

Before each and every club in the coarse inescapable present, however, is precisely the same character, someone named Rudi, or his cousin, or his brother, or even his father, a family destined to be doormen, a round, tubby figure in a dilapidated tuxedo, the remains of dinner yet glistening on his starched shirt-front, welcoming the sidewalk strays that cross in front of him in what he imagines is their native language, getting everything wrong—the inflection, the grammar, even the words—and rubbing his thumb and forefinger together to signify the delectable, roseate, peeled-peach quality of the merchandise inside.

Tawdry, no? But a sunburst of sorts is coming. Among the women who promptly sidle over to you as you are endeavoring to find the cheapest drink in the dim red light (beer, generally), there are certainly a fair number of battle-hardened veterans, slouch-eyed, puffy-cheeked, their cordial *Darf Ich hier sitzen?* an invitation only to order the inevitable undrinkable Sekt and keep the tab running. Yet in each and every bar, now and forever, there are one or two women of simply luxuriant loveliness, flowers in a faded field, their loveliness having come to life mysteriously, to everyone's amazement, as if it had been charmed into existence, charm the right word exactly, a kind of dissolute moist magic. They are young, poised, witty, these women, so many Mignonnes, Yvonnes, and damp Delilahs, French names being much in favor, and even an Elfrieda. That was her name! A great tawny mop of golden hair, clear level blue eyes, perfectly made up, a square face, pulpy bee-stung lips, the high Hapsburg forehead, a Fredericks of Hollywood gown draped over her lavish figure; and, of a sudden, the rosy impression the tourist or traveler gets, after a few words with the unkempt but understanding Rudi, of having entered a bad new, mad new world in which really only the most modest of business arrangements need be completed to persuade this drowsy delicious young woman to repair to the nearest hotel or disappear languidly into the *Separeé* at the back of the club, stretch out on the immaculate bed with its sparkling linen, the bottle of obligatory Sekt beside her head, and fall fast asleep, her curls framed about her warm young face.

VII. Interviews

22. A Conversation with *Le Figaro*

When in 2002, I published *A Tour of the Calculus* in French under the title *La vie rêvée des maths* (Saint Simon), *Le Figaro*, France's second largest national newspaper, sent one of their writers to my apartment and we chatted for an hour or so. The interview was published soon afterwards, together with my photograph, one of my cats seated tranquilly on my knee. I have gone through the interview, tidying up a few loose ends and providing a bit of connective tissue to complete various questions. I have decided to leave the interview in its original French. The French is lighthearted and slangy and it makes perfect sense. No matter how I fuss with an English translation, the result is uninspiring, the charm of the original lost.

Le Figaro: Ceux qui vous connaissent voient en vous un Pic de la Mirandole.

David Berlinski: Ah oui ? Pouquoi pas Leonardo ?

Le Figaro: Sans aucun doute. Avant d'expliquer les mathématiques aux autres, comment y êtes-vous parvenu vous-même ?

David Berlinski: De Pic de la Mirandole, je n'ai pas la nationalité, puisque je suis d'origine allemande, mais j'ai le même goût que lui de la France lorsqu'il décida de s'y replier pour échapper aux foudres de Rome. Je fuyais plutôt un autre type de pagaille. Je suis venu en France parce que les États-Unis étaient trop petits pour moi et mes ex-femmes. Et n'oubliez pas : j'avais des racines en France. Mon père, né à Leipzig, s'est battu contre son propre peuple, aux côtés des Français dans la Légion étrangère, puis s'est réfugié aux Etats-Unis où il est arrivé sans un sou au terme d'un difficile voyage en 1942. Je suis né à New York dans les mois qui suivirent.

Le Figaro: Avez-vous grandi en parlant français ?

David Berlinski: Pas un mot. Quel que soit le français que je connaisse, je l'ai appris ici à Paris. La langue à la maison était l'allemand.

Le Figaro: Qu'en est-il de votre éducation ?

David Berlinski: Un produit de diverses écoles publiques à Princeton.

Le Figaro: Avez-vous toujours été intéressé par les mathématiques ?

David Berlinski: Pas du tout. J'ai dormi la plupart de mes années de collège et de lycée. À Princeton, qui était encore à son apogée et presbytérienne et, bien sûr, interdite aux femmes, j'ai étudié la philosophie sans jamais manifester un quelconque attrait pour les mathématiques. Or, il se trouve qu'un jour, alors que j'avais déjà plus de vingt-cinq ans, me promenant chez les bouquinistes de New-York, j'ai repéré un livre étrange, et j'ai été absolument fasciné par la quantité de symboles, tous mystérieux pour moi, qu'il renfermait. Je me suis dit que c'était le moment où jamais de m'initier à cette discipline. J'ai décidé que je ne pouvais pas mourir sans comprendre tous ces signes qui me pénétraient et me parlaient avec tellement de force. Je me suis formé tout seul : cela a été une découverte à la fois terrible et épouvantable, mais dont je n'ai jamais eu le sentiment qu'elle m'ait coûté beaucoup d'efforts.

Le Figaro: Y a-t-il une méthode Berlinski ?

David Berlinski: Un livre, une table, un crayon, une lampe, un cigare, peut-être, et ce que les Allemands appellent *sitzfleisch*. Les Allemands ont un mot pour tout et c'est toujours le mot juste. Les mathématiques imposent une recherche solitaire et occupent l'esprit en permanence. J'ai donc passé mes journées à déchiffrer cette sorte de grimoire page par page et, au bout de cinq ans, j'ai pu dire que j'avais compris le sens des maths, quelque chose à propos de sa vie intérieure, une allusion, rien de plus, comme le vent dans les saules.

Le Figaro: Vous n'allez pas vous arrêter maintenant ?

David Berlinski: Bien sûr que non. Je me reposais simplement. Le français est la langue la plus proche de mon cœur, vous devez vous en souvenir, mais pas de ma bouche. Le fait est là. À un moment donné, les mathématiciens européens contemplèrent l'univers, remarquèrent l'effroyable pagaille qui y régnait et décidèrent qu'il devait exister une représentation simple du monde, qui pouvait être coordonnée par le monde des nombres. Remarquez la double exigence. Une *représentation* coordonnée par des *nombres*. Commençons par le commencement. L'appréhension mathématique du monde s'amorce avec la géométrie euclidienne, théorie statique, et donc stagnante, nul changement ne se reflétant dans son lumineux miroir. Pour les Grecs, les choses sont ce qu'elles sont, maintenant et pour l'éternité; mais *nous* hommes du XXIe siècle qui d'une certaine manière sommes passés de l'autre côté du miroir, nous vivons dans une explosion d'épanouissement et de déclins incessants, avec des choses qui se meuvent frénétiquement à la surface de la terre, des planètes qui surgissent en virevoltant dans le ciel nocturne, des galaxies qui naissent puis disparaissent, avec l'univers lui-même qui résulte d'un grotesque *Bang!* (un cousin comique, kidnappé à la naissance par des gitans, au *Bong*! de ces bandes dessinées que j'ai tant appréciées dans mon enfance – donc le *Bong Bang*! comme disent les physiciens) et qui est destiné, un jour, à se dilater indéfiniment dans le vide ou à se recroqueviller sur lui-même tel un vieux pruneau fripé. Sans doute la géométrie sert-elle de squelette, mais le Calcul est une théorie vivante qui a besoin de chair, de sang, et d'un dense réseau de nerfs. Contrairement à la géométrie euclidienne, l'arithmétique provient directement du cœur humain, du *boum-boum* sous le stéthoscope du médecin ou de l'oreille de l'amant, impossible à entendre sans un mélancolique écho fondamental «1, 2, 3, 4...» une série qui dure un peu, puis s'arrête, hélas.

Le Figaro: Mais dès lors que "Calcul" avec une majuscule signifie "calcul différentiel et intégral," les choses deviennent moins simples.

David Berlinski: Vous croyez ? Eh bien laissez-moi vous raconter une petite histoire aussi rassurante qu'effrayante. J'insiste. Il y a bien longtemps, j'ai suivi un cours de logique mathématique d'Alonzo Church. J'avais beau me sentir assez assuré dans le décryptage des signes, je m'y étais rendu avec une certaine forfanterie car je n'étais pas assez *préparé* aux exigences du raisonnement ni au style glacial de ce mathématicien extrêmement distingué. Le sujet était si difficile que quelqu'un, un jour, se plaignit de la complexité d'une démonstration. Church détourna alors son large torse du tableau pour faire face à la dizaine de personnes assises dans la salle. " N'importe quel imbécile, déclara-t-il placidement mais avec une profonde conviction, peut apprendre n'importe quoi en mathématiques. Ce n'est qu'une question de patience." Il semblait ému. Ses yeux s'embuèrent. "Cependant," ajouta-t-il, "créer quelque chose, c'est une autre histoire" Church, en cette seconde de vérité, ne se réjouissait nullement de ses propres compétences. Les yeux fixés sur les objectifs inaccessibles auxquels il avait aspiré, il nous avouait discrètement, à nous, simples blanc-becs, qu'en matière de mathématiques lui aussi figurait parmi les imbéciles de l'humanité. Comme nous tous.

Le Figaro: Et dans l'accomplissement de l'imbécile que vous êtes, que vous ont apporté concrètement les mathématiques ?

David Berlinski: Concrètement ? Pas tant que cela. *Qu'avaient les Césars excepté leurs trônes?* J'ambitionnais de devenir un maître des symboles. Je voulais être ce contre-maître égyptien aux tresses huilées devant lequel le plus inabordable des pharaons, le Roi-Dont-Nul-N'ose-Prononcer-Le-Nom, s'inclinerait, reconnaissant celui qui était capable de déterminer la superficie de ses champs cultivés ou le volume de son effroyable pyramide. Voilà pour la géométrie. Et le Calcul ? Il est ce que ne peuvent retranscrire les mots. C'est dans le Calcul, conçu par nous, pauvres êtres finis, que l'infini est, pour la première fois, charmé jusqu'à la docilité, et que sa luxuriance est subordonnée au dur concept d'une limite. Le *hic et nunc* d'une vie ordinaire est coordonné au moyen d'une *fonction* mathématique, noble et impénétrable création de l'imagination - impalpable et indestructible fil de soie qui relie les uns aux autres les concepts disparates d'un monde vagabond. Le calcul, avec ses formules, est un mode de pensée flamboyant, friand de grands gestes intellectuels, une théorie de l'espace et du temps, indifférente à toute description détaillée du monde. Quel paradoxe. Aussi ai-je mesuré, pour moi, la prééminence des mathématiques sur toutes les questions philosophiques.

Le Figaro: Vous voulez dire que vous avez trouvé grâce à elles un soutien métaphysique ?

David Berlinski: Si l'on considère la *métaphysique* selon le jeu de mot anglais: *better physic,* les mathématiques, avec leur vie rêvée, couvrent l'espace infime qui sépare la métaphysique de la physique, qu'elle soit mécanique ou quantique. Elles ouvrent là un débat fructueux et efflorescent.

Le Figaro: Vous affirmez cependant de façon assez fataliste que l'homme est fait pour souffrir et mourir.

David Berlinski: *L'homme naît pour souffrir comme l'étincelle pour briller* .

Le Figaro: Vous n'êtes pas sympathique à l'idée que le monde de la souffrance est une illusion ?

David Berlinski: Une illusion ? Ils plaisantent sur les cicatrices qui n'ont jamais senti une blessure.

J'ai pu constater qu'il en allait de même pour mon père : à la fin de sa vie, il n'avait toujours pas accepté de lui donner un caractère illusoire. Tel père, tel fils.

Le Figaro: Quelles sont les consolations des mathématiques ?

David Berlinski: Quoi qu'il en soit, je trouve beaucoup plus extraordinaire de disposer d'un système de symboles qui permette de représenter simultanément l'espace et le temps qui sont les deux théâtres de nos expériences recouvrant une unité. C'est une découverte fondamentale pour l'être humain dans la mesure où elle peut faire tomber tout un pan d'illusions.

Le Figaro: Qu'entendez-vous par illusions ?

David Berlinski: Penser, par exemple, que nous partageons des expériences. Nos expériences ne sont jamais communes, mais toujours divisées, même si chacun, dans son cœur, cherche toujours à en franchir les frontières, que ce soit sur le plan amoureux, familial ou social. Grâce aux mathématiques, on tente d'échapper à l'isolement pour accéder à l'universel par une démarche qui n'est guère différente de la démarche amoureuse, à cela près que l'amour est éphémère.

Le Figaro: Tandis que les mathématiques, elles, sont éternelles ?

David Berlinski: Eh bien non, malheureusement. Sujet humain, elles sont nées à une époque donnée, et, partant, soumises à un destin, condamnées à disparaître après floraison. Ce n'est pas une question de civilisation, mais de trajectoire : complexes et rébarbatives elles seront remplacées par l'informatique qui repose sur la logique. Reléguées au musée de la pensée pour l'intérêt de leur mécanique, elles entament déjà leur consomption, faute d'enseignants, d'adeptes et de raison d'être. La grande époque du XVIIe siècle offrant au monde dans son sillage les Newton, Lagrange et Einstein, est révolue. Nous n'en conservons que les grandes théories. L'ordinateur, plus *discret* avec les chiffres, façonne différemment les esprits. Les sciences et notamment la biologie sont aujourd'hui devenues plus importantes pour l'être humain, dans la mesure où elles peuvent en changer la nature. Regardez bien ce qui se passe en ce début de siècle : la biologie va, à son tour se trouver confrontée à la philosophie et au mystère du système vivant.

Le Figaro: Vous n'êtes guère optimiste pour la discipline qui apparaît votre raison d'être.

David Berlinski: Mais non, détrompez-vous, d'abord parce que les mots sont importants et que j'ai plusieurs vies : celle d'un écrivain et d'un poète. Ensuite par ce que l'esprit mathématique, à défaut de la discipline, est éternel. En voulez-vous un exemple ? Mon ami français Schützenberger m'a raconté que les mathématiciens Stanislaw Ulam et Edward Teller butaient sur le problème de la bombe à hydrogène. Le premier était, paraît-il, d'une paresse inégalée et passait tout son temps étendu sur le lit, un journal sur le nez. Un jour que ses collègues s'épuisaient à trouver une solution à cette question, il a ouvert les yeux deux minutes, annoncé qu'il détenait la clé du problème et l'a communiquée à sa femme de ménage avant de replonger dans un sommeil hébété. L'anecdote est délicieuse : le génie du mathématicien ne dépend pas du travail, de la diligence ou de la persévérance. Il tient aux idées qui peuvent arriver brutalement, au beau milieu de la nuit, comme les pompiers avec leurs sirènes. Comme tous les autres, j'attends ces sirènes, et j'ai bon espoir qu'un jour elles vont se manifester.

Le Figaro: Par quelle formule mathématique, pourriez-vous expliquer l'actualité ?

David Berlinski: Honnêtement, je n'en vois pas. Les événements qu'a traversé notre société le 11 septembre dernier dépassent les normes et relèvent du domaine de la malignité pour lequel les mathématiques se révèlent tout à fait inutiles. Si elles permettent d'unir l'espace et le temps, elles sont impuissantes à donner une lecture de l'histoire.

Le Figaro: Votre ouvrage affranchira-t-il certains de vos lecteurs de l'obstacle que représente pour eux la complexité des maths ?

David Berlinski: On dit en Allemagne qu'un livre est comme un miroir. On peut y trouver des trésors pour peu qu'on le veuille, mais si c'est un singe qui découvre la glace, aucun apôtre ne sera en mesure de l'éclairer sur les images qu'elle renvoie. Ne croyez pas qu'en vous répondant ainsi je fasse acte d'orgueil. Ni apôtre ni démiurge, je ne puis transformer les êtres. Pour autant, Wittgenstein prétendait qu'en philosophie, il n'y avait pas de problèmes, mais seulement des perplexités, lesquelles se ramènent le plus souvent à une mauvaise position des problèmes. Je m'y suis donc attelé avec fierté. D'où une ineffable source d'espoirs. Dans une célèbre lettre de reproche adressée à Lord Chesterfield, le Dr Johnson observait que : *le berger en Virgile chercha l'amour et le trouva de pierre.* Par cette obscure remarque, Johnson signifiait à un esprit de formation classique que l'amour peut être source de douleur et de désespérance. J'ai toujours été hanté par ces lignes qui mettent en évidence l'énigme profonde que sont nos états émotionnels - le fait que, si *habituels* qu'ils soient, ils n'en sont pas moins infiniment mystérieux. Or malgré leur caractère *inhabituel,* les concepts mathématiques, eux, sont infiniment accessibles. À l'heure de leur mort, ceux qui se seront intéressés aux mathématiques auront connu les fonctions continues bien plus intimement que le cœur humain et ses tortueux détours. Qu'un sujet aussi abstrait soit pour finir si lumineux ne peut que susciter l'émerveillement.

Le Figaro: Comme il y a le paradoxe de Zénon que vous racontez avec humour dans votre livre - l'homme qui ne pourra mathématiquement pas franchir complètement l'espace de sa propre chambre - existe-t-il un paradoxe de Berlinski ?

David Berlinski: Le fait que je ne possède pas une grande fortune m'a toujours semblé paradoxal. Sûrement j'en mérite un, ne pensez-vous pas?

23. A Conversation with *Evolution News*

In Anticipation of Berlinski's *The Deniable Darwin & Other Essays*

David Klinghoffer: Were you always subversive? Tell us about the childhood David Berlinski.

David Berlinski: I am not sure that I would care to think of myself as *subversive*. It is a mole-and-badger kind of word, isn't it? So long as we are searching for similes, I would prefer *lion*-like. *Regal* is another fine word.

I *was* from an early age indisposed to accept what I had been told. Having been urged not to insert a fork into an electrical outlet, I stuck one in anyway; I was shocked to discover that it *was* a poor idea, just as my mother had maintained. An impatient child, I became a school-yard terror, and a high-school bully. At the Bronx High School of Science I was a part of the clique—Moose Moscowitz, Steven Parker, Arthur Klein, June Tauber, Alan Abramson—that inflicted a life-long feeling of inadequacy on everyone else. I am often astonished that we got out of high school alive.

I have always been haunted by the meaning of my childhood. I was born in New York just a few months after my parents left Europe in flight from the Nazis. My parents having escaped Spain on virtually the last passenger ship to leave occupied Europe—the *Marquis de Camellia*—I assign to myself a most romantic *Spanish* conception. My father served in the French Foreign Legion and he had fought throughout the battle of France, his regiment decimated, 250 men left alive from the 2,500 men entering combat. Nonetheless, he had been thrilled, he told me late in his life, to be able *at last* to face the Germans with a weapon in his hands. It was, unfortunately, a 1916 water-cooled Hotchkiss machine gun, but, my father assured me ominously, it got the job done all the same.

My mother's hatred of the Germans and Germany continues unabated into her one hundredth year.

There has been that constant reminder throughout my life of exile and expatriation, the loss of language. I live my life within the English language—obviously so; but to this day, it is the sound of the German language that conveys *die Heimat* to me. Not *das Vaterland*, God forbid, but *die Heimat*.

In the early 1980s, a little French and German production company asked me to write a screenplay based on Kurt Götz's fluffy little novel, *Tatiana*. They needed a screenwriter who could read the German original. So I had an advantage. The book was little known then and unknown today, but it prefigured Nabokov's *Lolita*, and so remains a curiosity among literary scholars. Götz had achieved a success of sorts in Hollywood; he was known as a *boulevardier*, a man about town. He ended his days as a California chicken farmer. This, too, is a part of it, a writer talking to chickens, a weathered hand against the sun.

Ten years before they fled France, my parents had fled Germany; theirs was thus a double flight and a double expatriation. They had together grown up together in Leipzig, and they were both graduates of the Leipzig Conservatory. In France, they repeated their education at the *École Normale de Musique*, my father studying composition with Nadia Boulanger and piano with Alfred Cortot. The story of their escape from occupied France in late 1941 was the drama of my childhood: Hiding from the Gestapo in Marseilles, entry visas *to* the United States, exit visas *from* France, entry visas *to* Spain, exit visas *from* Spain; black market intrigues, Varian Frey, the flight across the Pyrenees, Spanish months spent waiting. It is odd now to think of Franco's Spain as a refuge, but it was theirs and obviously it was mine.

Growing up under these circumstances and growing up, too, in northern Manhattan, every last neighborhood ghost gabbling away in German, the greengrocer, Selig, a refugee from the *Kaiser's* Germany, my greatest need in childhood was to escape the culture that my parents embodied. My greatest need thereafter was to reclaim it. These historical convulsions ramify downward through the generations. Both my children are expatriates.

My education was a straight shot: P.S. 84, the Bronx High School of Science, Columbia College, Princeton, my PhD, an accessory before the fact. What remains today of my institutional education is a three-part memory: an excellent year-long course in Euclidean geometry taught by Mrs. Mazen at the Bronx High School of Science; Norman Cantor's course in medieval history at Columbia College; and Alonzo Church's graduate course in mathematical logic at Princeton.

Thereafter, whatever I learned, I learned on my own.

David Klinghoffer: When did you start thinking, as a critic, about Darwinian evolution? Did anything in your biography incline you to freethinking in that area?

David Berlinski: It was the fall of 1965. My graduate school roommate Daniel Messenger and I were ambling along Nassau Street in Princeton. We were munching the kind of wonderful Winesap apples that seem to have disappeared as a variety. I wonder why that is? Daniel's girlfriend, Sandra Petersen, was there too. Daniel was a fine philosopher and Sandra was doing a degree in classical philosophy. We walked over to Darwin's theory of evolution, living at the time in one of Princeton's back alleys.

A back alley was the right place to look for Darwin. No one in the philosophy department at Princeton had *ever* introduced his name into a seminar, or thought to argue that *his* theory was relevant to *our* concerns.

At Columbia College I had been given a ten-minute introduction to the *theory* of evolution in a class otherwise devoted to comparative anatomy. The impression conveyed was that Darwin's theory was far less interesting than the details embedded in the anatomy of the Dogfish.

—*Now if you will turn to your specimens, Gentlemen…*

If I had had those ten minutes to count on, Daniel had more. At Brown, he had once *read* Darwin's *On the Origin of Species*. This made him a considerable expert in my eyes. He knew what it was all about. I asked the obvious question: *So is that it?*

Apparently it was.

Daniel shrugged his rounded shoulders. Someone, he said, had figured it all out. As she always did, Sandra kept her counsel. She was fond of Daniel; she thought me an idiot.

A year later, I found myself promoted from East Coast snow to West Coast sunshine. And promoted to more, far more. I was an assistant professor at Stanford: *that* was more. And I had been given access to the splendor of northern California: *that* was far more. What is that wonderful line by Robert Lowell? *All of life's grandeur is something with a girl in summer.*

One night I was having dinner with my great friend, Daniel Gallin. At the time, he lived in San Francisco, his Delmar Street apartment high above the city. We could see the fog roll in, Nassau Street Daniel emerging briefly to offer Delmar Street Daniel the same reprise of Darwin's theory that he had once offered me. Delmar Street Daniel was doing a PhD at Berkeley with Dana Scott; he was an excellent mathematician, and an even better logician. He reserved his approval for mathematical model theory, and his admiration for Alfred Tarski.

"Can you imagine?" he would ask on reading something absurd.

And Darwin?

Can you imagine!

At some time in the early 1970s, I came across the papers that Murray Eden and M. P. Schützenberger had delivered to the 1966 Wistar Symposium, mathematical objections to Neo-Darwinism.[1] I read them closely; I was impressed; and I discussed them at Columbia with Josh Kornberg, a molecular biologist, and George Pieczenik, a biochemist. Pieczenik had just finished his PhD, writing a thesis on the grammatical constraints embedded in the nucleic acids. Sympathetic to Murray's position, he had discovered two facts: the first, that the nucleic acids contain internal terminator codons, and the second, that they often express very long palindromes. Josh Kornberg, on the other hand, had no intellectual capital to invest in either Murray or Marco. Not a dime, he said.

Who cares, he added?

For a while, I thought I might find a way to represent an evolutionary process in automata-theoretic terms. And for obvious reasons. The construction of a complex system demands some scheme of anticipation and deferral—*anticipation* to determine where things are going, *deferral* to keep intermediates in reserve for later use. Finite state automata will not do; push-down storage automata are needed.

Sidney Morgenbesser accepted my paper for the *Journal of Philosophy* without asking for revisions. That my paper had very little to do with philosophy, he regarded as nothing more than an inconvenience. "Stick the word 'philosophy' in the title somewhere," he said. So I called my paper, "*Philosophical* Aspects of Molecular Biological Systems." Everyone was well satisfied, the philosophers because I was writing about biology, and the biologists because I was writing about philosophy.

It was my introduction to irrelevance, the writer's natural state.

Somewhat later, Noam Chomsky gave me a letter of introduction that allowed me to meet Marco Schützenberger in Paris.

I've written about Chomsky and Marco in *Black Mischief: Language, Life, Logic, Luck.*[2]

But this is the way it was. Darwin and I go back. He has long since moved from that scruffy back alley to something grand—near Lake Cuomo, I believe. Still, it is lucky that we met. I might have encountered Marx instead of Darwin on Nassau Street, another one of the back-alley boys, the fall of the Berlin Wall leaving me, like Roger Kimball, dancing with ghosts.

David Klinghoffer: Did anyone in particular, a colleague or friend, influence the conclusions you reach in these essays?

David Berlinski: No, I don't think so. Daniel Gallin *has* been an influence on my thinking, but our friendship ended some thirty years ago, and so his influence is no longer of this time or place. Daniel introduced me to model theory. That was his gift to me. After studying with Church at Princeton, I regarded model theory as an immersion into cool water. Such ease, such elegance, such freedom! Had I stayed in mathematics as a research mathematician, I would have stayed in model theory.

In the 1980s, I wrote a monograph for the Princeton University Press in which I reached the conclusion that mathematics has no applications beyond finger counting. I stopped for fear that I would find myself affirming that it has no applications at all, circumstances that would have made it difficult for me to justify my work. I never published the thing. It is still sitting in my drawer together with my short stories and poems. But in writing it, I found myself using model-theoretic methods over and over again. I've not gone back to the subject. Just a few years ago, I tried to catch up, reading Wilfrid Hodges's *Shorter Model Theory*. Anyone who writes the shorter *anything* gets my vote.

It may seem odd to say that Marco had *à la longue* little effect on what I have written, but it is true. I loved the man; but what I took from our friendship and what I have written in these essays are two different things.

I have been influenced in a *general* way by a number of mathematicians: Daniel Gallin, as I have said, Marco, René Thom, Lipman Bers,

Gian-Carlo Rota, and even Irving Siegel, whose friendship I acquired by correspondence. I admired these men, but by the time I came to write these essays, I had already developed my own way of thinking, and as often as not, what I took from them, now that I think about it, was as much an *attitude* as anything else. Gian-Carlo remarked to me once that mathematics was the last honest discipline. I was struck by the remark—one reason, of course, that Gian-Carlo made it; I thought then that it was true, and I think so now as well.

That is the kind of attitude I mean.

David Klinghoffer: Darwinism is fiercely guarded by a scientific guild. What does the guild have at stake in this? Prestige? Money? To some observers, the defense seems impermeable. Do you see cracks in the fortress wall opening up?

David Berlinski: Fiercely guarded, but not, mind you, *effectively* guarded. If the Darwinian Guild, to adapt your phrase (since science has nothing to do with it), was interested in rational self-promotion, the Guild would have never allowed its members to display in public their characteristic attitude of invincible arrogance and sheep-like stupidity. Just listen to them as they limber up in the insult room: *Dumbski, Little Mikey Behe, Stevie Meyer* (a regression to school-yard taunts irresistible at both The Panda's Thumb and Talk Reason), *the creationist playbook, creationist pabulum, creationism in a cheap tuxedo, tired creationist canards, creationist cranks, IDiots, creotards, creos, sky fairies, liars for Jesus.*

I've even seen *Disco 'Tute,* this the invention of an elderly fellow at The Panda's Thumb who, like Polonius, imagines that he is the soul of wit. One lunatic named Quick or Quack—or is that simply the sound of his posts?—has become fond of the phrase *mendacious intellectual pornography* and has so overused it that his fellow bloggers have taken to attacking *him.* When they do, Quick as a Quack responds that they are guilty of mendacious intellectual pornography. The gabble is as unedifying as it is unending.

What is wonderful, I think, is the way in which membership in the Guild so runs to *type*, P. Z. Myers, to take the loudest case, reveling in his role as the hearty American rustic, a man prepared as circumstances demand either to desecrate the Catholic wafer or at dinner to immerse his feet in a platter of *boeuf bourguignon*. If in public he now refrains from withdrawing long spools of lint from his navel and examining them studiously, that is because Richard Dawkins has advised him that at Oxford, it is no longer done.

When it is late at night and my old war wounds ache, I very much enjoy chasing down discussions on The Panda's Thumb in which members of the Guild begin to abuse *one another*, their indignation discharging itself in a series of menopausal hot flashes, the discussion skipping from disagreement to disgruntlement to peevishness and finally to insult, until at last someone stands accused of being a lying scum for Jesus.

I offer nothing as invention. I have made nothing up.

What I find most remarkable about the Darwinian Guild is what is least remarked. There is not a single first-rate intelligence in the bunch.

Not one.

Let's go back. At some time in the late 1980s or so, Darwin found himself promoted from the back alley to the Big Tent, where he very profitably employed himself in peddling a universal acid, one said to cure warts as well as it explained speciation. A world view was in prospect. And cheap, too. Academics who had grown weary of being foxes were delighted to become hedgehogs. They turned to *radical* Darwinism and Richard Dawkins because they could find no other place to turn. Stephen Jay Gould had already straddled so many fences, after all, that friends were concerned for the integrity of his genitals. His supporters were never quite clear whether NOMA designated a position in thought or a wing of the Museum of Modern Art. There was no turning to *him*.

How much better Darwin's theory; once it had passed through the Dawkins mangler it emerged radical, simple, scientific, easy to grasp, and, of course, free of large wrinkles.

Academics who ten minutes before had been occupied in affirming their allegiance to Mao, and before Mao to Freud, affirmed their allegiance to Darwin. They had sworn—*sworn!*—never to be swept off their feet again. Darwin swept them up anyway.

Love is like that.

But still, trend-setters tend to drop trends the very moment that trends become trendy. If you have taken the trouble to evacuate Cannes in order to become a radical Darwinist in Toulon, the last thing you would wish to see at that darling little restaurant on the Quai is Barbara Forrest preparing herself to barge right in, and *my goodness that woman positively honks.*

There is a sense, then, that so far as radical Darwinism goes, the tide is beginning to move out. Even David Brooks at the *New York Times* is persuaded that if someone like Susan Blackmore is now babbling about memes and genes, it really may be time to cough discreetly and withdraw. There is a difference, after all, between favoring the latest fad and indulging the feeble-minded. A number of academics—Tom Nagel and Jerry Fodor come to mind—say *now* that they knew it all along.

Perhaps this is so.

Is there more in all this than fashion? A little more. It is good for the cause that evolutionary psychology flamed and went. It revealed the gap that haunts all of evolutionary thought, and that is the gap between what life is and what the theory explains. Ideological systems do not crumble from the center; it is the margins that are the first to go.

This sense of a withdrawal from commitment is hardly unique to Darwinism. A retreat from theory is general. For more than thirty years now, bright physicists have very diligently attempted to unify the Standard Model of Particle Physics and General Relativity. The result has been string theory. The hoped-for unification still seems far away.

Peter Woit and Lee Smolin have both made the case to the general public. Although physicists were indignant, those with a certain kind of sensitivity began to hedge their bets. Just recently, Steven Weinberg gave a fascinating talk at CERN. A great physicist, Weinberg had during the 1990s offered string theory his support, and using the anthropic principle, he had correctly predicted the positive value of the cosmological constant. At CERN, he was more tentative.

This sort of thing cannot be learned. It is a gift. Some men are born knowing how to tip-toe across the lawn at night, shoes in hand. Leonard Susskind, on the other hand, is not one of them. Just recently, he has proposed uniting the implausible in physics with the absurd in biology, writing dreamily about Universal Darwinism, its role in cosmology, the subordination of chance to the multiplication of possibilities, the anthropic principle, the Landscape.

The physicists who discovered Toulon when it was just a dreary fishing village have already made plans to move on.

Rumor has it that Edward Witten and Steven Weinberg are thinking of Port-au-Prince.

They believe it is the coming thing.

David Klinghoffer: You describe yourself as a "secular Jew" and "remarkably indifferent to the religious life." Yet so much of your writing bears directly on whether religion has been intellectually defeated by secular, science-flavored ideologies. You can't have given no thought to religious questions. Would you share with us your hunches and suspicions about spiritual reality, the trend in your thinking, if not your firm beliefs?

David Berlinski: No. Either I cannot or I will not. I do not know whether I am unable or unwilling. The question elicits in me a stubborn refusal. Please understand. It is *not* an issue of privacy. I have, after all, blabbed my life away: Why should I call a halt here? I suppose that I am by nature a counter-puncher. What I am able to discern of the religious experience often comes about *reactively*. V. S. Naipaul remarked recently that he found the religious life unthinkable.

He does? I was prompted to wonder. *Why* does he?

His attitude gives rise to mine. That is the way in which I wrote *The Devil's Delusion: Atheism and Its Scientific Pretensions*.[3]

Is there anything authentic in my religious nature?

Beats me.

David Klinghoffer: Your recent work is concerned with critiquing the myths of a materialist science. How does that theme relate to your earlier teaching and writing?

David Berlinski: I *do* think that my essays share a common concern. I agree with you. I am not sure whether "myths of a materialist science" quite describes what I have always had in mind. It is something less grand, I suppose.

I don't think any of this ever made it into my classrooms. I was pretty much occupied in getting the calculus across to my students. I did not have much time for anything else.

David Klinghoffer: Why do you live in Paris?

David Berlinski: What is it that Horace says? *Coelum non animum mutant qui trans mare currunt*.[4]

David Klinghoffer: In Ben Stein's documentary, *Expelled*, you mentioned that you live in the oldest (one of the oldest?) apartment buildings in Paris. What is your life there like? Give us a quick slice of it.

David Berlinski: Up at four; at work at five; lunch in the local café, where I am a regular; exercise or walking in the afternoon; dinner out most nights; from time to time, the theater or a concert. I seem to have separated from the friends I made and I've not made new ones. I am by temperament solitary, like the mole or the badger, now that I come to think about it, the Old Mole of Rue Chanoinesse.

Endnotes

Introduction

1. Steven Weinberg, "The Trouble with Quantum Mechanics," *The New York Review of Books*, January 19, 2017, 3, repr. in *Third Thoughts* (Cambridge, MA: Belknap Press, 2018).
2. Samuel Johnson, preface to *A Dictionary of the English Language* [1755].

1. The First World War

1. Winston Churchill, *The World Crisis: 1911–1914* (New York: Charles Scribner's Sons, 1924), 205.
2. See "The Best of Times" in this volume.
3. See Emile Zola, *Le Ventre de Paris*, for a fine description of those rumbling wagons.
4. The sense that the war would have a cleansing effect, rather like a brisk cold shower taken after exercise, was common. It is a sense that Arthur Conan Doyle assigned to Holmes in "His Last Bow." The war, Holmes remarks, "will be cold and bitter... and a good many of us may wither before its blast. But it's God's own wind none the less, and a cleaner, better, stronger land will lie in the sunshine when the storm has cleared." Arthur Conan Doyle, "His Last Bow: The War Service of Sherlock Holmes," *The Strand Magazine*, September 1917, https://en.wikisource.org/wiki/His_Last_Bow.-_The_War_Service_of_Sherlock_Holmes.
5. R. G. Collingwood, *An Autobiography* (London: Oxford University Press, 1939), 90.
6. See A. J. P. Taylor, *The Struggle for Mastery in Europe*: 1848–1914 (Oxford: Oxford University Press, 1954).
7. With the publication of *Griff nach der Weltmacht: Die Kriegzielpolitik des kaiserlichen Deutschland 1914–1918* (Düsseldorf: Droste, 1961), the German historian Fritz Fischer affirmed, or admitted, that the primary responsibility for the outbreak of the First World War rested with Imperial Germany. It would seem that a war-like government had long harbored war-like intentions and very often conveyed war-like sentiments. Who knew? The very great virtue of Fischer's work was that it rested on an examination of German archives from 1870 to 1914 unprecedented in its thoroughness. In many respects, Fischer's discussion of the First World War reprises Luigi Albertini's *The Origins of the War of 1914*, translated and edited by Isabella M. Massey (Oxford University Press, 1952), but first published in Italian in the 1930s, a matchless work of diplomatic history. Albertini was the last major historian of the First World War in a position to interview some of its leading figures. Isabel V. Hull, *Absolute Destruction: Military Culture and the Practices of War in Imperial Germany* (Ithaca: Cornell University Press, 2004) has recently endorsed and extended Fischer's thesis. She has come somewhat late to the understanding that the German Imperial army was committed to, and as often celebrated for, the principle of *Vernichtungskrieg*. Better late than never. See Gilli Vardi, "Review of Isabel V. Hull, *Absolute Destruction: Military Culture and the Practices of War in Imperial Germany*," in *University of Sussex Journal of Contemporary History* 10 (2006). Imperial Germany did not lack for military men prepared to be bloodthirsty in print and in practice. The most conspicuous example was

General Friedrich Bernhardi, whose *Deutschland und der nächste Krieg*, published in 1911, celebrated war as a Darwinian imperative. Bernhardi was an exceptionally able general and a man of outstanding courage. His book is repulsive.

A counter-current in scholarly opinion has, it goes without saying, already formed itself, one that assigns some responsibility for the outbreak of war to every party and all of it to none. See Christopher Clark, *The Sleepwalkers: How Europe Went to War in 1914* (New York: HarperCollins, 2013), and Sean McMeekin, *July 1914: Countdown to War* (New York: Basic Books, 2013). Neither writer, it is satisfying to observe, has a good thing to say about Serbia or the Serbians. Whatever the revisions in prospect, Niall Ferguson has already taken revising one step beyond revolting. It remains for him only to argue that in 1914, Belgium violated German neutrality. In his extended essay, "Germany and the Origins of the First World War: New Perspectives," *The Historical Journal* (September 1992): 725–52, Ferguson argued that Imperial Germany was steadily and systematically falling behind the Entente powers in the resources it could devote to its military. German fears of the Russian "steamroller" were widespread, but as events revealed, much exaggerated. Ferguson has amplified this thesis in a popular book, *The Pity of War* (New York: Basic Books, 1999). On Ferguson's view, it was England that bore primary responsibility for the outbreak of war, and the world would have been far better off had Germany prevailed on the battlefield and then been left in tranquility to administer a new German empire. Considering the empire that the Germans *did* administer in the Second World War, this is a thesis that does not immediately commend itself as self-evident.

Still other historians have thought to ask whether the First World War was inevitable, or even probable. See *An Improbable War?: The Outbreak of World War I and European Political Culture before 1914*, eds. Holger Afflerbach and David Stevenson (Oxford: Berghahn Books, 2007). Contributors agree that just possibly the war was improbable, probable, likely, unlikely, nearly inevitable, or not inevitable at all. It is owing only to God's grace that not one of them thought to invoke the now-mythical Black Swan to explain events.

8. Princip had determined to assassinate Franz Ferdinand when he did for no better reason, apparently, than the fact that the Archduke had chosen June 28th to visit Sarajevo. It was on June 28, 1389 that the Serbs lost the battle of Kosovo to the Turks on the Field of Blackbirds. Like the Shiite Iranians, the Serbians are uncommonly attached to their misfortunes, which they regard as relics and worship accordingly. The larger issue that occupied Princip and his collaborators was the annexation in 1908 of Bosnia and Herzegovina by Austria, thus bringing a great many Serbs under Austro-Hungarian rule. The annexation ratified in formal terms the Austrian domination of Bosnia and Herzegovina that had been a simple fact of life since the Congress of Berlin in 1879. There is no doubt at all the Princip was involved with and supported by the sinister Serbian terrorist cell called The Black Hand. Members assured one another of their high ideals, which involved the promotion of the Serbian people into a single political unit, and were fond of initiating one another into the cult by means of dark rooms, votive offerings, flickering candles, blood oaths, and a good deal of chanted Serbian poetry of which *The Mountain Wreath* by Petrović-Njegoš is an example. The Black Hand was in turn the smaller conspiratorial arm of a much larger conspiratorial torso, the *Narodna Odbranda*, which though officially disbanded in 1909 had by 1914 unofficially penetrated every part of the Serbian government.

9. That the war might have been caused by some other event is true enough, if by the war is meant some other war. But if some other event caused the war as it was, then its cause must have been the cause that it had. C_1 causes E_1, and C_2 causes E_2. Say that this is so. If $E_1 = E_2$

then $C_1 = C_2$. The argument is obvious enough. C_1 is the cause of E_1, and since $E_1 = E_2$, it is the cause of E_2 as well. But C_2 is the cause of E_2, by assumption, and so $C_1 = C_2$.

10. That the war could have been caused by the cause that it had only if conditions were as they were implies that the war could not have been caused by the cause that it had if conditions were *not* as they were. This is true enough. But conditions *were* as they were. This argument does not establish that the assassination of Franz Ferdinand was the cause of the First World War. It establishes only that one reason for thinking it was not is misconceived—a weaker claim.

11. The real cause of an event, Mill had argued, is the "whole of its necessary antecedents; and we have, philosophically speaking, no right to give the name of cause to one of them exclusively of the others." J. S. Mill, *A System of Logic* [1843], 8th ed. (New York: Harper & Brothers, 1882), 402. If the antecedents to an event are themselves events, they could not be necessary, and if they are necessary, they could not be events.

12. Jonathan Glover, *Humanity: A Moral History of the 20th Century* (New Haven, CT: Yale University Press, 2000), 177–199. Within the English-speaking world, it has been Barbara Tuchman's *The Guns of August* (New York: Macmillan, 1962) that has more than any other book shaped the popular impression of the First World War. It is a book that offers many lessons, some of them in conflict, and few assurances, most of them negligible. It is no surprise that President John F. Kennedy studied this book closely and assigned to it an improvement in his understanding of world events.

13. "Well tell me, at least," Prince von Bülow asked of Bethmann Hollweg, "how it all happened." Bethmann raised his arms. "If only I knew," he said. Prince von Bülow, *Memoirs, 1909–1919*, trans. F. A. Voigt and Geoffrey Dunlop (Boston: Little, Brown and Company, 1932), 145, quoted in Glover, *Humanity*, 184. Von Bülow was Bethmann's predecessor as Chancellor. A. J. P. Taylor describes his memoirs as "vain, inaccurate and vague." They are also gossipy, informed, and irresistible. Taylor, *The Struggle for Mastery*, 586.

14. Most notably by Sir Edward Gray, who on the first, third, and fourth of August occupied three inconsistent diplomatic positions with apparent indifference. On this point, see McMeekin, *July 1914*, 404. Throughout the July crisis, both Gray and Prime Minister H. H. Asquith attempted to parse the distinction between an alliance and an entente with France down to the molecular level. In his autobiography, *The Genesis of the War* (London: Cassell and Company, 1923), 99, Asquith remarks favorably of his policies that they preserved a studied indecisiveness in statecraft. Given the confusion between an entente, which is by nature vague, and an alliance, which is not, the English would not know whether they were to go to war until they went to war. Why anyone should think this a good thing is a matter about which Asquith never inquires.

15. A point emphatically denied by Tuchman, *Guns of August*, 80. Tuchman cites General von Staab, Chief of the German Railway Division, but does not specify a source. She was, perhaps, referring to H. von Staabs, *Aufmarsch nach zwei Fronten: Auf Grund der Operationspläne von 1870-1914* (Berlin, 1925).

16. For the connection between competitive armaments and the outbreak of war, see Michael D. Intriligator and Dagobert L. Brito, "Can Arms Races Lead to the Outbreak of War?" *The Journal of Conflict Resolution* 28, no. 1 (March 1984): 63–84.

17. To draw the connection between Darwin's thought and Nazi ideology is widely considered a profanation. Glover draws it. Good for him. He also indicts Nietzsche by quoting him, and thereafter challenges the very common impression that Nietzsche, when he was most objectionable, was least serious.

18. This is misleading. The diplomatic record indicates that every foreign office was aware of the threat of a general European conflict; what none quite realized was its likely *magnitude*, another matter entirely. European military leaders did no better. Lord Kitchener had predicted a long war involving millions of men; and the Polish banker, Jan Bloch, writing in 1899, had published a very grim, but very accurate, forecast of the future course of war, *Is War Now Impossible?* (London: Grant Richards, 1899); but by and large, neither the diplomatic nor the military service of any of the European states predicted the course of the war successfully. Had the Prussian General Staff, for example, better attended to the American Civil War, they would have been less eager to rush into combat. Union and Confederate armies included 2.75 million men; roughly 700,000 died in combat. Combined armies during the First World War totaled 60 million men, of whom 9 million died in combat. See Jay Luuvas, *The Military Legacy of the Civil War: The European Inheritance* (Lawrence, KS: University Press of Kansas, 1988). The truth was not very long delayed. In a bitter note to Italian representatives and foreign governments, Baron Sonnino, the Italian minister for Foreign Affairs, wrote of Italian efforts "to spare Europe from a vast conflict certain to drench the continent with blood and to reduce it to ruin beyond the conception of human imagination..." The date, however, is May 23, *1915*, and while the Italian Foreign Office may well have made efforts to spare the continent from war, Italian diplomats writing *before* 1914 expressed no real anxieties about the possibility that war would drench the continent in blood, or in anything else. Reprinted in *Diplomatic Documents Relating to the Outbreak of the European War*, ed. J. B. Scott (New York: Oxford University Press, 1916). Italy had been formally allied to Germany and Austria and was determined not to join either the Allied or the Axis powers in combat until it could determine the side likely to prevail. It is a policy that even today inspires admiration.
19. When the war came, Conrad discovered the very considerable difference between calling for and using arms. Conrad's memoirs, *Aus meiner Dienstzeit*, published in four volumes by Rikola–Verlag (1921–1925) succeed in conveying the impression that their author was in every respect rather dim.
20. Berchtold's reputation for diffidence was unfair. In May of 1913, the Austrian foreign office, under his instructions, issued an ultimatum to Montenegro, demanding the withdrawal of Montenegrin forces from Albania, a state newly created by the great power conference of 1912; and in October of 1913, Berchtold, on witnessing great power indifference to Serbian incursions in Albania, acted unilaterally to force a Serbian withdrawal. Berchtold had taken office in 1912. See Hugo Hantsch, *Leopold Graf Berchthold: Grandseigneur und Staatsmann* (Graz: Verlag Styria, 1963). The greater part of this book comprises a record of Berchtold's speeches, notes, memoranda, and letters. Curiously enough, it appears to be the only widely available biography of Berchtold in any European language.
21. Historians once content to blame Imperial Germany for the outbreak of war have recently turned their attention gratefully to Austria. See Richard J. W. Evans, "The Habsburg Monarchy and the Coming of War," in *The Coming of the First World War*, eds. R. J. W. Evans and Hartmut Pogge von Strandmann (Oxford University Press, 1990); F. R. Bridge, *The Habsburg Monarchy among the Great Powers, 1815-1918* (Oxford University Press, 1990); Graydon A. Tunstall, Jr., "Austria-Hungary," in *The Origins of World War I*, eds. Richard F. Hamilton and Holger H. Herwig (Cambridge University Press, 2003); Alma Hanning, "Die Balkanpolitik Österreich-Ungarns," in *Der Erste Weltkrieg auf dem Balkan: Perspektiven der Forschung*, eds. Jürgen Angelow et al. (Berlin: Bebra Wissenschaft, 2011). All that can justifiably be said is that Austrian policy was remarkably inept, but *not* that it was unjustified. Events in July of 1914 did not improve the luster of any diplomatic service.

22. *Morgen, morgen, nur nicht Heute, sagen alle faulen Leute,* runs an old German proverb. Among Germans, the proverb is considered an admonition; among Austrians, an encouragement.

23. Tisza was assassinated on the 4th of November, 1918, by Hungarian leftists who held him responsible for the outbreak of war.

24. Men such as Voja Tankositch, one of the founding members of the Black Hand, or Drugutin Demetrijevitch, known generally as Apsis (the bull), the Head of Serbian military intelligence and the leader of the Black Hand. Although both men were thugs, Apsis was said on the strength of no discernible evidence to be cunning. He was in any event not cunning enough to avoid his own execution.

25. The Franco-Russian alliance dated to 1891. It was the Military Convention between France and Russia of August 1892 from which the French took comfort. "If France is attacked by Germany," its first article read, "Russia shall employ her available forces to fight Germany." See *Documents Diplomatiques, L'alliance Franco-Russe* (Paris, 1918), 92; also A. F. Pribram, *Die politischen Geheimverträge* Österreich – *Ungarns, 1879–1914* (Vienna, 1920), 1:25–31, esp. n40. On its acceptance by the Russian Minister of Foreign Affairs and the French Ambassador to Russia in 1893, the convention acquired the force of a treaty.

26. It did them little good. Serbia defaulted on its French loans in 1918. France was in no position to argue, and Serbia in no condition to pay. The French held no grudges and continued to support Serbia in various international forums throughout the twentieth century. The origins of French policy toward Serbia are to my mind an utter mystery.

27. Austria and Germany had signed a Joint Memorandum on September 24, 1879, and a treaty on October 7. The treaty was conceived as an alliance of "peace and mutual defense." Pribram, *Die politischen* (Vienna, 1920) 1:25–31.

28. McMeekin (*July 1914*, 95) assigns to Tisza the inspiration for the memorandum. There is no evidence that this is so. Clark (*Sleepwalkers*, 115) refers to the Matscheko memorandum as a paranoid document, one characteristic of *fin de siecle* Vienna. The memorandum was composed fourteen years after the century ended and, as events would promptly reveal, it contains nothing that indicates paranoia. A. J. P. Taylor (*Struggle for Mastery*, 521) refers to Matscheko's memorandum as if it had been written by Berchtold—*his* memorandum—but neglects to provide a cross-reference. It cannot be said that this document has inspired the most impeccable scholarship. John Leslie's essay, "The Antecedents of Austria-Hungary's War Aims," in *Archiv und Forschung: Das Haus-, Hof-, und Staatsarchiv in seiner Bedeutung für die Geschichte* Österreichs *und Europas*, eds. Elisabeth Springer and Leopold Kammerhofer (Wien, 1993), is, at least, accurate in assigning the right authors to the right documents.

29. See Österreich-Ungarns *Aussenpolitik von der Bosnischen Krise 1908 bis zum Kriegsausbruch 1914*, eds. Ludwig Bittner and Hans Übersberger (Vienna, 1930), vol. 8, no. 9918 (24 Juni 1914): 189–93. Many of these documents are online at The World War I Document Archive, ed. Richard Hacken, Brigham Young University Library, http://wwi.lib.byu.edu.These documents have not been carefully edited, and, so far as I can tell, incorporate a number of abbreviations that could not be part of the originals.

30. See Szögyéni to Berchtold, in Österreich-Ungarns *Aussenpolitik*, vol. 8, no. 10076:320.

31. See *British Documents on the Origins of the War, 1898–1914*, eds. G. P. Gooch and Harold Temperely (London, 1926), 10:655 et seq. These agreements were not treaties and concerned Persia, the Persian Straits, and Afghanistan.

32. The concepts of push and the correlative doctrine of pull explain an astonishing amount about nineteenth-century diplomatic promotions. Maurice Paléologue, the excitable, ostentatious, unreliable and romantic French ambassador to Russia, owed his career to being pushed forward in 1905 by Théophile Delcassé and pulled upward in 1912 by Raymond Poincaré. Paléologue was ardently apprehensive about German policy and in conversations with Sazanov, the two men, no doubt, confirmed to each other's satisfaction that they were doing battle with the forces of the night, at least until Paléologue learned by means of various diplomatic sources that Sazanov had not meant quite what he said nor said quite what he meant. Neither man should have occupied a senior diplomatic position, Paléologue because he was without nuance in his judgment, and Sazanov because he was erratic in his.

33. Thirteen years after the outbreak of the First World War, Sazanov published his memoirs in Paris, *Les Annés Fatales* (Payot, 1927). They express the sentiment expressed by all memoirs about the First World War, and that is bafflement that such a thing should have happened. Churchill's memoirs are the exception.

34. Hannah Arendt's celebrated phrase, *the banality of evil*, might better be applied to the foreign ministers of the Great Powers in 1914 than the fanatical and demented bureaucrats of the Third Reich.

35. Jurisprudence, as it happens, a discipline in which he achieved a Third on his examinations.

36. Interesting evidence, as if any were needed, that Berchtold failed to grasp the enormity of the catastrophe in which he had played so conspicuous a role, for while he contemplated remaining an aristocrat if Austria were destroyed as an empire, he failed to ask whether he could remain an aristocrat were Europe to be destroyed as an idea. After the war he disappeared into his inherited fortune, which he spent on women and horses, circumstances that recall Oscar Wilde's mordant little poem, "The Harlot's House." The dead *were* dancing with the dead.

37. Thus Plan XVII, which in the event of war called for a direct attack on Germany through the Ardennes. Employed in the first weeks of the war, the Plan failed ignominiously at the Battle of the Frontiers. It is odd that German military planners, who appreciated how easily a direct French attack across the Franco-German frontier could be blocked by a relatively small German force, did not properly integrate this idea into their own military strategy by giving up the Schlieffen plan and concentrating entirely their military aims on Russia.

38. The Austrian ultimatum in both the original German and an English translation is available at The World War I Document Archive cited above.

39. The ultimatum was written in German, with no ancillary Serbian translation, circumstances that are odd considering the fact that the Austro-Hungarian monarchy encompassed twelve official languages, Serbian among them. Of these languages, Bosnian, Croatian, and Serbian are fundamentally the same.

40. The 5th and the 6th demands, as it happens, which seemed to compromise Serbian sovereignty by demanding foreign representatives, Austrians, in fact, on any Serbian committee charged with investigating the assassination. The sovereignty of the Serbian state was said to be sacred by both English and French foreign offices, a gesture of diplomatic piousness entirely at odds with its true nature as an interlocking series of terrorist cells.

41. Not one of the great powers was in any significant sense a complete or even a thoroughgoing autocracy, and neither in Russia nor Germany nor Austria did decisions flow down from a monarch to his offices.

42. In his very first page, Clark (*Sleepwalkers*) cites a figure of twenty million deaths, some five million deaths more than the figure offered by most other historians. He offers no sources; but then again, neither do they. No one is counting. The number 5,000,000 may represent a minor bank error; but human deaths are another matter. If the figure is accurate, it represents men, women, and children who have not even been remembered as gross statistics.

43. The Russian, German, Austro-Hungarian, and Ottoman empires. Within two decades, the British Empire would follow them.

44. Russia, which in 1912 had been a net exporter of grain, suffered a catastrophic famine in 1921, an event widely noted at the time but overshadowed entirely by the far more devastating famine of 1932–1933—the Holodomor.

45. Many survivors of the Austro-Hungarian Empire lamented its disappearance; not so the Ottoman Empire. But the latter was not without its virtues. In an interesting little book about his experiences in Cairo in the mid-nineteenth-century, *Les Femmes du Caire*, Gerard de Nerval described a city almost perfectly at ease in its multi-cultural aspect—Egyptians, Jews, Nestorians, Syrians, Armenians, and Turks living in isolation from one another but, within reason, living amicably.

46. There is, for example, Winston Churchill's *The World Conflict*, a masterpiece in which Churchill manages to accept credit for his strategic initiatives while declining responsibility for their failure. The old-fashioned view, expressed brilliantly by Paul Fussell in *The Great War and Modern Memory* (Oxford University Press, 1975), that military leaders were uniformly unimaginative, incompetent, reckless, stupid, and if not positively thirsty for blood then careless of its waste, has now been revised. It would seem that men such as Joffre and Haig and Foch were a good deal more capable than the evidence might indicate. They had, after all, won the war. The traditional military view of the First World War has always been that the mysterious balance between mobility and weight was, because of improvements in defense, unhinged until late 1916 when the Allies at last mastered the creeping artillery barrage. See Peter Hart, *The Somme: Darkest Hour on the Western Front* (New York: Pegasus Books, 2008). For a contemporary view, one assigning credit for Allied victory to the arrival of American forces, and *not* the supposed effectiveness of a unified Allied high command, see A. F. Pollard, *A Short History of the Great War* (London: Methuen, 1919). Pollard was a distinguished Tudor historian who served on the Western Front.

Fussell's book has offered to several generations of literary historians a view of twentieth-century literature limited to English sources. It is a defect of which Fussell was perfectly aware. See, for example, Arnold Zweig, *Erziehung vor Verdun*, Roman. Nachw. v. Eva Kaufmann 2001. German writers of the First World War were as earnest leaving the war as they were entering it. Zweig's experience had made him a pacifist but not an ironist. See as well Nicolas Beaupré, "Les écrivains combattants français et allemands, témoins de la fin de guerre," *Revue du Nord* 80 (1998): 383–91; or Nicolas Beaupré, "Ecrire pour dire, écrire pour taire, écrire pour tuer? La littérature de guerre face aux massacres et aux violences extrêmes du front ouest (1914–1918)," in *Le massacre, objet d'histoire*, ed. David El Kenz (Paris: Gallimard, 2005), 305–17; or Léon Riegel's survey, *Guerre et Littérature. le bouleversement des consciences dans la littérature romanesque inspirée par la Grande Guerre (littératures française, anglaise, anglo-saxonne et allemande), 1910–1930* (Paris: Klincksieck, 1978). A study of Russian, Italian, and Turkish sources would, of course, offer entirely different perspectives.

47. What is wished for is some sign from the historical literature, however faint, of modal propositions of the form $p \rightarrow \Box q$ or $\Box (p \rightarrow q)$. These forms are certainly not equivalent, but no historian has ever discovered evidence for either.

48. Steven Pinker, *The Better Angels of Our Nature* (London: Penguin Books, 2011), 248. See "The Cause of War" in this volume.

49. Pinker's views represent a confusion between a Poisson distribution, which by its nature is concerned with a series of events—it is a *distribution*—and the specific causal conditions responsible for any one of them. A series of deterministic events may be described by a Poisson distribution very well, and with the exception of beta-decay, all of the classical examples are of this form. In 1898, Ladislaus von Bortkiewicz analyzed fatal horse kicks in the Prussian cavalry. See *The Law of Small Numbers* (Leipzig: Teubner, 1898). Bortkiewicz never imagined that individual horse kicks were random. For all Bortkiewicz could determine, or imagine, each fatality might well have occurred for reasons known best to the horses. A statistical fallacy runs straight through Pinker's analysis—and Richardson's as well. While it is true that every Poisson process yields a Poisson distribution, the converse is not necessarily true, and it is almost always false.

50. In both minor and major respects. The twentieth century was a century of famine, among other afflictions. See in this regard "Gadzooks" in this volume. It was also a century of almost forgotten massacres. The Turkish massacre of the Armenians has entered into general consciousness, but it has entered into general consciousness recently; the Turkish massacre at Smyrna in 1923 is known only to specialists. In *A Coffin for Dimitrios* (New York: First Vintage Crime, 2001), Eric Ambler describes it vividly. By a process of action at a distance that no historian understands, events in Smyrna leapfrogged decades to acquire a murderous pertinence in Cyprus during the 1950s.

2. The Best of Times

1. Joseph Conrad, *Heart of Darkness* [1902], ed. Paul O'Prey (London: Penguin, 1983), 31. The speaker is Marlow.

2. Paulus Orosius, *Seven Books of History against the Pagans*, trans. A. T. Fear (Liverpool: Liverpool University Press, 2010).

3. See "The First World War" in this volume. If the twentieth century seems short, the nineteenth century seems long. David Blackbourn, *The Long Nineteenth Century* (Oxford: Oxford University Press, 1997).

4. Anna Akhmatova, *Plantain*, quoted in Bernard Wasserstein, *Barbarism and Civilization* (Oxford: Oxford University Press, 2007), 793.

5. Milton Leitenberg, *Deaths in Wars and Conflicts in the 20th Century*, 3rd ed., Cornell University Peace Study Program, Occasional Paper No. 29, https://www.clingendael.org/sites/default/files/pdfs/20060800_cdsp_occ_leitenberg.pdf.

6. John Fairbank, *China: A New History* (Cambridge, MA: Harvard University Press, 1994). See Benjamin Valentino, *Final Solutions: Mass Killing and Genocide in the Twentieth Century* (Ithaca, NY: Cornell University Press, 2005). Valentino estimated that the Chinese Civil War resulted in the death of between 1.8 million and 3.5 million people between 1927 and 1949.

7. See Michael Ellman, "Stalin and the Soviet Famine of 1932–1933 Revisited," *Europe-Asia Studies* 59, no. 4 (2007): 663–93, together with Ellman, "The 1947 Soviet Famine and the Entitlement Approach to Famines," *Cambridge Journal of Economics* 224, no. 5 (2000): 610n3. Ellman estimates over a million excess deaths in the third Soviet famine of 1947.

8. See R. M. Douglas, *Orderly and Humane: The Expulsion of the Germans after the Second World War* (New Haven, CT: Yale University Press, 2013) or Alfred-Maurice de Zayas, *A Terrible Revenge: The Ethnic Cleansing of the East European Germans* 1944–1950 (New York: St. Martin's Press, 1993). Hans Graf von Lehndorff's *Ostpreußisches Tagebuch: Aufzeichnungen eines Arztes aus den Jahren 1945–1947* (München: Deutscher Taschenbuch Verlag, 1997) offers an account combining a certain moral shortsightedness and a biting sense of loss:

> *Was ist das eigentlich, so fragte ich mich, was wir hier erleben? Hat das noch etwas mit natürlicher Wildheit zu tun oder mit Rache? Mit Rache vielleicht, aber in einem anderen Sinn. Rächt sich hier nicht in einer und derselben Person das Geschöpf am Menschen, das Fleisch am Geist, den amn ihm aufgezwungen hat? Woher kommen diese Typen, Menschen wie wir, im Banne von Trieben, die zu ihrer äußeren Erscheinung in einem grauenvollen Mißverhältnis stehen? Welch ein Bemühen, das Chaos zur Schau tragen!... Das hat nichts mit Rußland zu tun, nichts mit einem bestimmten Volk oder einer Rasse —das ist der Mensch ohne Gott, die Fratze des Menschen.*

Von Lehndorff's appeal to the absence of God was never made, a sympathetic reader is bound to observe, when the German army was advancing *into* Russia. Perhaps revenge had something to do with the fate of the east Prussians and ethnic Germans after all. What de Zayas calls *the terrible revenge* lacks for a common name and a place in the standard histories of the twentieth century.

9. The twentieth century was marked by a depraved indifference to human life on almost every scale. The Turkish devastation of Smyrna in 1922 is an example. Eric Ambler offers a fine description in *A Coffin for Dimitrios*. See "The First World War" in this volume for further details.

10. Alan Taylor, *The Struggle for Mastery in Europe: 1848–1914* (Oxford: Oxford University Press, 1954), 255.

11. The destruction of German *and* European culture—how does that figure in an assessment of twentieth-century violence and according to what metric? See Stefan Zweig, *Die Welt von Gestern* (Leck: Claussen & Bosse, 1992); or Jean-Michel Palmier, *Weimar in Exile: The Antifascist Emigration in Europe and America* (London: Verso, 2006). German bureaucrats and propaganda officials under the third Reich required a language adequate to their endeavors; but the damage done to the German language itself hardly lends itself to any simple scheme of assessment. Victor Klemperer's *The Language of the Third Reich* [1947], trans. Martin Brady (London: Continuum, 2011) is useful, but incomplete and anecdotal. In a well-known interview with Günther Grass, Hannah Arendt argued that no matter what the German people under Hitler may have been doing, their language did not become insane. See Hannah Arendt, "What Remains? The Language Remains: A Conversation with Günter Grass," in *Essays in Understanding, 1930–1954: Formation, Exile, and Totalitarianism*, ed. Jerome Kohn, trans. John Stambaugh (New York: Shocken Books, 1994), 13. Arendt's views are, in this regard, at least, at odds with her penetrating analysis of Nazi neologisms, linguistic habits, and the like. In 1933, German was still the world's scientific language; it is no longer a global language in any sense, and the population of German speakers is shrinking. If the German language did not become insane, it nevertheless underwent an internal deformation, a disfigurement so appalling that its use in ordinary contexts acquired a sinister aspect. No translation of *im Krieg geht es oft um die Vernichtung des Gegners* conveys its sense, nor the sense of a legal decree entitled *Nacht und Nebel*. The crimes of the Third Reich against the German language were their own punishment.

Among the ironies of the twentieth century is the fact that the First World War put an end to an emerging sense of European civilization, while the Second World War attempted to resurrect it. See in this regard Prince Alfons von Clary-Aldringen, *Geschichten eines alten Österreichers* (Frankfurt: Ullstein, 1977), for a description of the common attitude among the vanishing aristocrats of Europe that they were a part of an ancient European experience. It was an attitude, I suspect, from which von Clary was liberated by his service in the German *Wehrmacht*. Gregor von Rezzori, *Memoirs of an Anti-Semite* [1979] (New York: New York Review of Books, 2007), offers a far more subtle account. Von Clary's memoirs suggest that despite the loss of his family's wealth, position, and acquisitions, he remains a European. This is what von Rezzori suggests as well, but with an entirely different and far more sinister implication.

12. Thomas Macaulay, "A Review of Southey's Colloquies," *Edinburgh Review* [1830], repr. in the *Norton Anthology of English Literature* (New York: W. H. Norton & Company, 1962), 1:620–25.

13. Herbert Butterfield, *The Whig Interpretation of History* (London: G. Bell and Sons, 1931), 12.

14. Butterfield, *The Whig Interpretation of History*, 13. See Adrian Wilson and Timothy Ashplant, "Whig History and Present-Centered History," *The Historical Journal* 31, no. 1 (1988): 1–16, and William Cronon, "Two Cheers for the Whig Interpretation of History," *Perspectives on History* 50, no. 6 (2012): 5. The Whig historians constitute a group that, according to Michael Bentley, includes William Stubbs, James Froude, Edward Freeman, John Richard Green, William Lecky, Lord John Dalberg-Acton, John Seeley, Samuel Gardiner, Charles Firth, George Macaulay Trevelyan, and John Bagnell Bury. See Michael Bentley, *Modern Historiography: An Introduction* (London: Routledge, 1999), 64–65. As for Acton, his relationship to the Whigs is contested. As Cronon commented in his discussion of Butterfield's book, "E. H. Carr famously joked that although the book 'denounced the Whig interpretation over some 130 pages, it did not... name a single Whig except [Charles James] Fox, who was no historian, or a single historian save [Lord] Acton, who was no Whig.'"

15. "According to widespread popular belief, the period of European history known as the Middle Ages or medieval period (roughly the years 450–1450) was a time of barbarism, ignorance, and superstition. The epithet 'Dark Ages,' often applied to it, nicely captures this opinion. As for the ills that threatened literacy, learning, and especially science during the Middle Ages, blame is most often laid at the feet of the Christian church, which is alleged to have placed religious authority above personal experience and rational activity, thereby snuffing out the faint sparks of scientific and other forms of intellectual creativity that had survived the barbarian invasions of late antiquity." David Lindberg, "The Medieval Church Encounters the Classical Tradition: Saint Augustine, Roger Bacon, and the Handmaiden Metaphor," in *When Science and Christianity Meet*, eds. David Lindberg and Ronald Numbers (Chicago: University of Chicago Press, 2003), 7. Lindberg knows perfectly well that these widespread and popular beliefs are entirely untrue—absurdly so. I mention this *pour encourager les autres*.

16. Steven Pinker, *The Better Angels of Our Nature* (London: Penguin Books, 2011), xix. Pinker's book contains a great many secondary theses about animal and women's rights, child rearing, bullying, slavery, torture, and psychology; they are fatuous without in any way being interesting.

17. Timothy Snyder is an example. A fine historian, Snyder suspects that something is wrong with Pinker's thesis. He is unable to say what it is. Timothy Snyder, "War No More: Why the World Has Become More Peaceful," *Foreign Affairs*, January/February, 2012.

18. Pinker, *The Better Angels*, xx–xxi.

19. Pinker, *The Better Angels*, 228–347.

20. Both Guy de Maupassant and Leonardo Sciascia are uncommonly adept at depicting an atmosphere of suggested or implicit violence. Guy de Maupassant's short story "Histoire Corse" is a brilliant example; so is Leonardo Sciascia's novel *The Day of the Owl.*

21. In "Without Respite, *The Nation*, November 25, 2013, Vivian Gornick remarks of the Nazis,

> What they never reduced their interest in, however, was the application of what [Primo] Levi called "useless violence": administering blows and curses for no reason; withholding food and drink for no reason; ordering prisoners to stand naked in the yard for no reason ("in the blue and icy… dawn… all our clothing in our hands"). At first, Levi writes, "It was so new and senseless that we felt no pain… Only a profound amazement: How can one hit a man without anger?"
>
> *Why?* is the question that the 24-year-old Primo—a child of the Enlightenment, committed to the rule of reason—kept asking himself. Why, when the Germans had already determined on mass murder, was it necessary to torment the prisoners every hour that they lived? He knew that "our language lacks words to express this offence, the demolition of a man," but the Primo Levi who had trembled before women now stood remarkably alert before the Nazis, and was becoming a man who would spend the rest of his life absorbed by an experience for which there would never be enough of the right words.

This is a very characteristic remark. It suggests that like Levi, Gornick, on considering the category of useless violence, can conclude only that the Nazis were not children of the Enlightenment and were not committed to the rule of reason. So much the worse for them. Why not, one is tempted to ask, so much the worse for the Enlightenment and the rules of reason? It is no surprise that Steven Pinker's recent book about the enlightenment assigns it credit for everything and blame for nothing. Steve Pinker, *Enlightenment Now: The Case for Reason, Science, Humanism, and Progress* (New York: Penguin Random House, 2018).

22. Gerd Schwerhoff, "Criminalized Violence and the Process of Civilization: A Reappraisal," in *Crime, History & Societies* 6, no. 2 (2002): 103–126, https://journals.openedition.org/chs/418.

23. See the website of Germany's *Bundeskriminalamt.* Great pains have been taken to make it comprehensive, user-friendly, entirely unthreatening, and consequently, faintly comical. Homicide rates began to decline in seventeenth-century England, to take another example at will, but punishments, often of an appalling ferocity, began proportionately to increase, and deaths in the English civil wars often approached twentieth-century levels. Thomas Hobbes wrote the *Leviathan* for every good reason. By any conceivable standard, seventeenth-century England became *more* violent as its homicide rates declined. For references, see Note 34 of this essay.

24. Robert Conquest, *The Great Terror* (New York: Macmillan, 1968). The story told by the Soviet archives is grim, but it does not support the account initially offered by Conquest. As Father Leo Naptha remarks in *The Magic Mountain*: "The mystery and precept of our age is not liberation and development of the ego. What our age needs, what it demands, what it will create for itself, is—terror." *The Magic Mountain* (Vintage, 1993), 396.

25. Karl Schlögel, *Moscow 1937* (Cambridge, UK: Polity Press, 2012). This fascinating book answers every question about the Great Terror except why it occurred. However correct their assessment of deaths during the Great Terror, scholars such as Conquest or Schlögel are, at least, rational. Pinker's only source for this period—Rudolf Rummel—has more people perishing in than entering the Gulag.
26. David Shearer, "Crime and Social Disorder in Stalin's Russia: A Reassessment of the Great Retreat and the Origins of Mass Repression," *Cahiers du Monde Russe: Russie, Empire Russe, Union Soviétique, États Indépendants* 39, no. 1–2 (1998): 119–48. In his 1936 report to the *Sovnarkom*, Genrikh Iagoda, the head of the NKVD, "boasted that there were fewer murders in the whole of the USSR in 1935 than in the city of Chicago." Iagoda's report is cited in David Shearer, "Social Disorder, Mass Repression, and the NKVD during the 1930s," *Cahiers du Donde Russe: La Police Politique en Union Soviétique, 1918–1953.* If true—who knows?—would it follow that Moscow was *less* violent than Chicago? In his note, "Soviet Repression Statistics: Some Comments" (*Europe-Asia Studies*, 54, no. 7 (2002): 1151–1172), Michael Ellman remarks that in 1937–38, the NKVD shot 850,000 victims out of hand under the notorious Section 58 of the penal code; he estimates the actual number of deaths in detention at 200,000, but the actual number of excess *non*-Section 58 deaths at 5,000. The ratio of one million to five thousand offers some idea of the proportional significance of ordinary crime in the Soviet scheme of things in the mid-1930s.
27. For a collection of essays, some of them interesting, few of them penetrating, see *Crimes Histoires & Sociétés, La Violence Dans la Longue Durée* 5, no. 2 (2001).
28. Fahui Wang and Van O'Brien, "Constructing Geographic Areas for Analysis of Homicide in Small Populations: Testing Herding-Culture-of-Honor Proposition," in *Geographic Information Systems and Crime Analysis*, ed. Fahui Wang (Hershey, PA: Idea Group Publishing, 2005), 84–101.
29. Albert Reiss, quoted in Wang and O'Brien, "Constructing Geographic Areas for Analysis of Homicide in Small Populations."
30. Hans Reichenbach, *The Theory of Probability* (Berkeley and Los Angeles: University of California Press, 1949), 374.
31. Pinker, *Enlightenment Now*, 83.
32. Pinker, *Enlightenment Now*, 85. Pinker is writing about the *Christian* Middle Ages, a period not ordinarily known for its sexual exuberance. "It is part of the essence of humans to be ashamed of their nakedness," Hans-Peter Dürr observes, quite correctly, "however this nakedness may be defined historically." Hans-Peter Dürr, *Nacktheit und Scham* (Frankfurt: Suhrkamp, 1988), 12. See also Oliver König, *Nacktheit und Moral: Zur sozialen Normierung der Nacktheit* (Wiesbaden: Herbst, 1990).
33. No forks? Really? See Pasquale Marchese, *L'invenzione della forchetta* (Soveria Mannelli: Rubbettino Editore, 1989). The fork is in any case no measure of dining delicacy. Many refined cultures eat with their hands, no easy matter, as the neophyte soon learns. There is, of course, a word for slob in Arabic. The Chinese and Japanese eat with chopsticks. Forks are neither needed nor encouraged.
34. Lawrence Stone, "Interpersonal Violence in English Society 1300–1980," *Past & Present* 101, no. 1 (1983): 22–33. The same author's *The Past and the Present Revisited* (London: Routledge, 1987) contains Stone's observations, many of them in conflict, most of them trite. See also James Sharpe, "The History of Violence in England: Some Observations," *Past & Present* 108, no. 1 (1986): 206–15. To Stone, Sharpe credits the thesis that "deep

changes in society are indicated by variations in the homicide rate" (206). That variations in the homicide rate represent a change in society is trivially true. But that variations in the homicide rate represent something *deeper* than themselves is not obviously true at all. It is, in particular, not true that they inevitably represent a *decline or an increase* in homicide rates, a point I discuss below. See also J. S. Cockburn, "Patterns of Violence in English Society: Homicide in Kent 1560–1985," *Past & Present* 130, no. 1 (1991): 70–106. In *The Past and the Present Revisited*, 82, Stone remarks that "historians can no longer get away with saying "more," "less," "growing," "declining," all of which logically imply numerical comparisons, without ever stating explicitly the statistical basis for their assertions." Sure they can.

35. For an historian such as Lawrence Stone to regard with satisfaction a decline in homicide within the context of the *twentieth* century rather suggests a physician remarking to a patient suffering from a terminal disease that, at least, his impetigo is improved.

36. Ted Gurr, "Historical Trends in Violent Crime: A Critical Review of the Evidence," in *Crime and Justice: An Annual Review of Research*, eds. Michael Tonry and Norval Morris (Chicago: University of Chicago Press, 1981), 3:295–353.

37. James Buchanan Given, *Society and Homicide in Thirteenth-Century England* (Stanford, CA: Stanford University Press, 1977). For an initial review of Given, see Thomas Green, "Review of *Society and Homicide in Thirteenth-Century England*, by J. B. Given," *Speculum* 54, no. 1 (1979): 137–40. For later comments, see Pieter Spierenburg, *A History of Murder* (Cambridge, UK: Polity, 2008).

38. Carl Hammer, "Patterns of Homicide in a Medieval University Town: Fourteenth-Century Oxford," *Past & Present* 78, no. 1 (1978): 3–23.

39. Gurr, "Historical Trends in Violent Crime," 295. Quoting an imprecisely identified 2002 work by Pieter Spierenburg, Schwerhoff asks, "Was the long-term decline of violence, from the 14th to the middle of the 20th century, real?" (Schwerhoff, "Criminalized Violence and the Process of Civilization," numbered para. 8 and n14.) Schwerhoff's answer is: not obviously. "The calculation of homicide rates from the 13th to the 15th centuries is fraught with so many problems that a comparison between these figures or even the determination of a trend on this basis seems to be methodologically inadmissible." (Schwerhoff, "Criminalized Violence," para. 14.) See also Pieter Spierenburg, "Long-term Trends in Homicide: Theoretical Reflections and Dutch Evidence, Fifteenth to Twentieth Centuries," in *The Civilization of Crime: Violence in Town and Country since the Middle Ages*, eds. E. A. Johnson and E. H. Monkkonen (Urbana and Chicago: University of Illinois Press, 1996), 63–105.

40. Manuel Eisner, "Long-Term Historical Trends in Violent Crime," *Crime and Justice* 30 (2003): 83–142. In a more recent paper, entitled "From Swords to Words: Does Macro-Level Change in Self-Control Predict Long-Term Variations in Levels of Homicide?" *Crime and Justice* 43 (2014): 65–134, Eisner offered an endorsement of Norbert Elias's theory that variations in homicide rates are tied to improvement in self-control. I should add that Eisner's endorsement is a model of self-controlled enthusiasm.

41. Hammer, "Patterns of Homicide in a Medieval University Town," 7; see also n3.

42. Michael Shermer is an example. Called upon to review *The Better Angels of Our Nature* in *The American Scholar* (Autumn 2011), he thought to entitle his review, "Getting Better All the Time." Were Pinker to assert that San Pedro Sula now embodied the lowest homicide rate in the western hemisphere, when, in fact, the reverse is true, Shermer would, at once, conceive a favorable impression of Honduras.

43. Hammer, "Patterns of Homicide in a Medieval University Town," 12–13.

44. Gurr, "Historical Trends in Violent Crime," 307.

45. Stone, "Interpersonal Violence in English Society," 30.

46. *English Government in the Thirteenth Century*, ed. Adrian Jobson (Suffolk: The Boydell Press, 2004) is valuable for an account of C. A. F. Meekings's archival research, which was incomplete at the time that Given undertook his own research.

47. For Sutherland's mature appreciation of the Eyre courts, see Donald Sutherland, "The Brotherhood and the Rivalry of English Lawyers in the General Eyres," *American Journal of Legal History* 31, no. 1 (1987): 1-8.

48. Introduction to *The London Eyre of 1276*, ed. Martin Weinbaum (London: London Record Society, 1976), xi–xl.

49. Josiah Cox Russell, *British Medieval Population* (Albuquerque: University of New Mexico Press, 1948).

50. Rodney Hilton, *A Medieval Society: The West Midlands at the End of the Thirteenth Century* (Cambridge, UK: Cambridge University Press, 2008).

51. Michael Prestwich, *Plantagenet England, 1225–1360* (New York: Oxford University Press, 2005). For a review of Prestwich's book, see Lorraine Attreed, "Review of Michael Prestwich, *Plantagenet England, 1225–1360*," *Speculum* 81, no. 4 (2006): 1243–45.

52. Henry Summerson, "Peacekeepers and Lawbreakers in London, 1276–1321," in *Thirteenth Century England XII: Proceedings of the Gregynog Conference 2007*, eds. Janet Burton, Philipp Schofield, and Bjorn Weiler (Boydell & Brewer, 2009), 107–22.

53. Gurr, "Historical Trends in Violent Crime," 295 citing Given.

54. Frederic Maitland, *Pleas of the Crown for the County of Gloucester Before the Abbot of Reading and His Fellows* (London: Forgotten Books, 2013), 36. "Any one who is willing to take a little trouble," Maitland remarked, "and to remember that the scribes were listening to English and thinking in English, will find the Latin of these rolls easy enough" (29). Maitland maybe; me, no; Pinker, never.

55. Warren Brown is an example. "I too am drawn to medieval violence," Brown remarks sheepishly at the beginning of his book, *Violence in Medieval Europe*. No kidding. Warren Brown, *Violence in Medieval Europe* (New York: Pearson Education, 2011), 1.

56. Eisner, "Long-Term Historical Trends in Violent Crime," 83.

57. Eisner, "Long-Term Historical Trends in Violent Crime," 84.

58. Quoted in *The Guardian* of March 31, 2015. Criminologists understand that homicide rates in the United States have always been higher than European homicide rates. The United States, so the argument goes, is an outlier. Really? Why isn't Europe the outlier since homicide rates in the United States are close to homicide rates in the rest of the world? The discussion is academic. When homicide rates are properly interpreted so that they include the great European crimes of the twentieth century, European homicide rates are far greater than homicide rates anywhere in the United States. Or the world. *Ever.* I discuss the point later in this essay.

59. Just when is it proper to speak of a *decline* in homicide rates? At the very least, when one has a homogeneous population either in space or in time. Thus New York underwent a remarkable *decline* in its homicide rates in the last decade of the twentieth century. *One* population seemed to respond to a complex and still mysterious set of circumstances, and changed *its* behavior. In writing about an 800-year decline in homicide rates, no homogeneous population is involved, and no single set of circumstances either. But this is true

of medieval and early European homicide statistics, as well. It is a point emphasized by Gerd Schwerhoff; see "Criminalized Violence and the Process of Civilization," 103 et seq. During roughly the same period during the first half of the sixteenth century, Schwerhoff observes, while homicide rates in Freiberg, Olmütz, and Krakow were very high, homicide rates in Basel, Regensburg, and Eger were rather lower, while homicide rates in Constance, Cologne, and Brussels were very much lower—comparable in every case to contemporary homicide rates in the United States. "In many cases," he remarks, "the sources are as heterogeneous as the categories for the various criminal acts." It is certainly true that heterogeneous data may reveal a long-term statistical trend. Whatever the trend during the sixteenth and seventeenth centuries, it is certainly not unambiguous. Were it otherwise, why would historians be arguing? See also Randolf Roth, "Homicide in Early Modern England 1549–1800: The Need for a Quantitative Synthesis," *Crimes Histoires & Sociétés, La Violence Dans la Longue Durée* 5, no. 2 (2001), 33–67.

60. "In his major work, *The Civilizing Process* (1978), Elias assumed that an interplay between the expansion of the state's monopoly of power and increasing economic interdependence would lead to the growth of pacified social spaces and restraint from violence through foresight or reflection. In an attempt to bridge sociological macro-theory and psychological insight, he suggested that the average level of self-control would increase to the degree that state institutions stabilize the flow of everyday interactions. Since these expectations match so well what crime historians have been finding, Elias has become the major theoretical reference for scholars who are working in the field and interested in theorizing about the long-term trend." Eisner, "Long-Term Historical Trends in Violent Crime," 87.

61. Norbert Elias, *Über den Prozeß der Zivilisation, Soziogenetische und Psychogenetische Untersuchungen* (Basel: Verlag Haus zum Falken, 1939). An abridged English translation is available as *The Civilizing Process* (Oxford: Blackwell, 1994).

62. Pinker refers to Elias as "the most important thinker you have never heard of." Pinker, *The Better Angels of Our Nature*, 59. Pinker, yes; you, maybe; everyone else, no.

63. In a remark now famous, Elias remarked that the Court served to "transform warriors into courtiers." Norbert Elias, *The Court Society* (Dublin: University College Dublin Press, 2006), 216. This view Elias based almost entirely on a study of the French court under Louis XIV, and the Duc de Saint Simon's memoirs. See *Norbert Elias and Violence*, eds. Tatiana Landini and Francois Dèpelteau (London: Palgrave Macmillan, 2017), 119.

64. Keith Thomas remarks shrewdly enough that if Elias sought "to find a theory that explains the spread of civility, we need look no further... than Montesquieu, who wrote... that 'the more people there are in a nation who need to deal with each other and not cause displeasure, the more politeness there is.'" *In Pursuit of Civility* (New Haven, CT: Yale University Press, 2018), 122. Throughout, Thomas offers a sympathetic but critical assessment of Elias's theories. Elias was no very sound historian, Thomas observes, and no close student of the handbooks on manners and propriety to which he devoted his somewhat indiscriminate attention. See 19–21 et seq. for details and references to the contemporary literature.

65. Johan Huizinga, *The Waning of the Middle Ages* [1924] (Mineola, NY: Dover, 2013).

66. See David Knowles, *Christian Monasticism* (New York: McGraw Hill Book Company, 1969).

67. These were precisely the features that Saint Bernard found vexing. See Saint Bernard's Apologia to William of Thierry for an indignant account of the sumptuousness and artistic grandeur of Cluniac life. "I shall say nothing," Bernard begins, "about the soaring heights

and extravagant lengths and unnecessary widths of the churches, nothing about their expensive decorations and their novel images, which catch the attention of those who go in to pray, and dry up their devotion." After saying nothing at some considerable length, Bernard goes on to say, "Good Lord, even if the foolishness of it all occasions no shame, at least one might balk at the expense." *Bernard of Clairvaux: Selected Works*, trans. G. R. Evans (Paramus, NJ: Paulist Press, 1967).

68. Elias's grasp of medieval history was insecure and out-of-date when he wrote his book in the early 1930s. Charles Homer Haskins's *The Renaissance of the Twelfth Century* (Cambridge, MA: Harvard University Press, 1927) makes an appearance in his index, but with the exception of an irrelevant quotation, not in his text—a pity, inasmuch as Haskins's pioneering work undermines Elias's thesis about the civilizing process. Elias seems unaware throughout of Percy Schramm, *Kaiser, Rom und Renovatio* (Leipzig: G. B. Teubner, 1929), and Ernst Kantorowicz, *Kaiser Friedrich der Zweite* (Georg Bondi, 1927). These are the great works of German medieval scholarship. Nor was he aware of Karl Lamprecht, whose three-volume *Deutsches Wirtschaftsleben im Mittelalter* (Leipzig: A. Dürr, 1885–1886) championed precisely the detailed examination of the minutiae of daily life that Elias advocated. Robert Lopez's *The Commercial Revolution of the Middle Ages: 950–1350* (Cambridge, UK: Cambridge University Press, 1976) undermines in every particular Elias's chronology, as the title itself might indicate, and while Elias cannot be faulted for not having anticipated the future, his admirers might, at least, have noted the past.

69. The Investiture Controversy of the eleventh century put an end to the Church's ambition to seize both the temporal and the sacerdotal sword. See Gerd Tellenbach, *Church, State and Christian Society at the Time of the Investiture Contest*, trans. R. F. Bennett (Oxford, UK: Basil Blackwell & Mott, 1940). Although Tellenbach and Elias published their great works at roughly the same moment, there is no evidence that Elias ever studied Tellenbach, and every reason that he should have done so. Tellenbach was interested in very many of the same issues that occupied Elias.

70. Norbert Elias, *Studien über die Deutschen* (Frankfurt: Suhrkamp Verlag, 1989).

71. Virgil, *The Æneid* 3.620. ("Gods, turn away such a plague from the earth!")

72. Timothy Synder, *Bloodlands: Europe between Hitler and Stalin* (New York: Basic Books, 2010).

73. Pinker, *The Better Angels*, 47.

74. I assume throughout that any set S used in these in calculations can be replaced by its cardinal meaure $|S|$. They are sets embodying populations, after all.

75. Pinker's conclusions to the contrary would make sense only if victims were homogeneously distributed. This is not the case. The underlying issue of statistical homogeneity is by no means trivial. See Vladislav Shvyrkov and Arch David III, "The Homogeneity Problem in Statistics," *Quality and Quantity* 21, no. 1 (1987), 21–36. In a widely quoted remark, Alexander Solzhenitsyn observed that "here always is this fallacious belief: 'It would not be the same here; here such things are impossible.' Alas, all the evil of the twentieth century is possible everywhere on earth." This is cant. If true, then one might expect that the evils of the twentieth century, if possible anywhere on earth, would, at least, be distributed randomly everywhere on earth. This is hardly the case. The Holocaust did not take place in Bulgaria or Denmark, nor did it take place in France to the same extent that it took place in Germany. The Gulag did not flourish in the United States or Great Britain. The great crimes of the twentieth century were specific and local, and not general and global. They were localized in space, but in time as well. They did not occur in the nineteenth century,

nor in any of the centuries that preceded it. I once asked my father, who had been active in the anti-Nazi resistance in Germany, whether he might have found Hitler compelling had he not been a Jew. He did not answer, and I did not ask again.

76. See Mathew White, https://necrometrics.com/wars19c.htm.

77. W. H. Auden, *New Year Letter* [1940].

78. Quoted in Simon Leys, *The Hall of Uselessness: Collected Essays* (New York: New York Review Books Classics, 2013), 408.

79. Pinker, *The Better Angels*, 235–36.

80. Both White and Pinker would have been better served by considering the nineteenth-century Taipeng rebellion, the subject of a fine book by Jonathan Spence: *God's Chinese Son: The Taiping Heavenly Kingdom of Hong Xiuquan* (New York: W. W. Norton, 1996). Spence puts death tolls for events occupying fourteen years at twenty-five million, or roughly two million excess deaths a year.

81. Yang Gufei, "The Song of Everlasting Sorrow."

82. See Pinker's website: https://stevenpinker.com/.

83. Stop, I am tempted to say, laying an avuncular hand on Pinker's shoulder. Ratios scale as a matter of arithmetic, but homicide statistics do not. Two deaths in a hamlet of one hundred, two thousand deaths in a village of one hundred thousand, and twenty thousand deaths in a city of one million are completely different events. Twenty thousand deaths in peacetime in a city of one million would be an unprecedented catastrophe; but two deaths in some obscure hamlet are entirely forgettable. I have forgotten about them already.

84. Pinker, *The Better Angels*, 234. There is a sort of savage nobility about his firm reliance on his own bad taste, as A. E. Houseman said of Eric Bentley.

85. If Julius Caesar = Richard Nixon, would Caesar have spoken English or Nixon Latin? Nelson Goodman raised many pertinent questions of this type in *Fact, Fiction, and Forecast* (Cambridge, MA: Harvard University Press, 1955). See also J. S. Levy, "Counterfactuals, Causal Inference, and Historical Analysis," *Security Studies* 24, no. 3 (2015): 378–402.

86. Alan Hájek, "The Reference Class Problem Is Your Problem Too," *Synthese* 156 (2007): 563–85. Hájek's paper is, except for its conclusions, correct in its diagnoses.

87. Steven Pinker, "Frequently Asked Questions," https://stevenpinker.com/pages/frequently-asked-questions-about-better-angels-our-nature-why-violence-has-declined. Pinker misses the reality that the crimes of the twentieth century were unprecedented in scope and that those committing them were officials of the state. The numbers of criminals *increased* rather than the reverse, their government uniforms notwithstanding.

88. Eisner, "Long-Term Historical Trends in Violent Crime," 106.

89. Jacques Semelin, writing in *Persécutions et entraides dans la France occupée* (Paris: Édition du Seuil, 2013), remarks with some satisfaction that "puisque environ trois cent trente mille juifs vivaient alors dans notre pays, cela signifie que 75% d'entre eux ont pu échapper à l'extermination. Pour les juifs français, cette proportion avoisine les 90%." A comparison to Belgium and Holland is the source of additional satisfaction: "Par comparaison, la Belgique n'a compté que 55% de survivants et les Pays-Bas 20%." Semelin is very largely correct, but his observation is also compatible with the fact that among *les juifs non-français*, death tolls approached 100%.

90. The French Wikipedia page is of an extraordinarily high quality, and contains an exhaustive list of French references. It could only have been written by a senior scholar in the

Centre National de la Recherché Scientifique. Unlike the Germans, the French have not felt themselves abject in virtue of their role in the Holocaust, but if not abashed, then at least they are embarrassed. And for obvious reasons. "The foreign Jews and immigrants were abandoned, and an effort was made to protect the native Jews. To some extent that strategy met with success. By giving up a part, most of the whole was saved." Raul Hilberg, *The Destruction of the European Jews* (New York: Holmes & Meier, 1985), 2:609. The site *Anonymes, justes et persécutés durant la période Nazie dans les communes de France* contains an exhaustive account of Jewish deportations organized by departments throughout France. The site is organized according to French principles of internet design, which is to say, it is virtually unreadable.

91. "Most criminologists don't consider themselves competent," Manuel Eisner wrote, "to analyze these kinds of levels of killings, believing that genocides and civil wars are something entirely different from criminal homicide, and better analyzed by sociologists or political scientists." Eisner, "What Causes Large-Scale Variation in Homicide Rates?" Institute of Criminology, University of Cambridge (working paper, July 2012): 6. Final revised version published in *Aggression in Humans and Other Primates*, eds. Hans-Henning Kortüm and Jürgen Heinze (Berlin: De Gruyter, 2012), 137-163. In a footnote reflecting on just this issue, Given remarks that "twentieth century Europeans seldom murder their fellow citizens; but in the course of two major wars in this century, they have systematically slaughtered several million people." If twentieth-century Europeans have systematically slaughtered several million people, then plainly they have often murdered their fellow citizens. A very great proportion of those murdered were *not* murdered during warfare; and far more than "several million people" were murdered. One is grateful that, at least, Given recognized that homicide statistics as criminologists understand them reflect little of twentieth-century violence. See Given, *Society and Homicide in Thirteenth-Century England*, 72.

92. Genesis 4:7.

93. "Whatever is the cause of human corruption," Dr. Johnson observed, "men are evidently and confessedly so corrupt, that all the laws of heaven and earth are insufficient to restrain them from crimes." James Boswell, *Life of Johnson* (Oxford: Oxford University Press, 1904), 1190.

94. Hannah Arendt, *Eichmann in Jerusalem* (New York: Penguin Books, 1994), 273.

3. The Cause of War

1. Heraclitus, translated and quoted in "Presocratic Philosophy," Stanford Encyclopedia of Philosophy (website), accessed September 9, 2019, https://stanford.library.sydney.edu.au/archives/fall2008/entries/presocratics/. This fragment (ca. 500 BC) of Heraclitus has been assigned the standard number of 22B80 (or Heraclitus B80) in the list of fragments of pre-Socratic philosophers compiled by Diels and Kranz, *Die Fragmente der Vorsokratiker*, 5th ed., 3 vols. (Berlin: Weidmann, 1934–38).

2. The first quotation is from Martial, *Epigrams* IV.60.5; the second from Ecclesiastes 9:11.

3. While some other war might have occurred, *it* would not have been *the* First World War.

4. This was Spinoza's view as well: singular causal statements are necessary. As Elizabeth Anscombe noted, Hume did not place this view in doubt. He asked, instead, for an analysis of necessity and found it in constant conjunction. See G. E. M. Anscombe, *Intention* [1957] (Cambridge, MA: Harvard University Press, 2000). Hume's view has now been elaborated in modal terms. Thus David Lewis remarked that "an event E *causally depends* on C if, and only if, (i) if C *had* occurred, then E *would have* occurred, and (ii) if C *had* not occurred,

then E *would* not have occurred." See Peter Menzies, "The Role of Counterfactual Dependence in Causal Judgements," in *Understanding Counterfactuals, Understanding Causation*, eds. Christoph Hoerl, Teresa McCormack and Sarah R. Beck (New York: Oxford University Press, 2011), 1 for references to Lewis, which are somewhat confused.

I would change 'would have' in (i) to *must* have. These counterfactuals are, in turn, embedded in an elaborate apparatus of possible world. Me? I do not find the analysis or the apparatus superior to the Aristotelian view: if *e* causes E then E *must* occur.

5. In 1963, Donald Davidson published an influential paper entitled "Action, Reason and Causes." The paper can be found in Donald Davidson, *Essays on Actions and Events*, 2nd ed. (Oxford: Oxford University Press, 2001), 3–19. I was Davidson's colleague at Stanford in 1966 and a participant in his seminar, where the paper was discussed, often at length. Davidson's chief thesis was simple enough: a man's reasons for acting are his desires and his beliefs, and these together are his causes for acting. Neither beliefs nor desires are typically events. What is the trigger that transforms them into action? A careful and sophisticated philosopher, Davidson declined to answer the question, although he understood perfectly well that it *was* a question. There is a symmetrical question, one that I raised in 1966, which seemed to me then, as it seems to me now, equally unanswerable: If a man's reasons are the cause of some effect in the world, must they not, as well, be the effect of some cause in the world, and immersed thus in the flux of events that happen because other events have happened? No analysis is adequate to the promotion of beliefs and desires into the effects of antecedent and exterior causes. Problems work in reverse. Before an event in the world can prompt a belief, it must be variously understood, grasped, interpreted, considered, appraised, or entertained. Fred Dretske makes a very similar point. Before the state of a system S can be the effect of some state or condition C, "it must be supplied with some sort of selective mechanism that is selectively sensitive to the presence or absence of C." Fred Dretske, "Reasons and Causes," *Philosophical Perspectives* 3 (1989): 1–15. Were this not the case, we would be returned to a full-fledged form of behaviorism. In that case, why bother with a man's reasons for action, when the causal chain runs by transitivity from antecedent causes to subsequent effects? My own view, then and now, is that the human mind cannot in large part be understood as the effect of some external cause for the same reason that it is not the cause of some external effect. Bishop Berkeley was roughly right: the only cause of an idea is another idea.
6. See Colin C. Flemming, "Understanding 'Chance and Uncertainty' in Clausewitz's *On War: Reflections on the Balkan Wars (1991–1995)*," European University Institute, MWP Working Paper, 2010.
7. Steven Pinker, *The Better Angels of Our Nature* (London: Penguin Books, 2011), 248. The metaphor in any case is due to Friedrich Schiller.
8. William Shakespeare, *Henry IV, Part I*, 3.1.55–57.
9. Lewis Richardson, *Statistics of Deadly Quarrels* (Chicago: Boxwood Press, 1960).
10. The Correlates of War Project at http://cow.dss.ucdavis.edu/contact-us maintains a number of interesting data sets about the outbreak of war. One surprise: the incidence of warfare declined during the eighteenth century, which rather resembled Europe during the thirteenth century from the battle of Bouvines to the end of the century.
11. The two statistical claims are frequently regarded as among the most solid and reliable achievement of political science. A representative encomium: "Richardson's finding that the severity of interstate wars is power-law distributed belongs to the most striking empirical regularities in world politics." See Lars-Erik Cederman, "Modeling the Size of Wars,"

The American Political Science Review 97, no. 1 (Feb. 2003): 135–150. Cederman goes on to remark that it is regularity in search of a theory. I have no idea what theory he might have in mind.

12. Skeptical because the data on which these statistical assessments rely is notoriously inadequate. No state before the twentieth century had the resources accurately to count its deaths in war; and even in the twentieth century, estimates for the First World War vary among historians. See "The First World War" in this volume for a reference to Christopher Clark's death tolls for the First World War. Population and death tolls before the twentieth century are no more than exercises in the imagination. In this regard David Henige, *Numbers from Nowhere* (Norman, OK: University of Oklahoma Press, 1998) is a very useful corrective. Historical Chinese death tolls are all of them based on tax or census records and are thus one very large step removed from the primary data.
13. "The Mandela of elementary functions" is the happy term that I used in *A Tour of the Calculus* (New York: Pantheon, 1995).
14. Aaron Clauset, "The Enduring Threat of Interstate War," OEF Research (website), September 20, 2017, 6, doi: http://dx.doi.org/10.18289/OEF.2017.018. His reference is to his own work, which, in this case, is of no relevance. Pinker, *The Better Angels of Our Nature*, 235.
15. Claudio Cioffi-Revilla and Manus A. Midlarsky argue that a power-law distribution accommodates "the highest-magnitude international wars and civil wars along dimensions of onset (time between onsets), fatalities (battle deaths or intensity) and duration..." This, of course, leaves open the possibility that it does not accommodate any of the others. See their "Power Laws, Scaling and Fractals in the Most Lethal International and Civil Wars," SSRN (website), July 11, 2013, 3 et seq., http://dx.doi.org/10.2139/ssrn.2291166.
16. So called because the descending distribution lies close to the axis. This is where the rare events occur.
17. Henk Houweling and Jan Kuné, "Do Outbreaks of War Follow a Poisson-Process?" *The Journal of Conflict Resolution* 28, no. 1 (1984): 51–61. The authors make the same point. From their abstract: "Richardson's finding that the distribution of war outbreaks in time conforms to the Poisson distribution has been repeated over and over again. In this article, we argue that the close correspondence between the two distributions does not imply that the mechanism generating the data is the Poisson process. Because the time sequence is broken down in Richardson's analysis, his finding does not imply that war outbreaks follow a distinct pattern in time. The Parzen test on arrival times revealed that war outbreaks are not generated by a Poisson random process."
18. Both homicide statistics and statistics about the outbreak of war induce a kind of ontological trance in criminologists and historians. The statistics are what they are, whether reliable or not. It is the inferences that they generate that are frequently suspicious. It is true that the outbreak of war seems properly to be described by a Poisson distribution. The distribution exhausts whatever meaning might be attached to randomness. No individual event in the series is random if only because assigning randomness to individual events is a category mistake. Quite the contrary. Every event in the series is determinate. No state has ever gone to war by throwing dice.
19. In what follows, I assimilate a Poisson process to a Poisson distribution on the grounds that a Poisson process is characterized by its Poisson distribution.

20. "The forces and influences governing a Poisson process," William Feller observed, must "remain absolutely unchanged." William Feller, *The Theory of Probability and Its Applications* (New York: John Wiley, 1950), 1:365. Such processes are, for this reason, called stationary.

21. The year 1950 is also taken as a turning point by criminologists, who observe, often with satisfaction but rarely with doubt, that homicide rates in London were then at their lowest historical point—roughly one in one hundred thousand. See "The Best of Times" in this volume for details. They were as low as they were because the natural-born killers and their victims had both perished in the preceding decade.

22. If the onset of war over 130 years is best represented by a homogeneous Poisson distribution, this, too, requires explanation. In a world in which everything is changing, why should λ have remained unchanged?

23. Aaron Clauset, "Trends and Fluctuations in the Severity of Interstate Wars," *Science Advances* 4, no. 2 (Feb. 2018): 3. "An ensemble approach is used on the basis of a standard non-parametric bootstrap procedure that simulates the generative process of events to produce a series of synthetic data sets {Y} with similar statistical structure as the empirical data X. Fitting a semiparametric model Pr(y|q) to each Y yields an ensemble of models {q} that incorporate the empirical data's inherent variability into a distribution of estimated parameters. This distribution is then used to weight models by their likelihood under the bootstrap distribution and to numerically estimate the likelihood of specific historical or future patterns."

24. Pasquale Cirillo and Nassim Nicholas Taleb have come to a similar conclusion based on their assessment of the power-law distribution. See "On the Statistical Properties and Tail Risk of Violent Conflicts," *Physica A: Statistical Mechanics and its Applications* 452 (June 15, 2016): 29-45, https://doi.org/10.1016/j.physa.2016.01.050. "The consequence of this analysis is that the absence of a conflict generating more than, say, 5 million casualties in the last sixty years [is] highly insufficient to state that their probability has decreased over time, given that the average inter-arrival time is 93.03 years, with a mean absolute deviation of 113.57 years! Unfortunately, we need to wait for more time to assert whether we are really living in a more peaceful era: present data are not in favor (nor against) a structural change in violence, when we deal with war casualties." This is an interesting and a provocative conclusion, but so far as the larger argument goes, it is based on a non-sequitur, for Cirillo and Taleb assume that "the number of conflicts over time is likely to follow a homogeneous Poisson process." This is the point at issue because it is precisely the point that Pinker denies in arguing that the long peace is evidence of an emerging inhomogeneous Poisson process. Monsieurs Cirillo and Taleb, allow me to introduce you to Monsieur Clauset.

25. Feller, *The Theory of Probability and its Applications*, 365.

26. Lewis Fry Richardson, *Statistics of Deadly Quarrels* (Pittsburgh: Boxwood Press, 1960), 35.

4. Relativism—A Fish Story

1. This is a somewhat revised version of my review of Stanley Fish, *There's No Such Thing as Free Speech... and It's a Good Thing, Too* (New York: Oxford University Press, 1994). The review was published some twenty-five years ago in an SF zine that appeared briefly and as briefly disappeared. It was put together and edited by Peter Collier, who is now dead. The zine reached about ten people, all in all. On the issues of substance, I find that I see no reason to change my mind. This is always a gratifying discovery.

6. Necessary Nature

1. Barry Mazur, "When Is One Thing Equal to Some Other Thing?" preprint on Mazur's Harvard site, June 12, 2007, 23, http://www.math.harvard.edu/~mazur/preprints/when_is_one.pdf.
2. □(Pluto = Pluto) means that *necessarily* Pluto = Pluto.
3. See "Essentialism," Geek Feminism Wiki, accessed September 2019, http://geekfeminism.wikia.com/wiki/Essentialism.
4. Ezra Furman, "Wobbly," verse 2, lines 1–5, https://genius.com/Ezra-furman-wobbly-lyrics.
5. A subset of a topological space is saturated if it is an intersection of open subsets of X. See "Saturated Set," Wikimedia Foundation, last modified 9 January 2019, 11:13, https://en.wikipedia.org/wiki/Saturated_set; and also "Saturated Sets and Topological Spaces," StackExchange: Mathematics, post 4, https://math.stackexchange.com/questions/1926040/saturated-sets-and-topological-spaces?rq=1.
6. Published in three volumes between 1830 and 1833, and thus a full twenty-nine years before Darwin published a word about evolution.
7. Charles Darwin, *The Origin of Species*, 6th edition [1872] (New York: P. F. Collier, 1902), 310.
8. Ian Tattersall, "The Genus *Homo*," *Inference* 2, no. 1 (February 2016), https://inference-review.com/article/the-genus-homo.
9. Why this thesis should be called the *Copernican* principle is entirely a mystery.
10. Although never at work, I should add, in discussions among *physicists*.
11. For the three-part article, see Michael Denton, "*Evolution: A Theory in Crisis* Revisited," *Inference* 1, no. 1 (October 2014), no. 2 (March 2015), and no. 3 (July 2015). The first installment (and through it the others) can be found at https://inference-review.com/article/evolution-a-theory-in-crisis-revisited-part-one.

7. Disgusting, No?

1. The pulled interview was originally recorded August 25, 2009, and put up on the Bloggingheads website August 26, 2009. (Not August 27, as erroneously stated on the site.) Later that day, the interview was pulled. See Behe's astonished comments on the affair, published on August 28, at http://behe.uncommondescent.com/2009/08/bloggingheads-tv-and-me/.
2. "John McWhorter feels, with regret, that this interview represents neither himself, Professor Behe, nor Bloggingheads usefully, takes full responsibility for same, and has asked that it be taken down from the site. He apologizes to all who found its airing objectionable." This statement was originally found in a comment on the site at http://bloggingheads.tv/forum/showthread.php?p=126767#poststop, but this link now appears to be dead; however, it is quoted in more than one place on the web, e.g., by "Mark H." on Nov. 4, 2009, in the comments section at http://commonsenseatheism.com/?p=4018. The interview was within a few days reinstated, apparently by Robert Wright, editor-in-chief of Bloggingheads. See the announcement of the reinstatement at https://uncommondescent.com/intelligent-design/behe-mcwhorter-back-online/. A discussion of the reinstatement by David Klinghoffer is found at https://www.beliefnet.com/columnists/kingdomofpriests/2009/08/wright-does-the-right-thing-reinstates-behe-on-intelligent-design.html. The interview itself can currently (August 15, 2019) be viewed at https://bloggingheads.tv/videos/2234. (Some browsers require the Flash player to be allowed for the site.)

3. World Summit on the Information Society, Document WSIS-03/GENEVA/DOC/4-E, December 12, 2003, Point A4, http://www.itu.int/net/wsis/docs/geneva/official/dop.html.

8. Majestic Ascent: *Darwin on Trial*

1. Richard Dawkins, *The Blind Watchmaker: Why the Evidence of Evolution Reveals a Universe Without Design* [1986] with a new introduction (New York: W. W. Norton, 1996).
2. Charles Darwin, *On the Origin of Species by Means of Natural Selection, or the Preservation of Favoured Races in the Struggle for Life*, 1st ed. (London: John Murray, 1859), ch. 9, p. 302. In all subsequent notes to this work (henceforth to be cited simply as *Origin of Species*), the 1st edition is to be assumed unless otherwise indicated. The chapter will always be indicated, to assist those who are consulting different editions with different paginations. For searchable full texts of the various editions of Darwin's works, see http://darwin-online.org.uk/.
3. Gert Korthof, "How to Attack Neo-Darwinism and Still End Up in Evolution Textbooks: The Neutralist–Selectionist Controversy," review of *The Neutral Theory of Molecular Evolution*, by Motoo Kimura, on Korthof's website Was Darwin Wrong?, January 1, 1999 (updated November 3, 2016), http://wasdarwinwrong.com/kortho37.htm.
4. Richard Lewontin, "Billions and Billions of Demons," review of *The Demon-Haunted World: Science as a Candle in the Dark*, by Carl Sagan, *The New York Review of Books*, January 9, 1997, https://www.nybooks.com/articles/1997/01/09/billions-and-billions-of-demons/.
5. Dawkins, *The Blind Watchmaker*, 6.
6. "California Science Center Pays $110,000 to Settle Intelligent Design Discrimination Lawsuit," *Evolution News*, Discovery Institute, August 29, 2011, https://evolutionnews.org/2011/08/california_science_center_pays/.
7. Casey Luskin, "University of Kentucky Pays $100,000+ to Settle Gaskell Discrimination Lawsuit," *Evolution News*, Discovery Institute, January 18, 2011, https://evolutionnews.org/2011/01/university_of_kentucky_pays_10/.

11. The Social Set

1. Conducted over many years, Christakis's research has revealed that "people's happiness depends on the happiness of others." J. H. Fowler and N. A. Christakis, "Dynamic Spread of Happiness in a Large Social Network: Longitudinal Analysis over 20 Years in the Framingham Heart Study," *BMJ* 337, a2338 (December 4, 2008): 1, doi:10.1136/bmj.a2338. This is not a conclusion that has ignited a firestorm of controversy. Or interest. On the other hand, *nous avons tous assez de force pour supporter les maux d'autrui*, as La Rochefoucauld observed.
2. Nicholas A. Christakis, *Blueprint: The Evolutionary Origins of a Good Society* (New York: Little, Brown Spark, 2019).
3. Christakis, *Blueprint*, 408, emphasis added.
4. Christakis, *Blueprint*, 408.
5. Facebook, in effect.
6. Thus, "Biology can prime—even if it does not completely govern—the flow of certain human behaviors," Christakis, *Blueprint*, 404. Who would scruple? Directly thereafter, Christakis writes that "the notion of a blueprint… is a kind of determinism." When he adds on p. 405 that "a crucial part of our species' genetic inheritance is, ironically, the

capacity *not* to be wholly tethered to our biology," he achieves communion with an almost Platonic degree of incoherence.

7. Christakis regards convergent evolution with unconcern, and given the frequency of its occurrence, it is odd that a system obviously as useful as language should have appeared only once in four billion years. The popularity of talking animals in world literature suggests that the oddity has itself been widely noted. See *Blueprint*, 284–89. For an account of convergent evolution, see Simon Conway Morris, *Life's Solution: Inevitable Humans in a Lonely Universe* (Cambridge, UK: Cambridge University Press, 2003). George R. McGee makes a more radical case in *Convergent Evolution: Limited Forms Most Beautiful* (Cambridge, MA: MIT Press, 2011). "The number of evolutionary pathways available to life," he writes, "is, in fact, not endless, but is quite restricted," xi. In some sense, this must be so. Pigs cannot fly. This tells us nothing of interest about the probabilities involved in finding those restricted paths, and, if determined, the probabilities involved when two remote species discover the same path.
8. Eusebius, *Chronicon*, in *Berossos and Manetho: Native Traditions in Ancient Mesopotamia and Egypt*, eds. and trans. Gerrald Verbrugghe and John Wickersham (Ann Arbor, MI: University of Michigan Press, 2001), 44. I have called attention to this haunting story in "The Origins of Mind," in *The Deniable Darwin* (Seattle, WA: Discovery Institute Press, 2010), 441. Berossus the Chaldean, as he was known, had a considerable reputation as an astrologer in the Greek world. See my own *The Secrets of the Vaulted Sky* (Orlando, FL: Harcourt, 2003), 25–30.
9. See Robert Berwick and Noam Chomsky, "The Siege of Paris," *Inference* 4, no. 3 (March 2019), https://inference-review.com/article/the-siege-of-paris.
10. Not one without water.
11. An example, one of hundreds. Why fear? Why ask? The question is simple; so, too, its answer. "Fear motivates us to escape or avoid danger and harm—to run away from the lion or avoid wandering too near to the edge of the cliff." When confronted with a lion, *my* fear is just along for the ride. I would just as well be served by a nervous system in which the middle-man is eliminated. Some men may avoid danger cold-eyed and without fear; and others may feel fear without avoiding danger. Fear is an evolutionary luxury, all things considered. For the quoted passage, see the interview with Steve Stewart-Williams, "Memes, Genes, and Sex Differences," *Quillette*, May 14, 2019, https://quillette.com/2019/05/14/memes-genes-and-sex-differences-an-interview-with-dr-steve-stewart-williams/.
12. Debra Soh, "Sex, Love, and Knowing the Difference," *Quillette*, May 3, 2019, https://quillette.com/2019/05/03/sex-love-and-knowing-the-difference/.
13. In the eleventh-century Heian court, Sei Shonagan remarked in her *Pillow Book*, men were expected to send a morning-after poem to the woman of their night. Assigning a common cause to behavior ranging from the composition of literate Chinese poetry to the grunt-and-leave characteristic of student hook-ups is rather like designating the creative urge as the common cause animating both Andrea del Sarto and Jeff Koons.
14. *Hübsch als es währte, Und nun ist's vorüber*, as Polly sings in *Die Dreigroschenoper*—one reason that civilized societies prefer to arrange their marriages.
15. "The underpinnings of society that we have come to understand—the social suite that is our blueprint—have to do with our genetic similarities," he writes, "not our differences." Christakis, *Blueprint*, 408.

16. Genomes are compared by means of a metric suitable for combinatorial objects—typically the Hamming distance. Human beings are not combinatorial objects; nor are they discrete; and no one has the faintest idea of what an appropriate metric for assessing their similarities and differences might be. Whatever the standard of similarity, it is not measured by the Hamming distance, so in talking about genotypes and phenotypes, two different metrics are loitering about. Their relationship is anyone's guess. We are left with the obvious: human beings are pretty much alike except when they are different.

17. Christakis, *Blueprint*, 119–27.

18. Phillip Mitteroecker and Simon Huttegger, "The Concept of Morphospaces in Evolutionary and Developmental Biology: Mathematics and Metaphors," *Biological Theory* 4, no. 1 (2009), 54–67. The stress is all on the word "phenotypic." There are no genetic sequences in morphospace. Human beings share their genes to ninety-nine percent, Christakis believes; and this may be true; but he has rested his argument on the existence of some close connection between the space of genetic and phenotypic possibilities—something like an isomorphism. No one has seen such a thing, if only because no one has ever seen a morphism between them. Human beings may be genetically alike and yet radically different. Of two *identical* twins, it is important to recall, one may go in for mail fraud and violations of the Mann Act, while the other may be devoted, as I am, to third-wave feminism and transgender rights. There is much wisdom in the story of Dr. Jekyll and Mr. Hyde.

19. It is a metaphor that Christakis attributes to Richard Dawkins. See *Blueprint*, 119. These ideas may be traced backward to D'Arcy Thompson's *On Growth and Form* (Cambridge, UK: Cambridge University Press, 1917). Thompson was interested in *continuous* transformations; the idea of a morphospace is otherwise. I know of only one substantial result in mathematical morphology, and that is Thom's Classification Theorem. For a discussion, see my *Black Mischief: Language, Life, Logic, Luck*, 2nd ed. (Orlando, FL: Harcourt Brace Jovanovich, 1988), 245–267.

20. Johann Peter Eckermann's record of his conversations with Johann Wolfgang von Goethe, first published in 1836 (vols. 1 and 2) and 1848 (vol. 3).

21. I made the same point years ago in *Black Mischief*, 97.

22. Writing in *The Guardian* of May 16, 2019, Lynn Eaton and Rossalyn Warren avow that "poor body self-image can affect all ages." The problem is serious. "The reactions it can trigger range from anxiety and self-disgust to suicidal thoughts." But why *disgust*? Almost everyone finds the human body disgusting some of the time, and some malcontents find it disgusting all of the time. Such are the facts of life. But what is odd is that these facts should embrace a livid form of repugnance, an attitude that gains no purchase in any scheme of evolutionary biology.

23. It is a taboo that reflects a deep human imperative to cover things up. To be naked before one's enemies is both literally and metaphorically an unwelcome position. The source of the taboo protecting nakedness is a mystery. It appears a part of human nature, and, as a part of human nature, it belongs to an ever-shifting system of rituals, prohibitions, imprecations, and anathemas, all of them irrational but strangely coherent.

24. Rather a waste of their time, in both cases, since the objective may far more easily be achieved. Birds may mate without bowers, and primitive man could take his pleasure at the end of a club.

25. Evolution is a mapping $(\mathbf{P} \times \mathbf{E}) \rightarrow \mathbf{P}^*$ from a phenotype **P** and an ecological niche **N** to another phenotype $\mathbf{P}^*$. **P** and **E** are both random variables; and so is $(\mathbf{P} \times \mathbf{E})$.

26. Christakis, *Blueprint*, 125.

27. In *Der SS-Stadt*, Eugen Kogon describes one: "*Die deutschen Konzentrationslager waren eine Welt für sich, ein Staat für sich—eine Ordnung ohne Recht, in die der Mensch geworfen wurde, der nun mit all seinen Tugenden und Lastern—mehr Lastern als Tugenden—um die nackte Existenz und das bloße Überdauern kämpfte. Gegen die SS allein? Beileibe nicht; genauso, ja noch mehr gegen seine eigenen Mitgefangenen! Das Ganze hinter den eisernen Gitterstangen einer terroristischen Disziplin ein Dschungel der Verwilderung, in den von außen hineingeschossen, aus dem zum Erhängen herausgeholt, in dem vergiftet, vergast, erschlagen, zu Tode gequält, um Leben, Einfluß und Macht intrigiert, um materielle Besserstellung gekämpft, geschwindelt und betrogen wurde, neue Klassen und Schichten sich bildeten, Prominente, Parvenüs und Parias innerhalb der Reihen der Sklaven, wo die Bewußtseinsinhalte sich wandelten, die sittlichen Wertmaßstäbe bis zum Zerbrechen sich bogen, Orgien begangen und Messen gefeiert, Treue gehalten, Liebe erwiesen und Haß gegeifert, kurzum die tragoedia humana in absonderlichster Weise exemplifiziert wurde.*" Eugen Kogon, *Der SS-Stadt: Das System der deutschen Konzentrationslager* [1946] (Munich: Kindler Verlag, 1974), vii. The SS state suggests Solzhenitsyn's "Gulag Archipelago," both Kogon and Solzhenitsyn arguing that these states within states represented an eschatological vision of the society they sought to bring into existence. In the end, Kogon observes, the SS was determined to impose its peculiar practices on Germany itself, the SS reveling in its power as well as in its imagined purity until, with no victims left, it proposed to turn upon itself. These societies were not sequestered in some inaccessible portion of ethnographic hyperspace. They are a part of the historical record.

28. V. S. Naipaul, *Among the Believers* (New York: Vintage Books, 1982), 381–382.

29. Naipaul, *Among the Believers*, 353.

30. The Freud of *Civilization and Its Discontents* understood that civilization, far from being the expression of biology, represents a perpetual, and demanding, struggle against the murderous chaos of instinctual life. This dark, sober, adult view is more obviously true than any of the brisk optimistic tracts offered by evolutionary psychology or sociology.

12. Godzooks

1. Jean Racine, *Phèdre*, act 5, scene 3. Margaret Rawlings translates this into English as "Fear, my Lord, fear lest Heaven, in revenge, Hate you enough to grant your prayer!" *Phèdre: Dual Language Edition* (New York: Penguin, 1991), 153.

2. Yuval Harari, *Sapiens: A Brief History of Humankind* (New York: Harper, 2011). In his review, published in *The Guardian* of September 11, 2014, Galen Strawson remarked that the book was "overwhelmed by carelessness, exaggeration and sensationalism." Fair enough. After a century in which serious historians regarded Big History as a Big Mistake, it is now again in fashion. See David Armitage, "What's the Big Idea?" *TLS*, September 20, 2012. For the first half of the twentieth century, the notoriety of Oswald Spengler's *Der Untergang des Abendlandes* and Arnold Toynbee's *A Study of History* persuaded serious historians not to go there or do that. All is now forgiven. David Christian, *Maps of Time: An Introduction to Big History* covers 14 billion years, the overwhelming majority of no relevance to human history whatsoever. Ian Morris's *Why the West Rules—for Now* is Small Time Big Time: it is limited to the past 10,000 years. *Sapiens* is Big Time Small Time, Harari going back some 250,000 years.

3. Yuval Harari, *Homo Deus: A Brief History of Tomorrow* (New York: HarperCollins, 2017).

4. V. S. Naipaul, "Our Universal Civilization," *The New York Times*, November 5, 1990.

5. Mark Humphrys, "The West—The Universal Civilization," undated column, http://markhumphrys.com/west.universal.html.

6. See James Oliver, "The Ruling Power: A Study of the Roman Empire in the Second Century after Christ through the Roman Oration of Aelius Aristides," *Transactions of the American Philosophical Society* 43, no. 4 (1953): 871–1003.

7. This is not a doctrine apt to survive an encounter with itself. The claim that whatever can be known must be known as a derivation from the sciences cannot itself be derived from any of the sciences.

8. Harari, *Homo Deus,* 319. When Harari's argument is stripped of its absurd and sentimental attachment to the idea of an algorithm, what remains is a re-statement of Hume's unpersuasive argument about the personality and its persistence over time. "For my part, when I enter most intimately into what I call *myself,* I always stumble on some particular perception or other, of heat or cold, light or shade, love or hatred, pain or pleasure. I never can catch *myself* at any time without a perception, and never can observe anything but the perception." David Hume, *A Treatise of Human Nature* (Oxford: Clarendon Press, 1896), 1.4.6.3. From this it follows only that the self is not an object of perception. So?

9. Harari, *Homo Deus,* 14.

10. Harari, *Homo Deus,* 14.

11. Brian Ferguson, "Pinker's List," in *War, Peace, and Human Nature: The Convergence of Evolutionary and Cultural Views,* ed. Douglas Fry (Oxford: Oxford University Press, 2013), 116. Ferguson is discussing Steven Pinker, not Yuval Harari, but the claims at issue are the same.

12. See "Global Action Keeping Famine at Bay but Failing to Prevent Suffering, UN Chief Warns," *UN News Centre,* September 21, 2017, https://news.un.org/en/story/2017/09/566162-global-action-keeping-famine-bay-failing-prevent-suffering-un-chief-warns.

13. Amartya Sen has argued that famines are less about the availability of food and more about its distribution. Amartya Sen, *Poverty and Famines: An Essay on Entitlement and Deprivation* (Oxford: Oxford University Press, 1981).

14. Like almost all numbers pertaining to excess deaths in the twentieth century, including deaths in combat, these numbers, although very roughly correct, vary widely from source to source. No comparable margin of error would be tolerated in any serious science. See Stephen Devereux, "Famine in the Twentieth Century," IDS Working Paper 105, Institute of Development Studies, January 1, 2000, https://www.ids.ac.uk/publications/famine-in-the-twentieth-century/.

15. See "The Best of Times" in this volume.

16. Harari, *Homo Deus,* 200.

17. Harari, *Homo Deus,* 83.

18. Harari, *Homo Deus,* 36.

19. Harari is not mistaken in assigning an immense intellectual importance to the advent of the algorithm in the twentieth century. His mistakes are local, not general. My own view is that the algorithm is one of two seminal concepts in the Western scientific tradition. The other is the calculus. I have developed these ideas first in *A Tour of the Calculus* (New York: Pantheon, 1995), and in *The Advent of the Algorithm* (San Diego: Harcourt, 2001). These ideas arise from quite different parts of the scientific experience, and it is not easy to see

how they might ever be reconciled in one completely compelling mathematical or logical structure. If they are not in conflict, neither are they the best of friends.

20. Harari, *Homo Deus,* 283.

21. Harari does not for a moment believe that free will is an illusion. Neither does anyone else. "All the predictions that pepper this book," he writes, "are no more than an *attempt* to discuss present-day dilemmas, and an invitation to *change* the future [emphasis added]." Harari, *Homo Deus,* 64. What would an *attempt* to discuss anything, or an invitation to *change* something, amount to in a world without freedom of the will?

22. Dante, *Inferno,* canto 26, lines 118–9.

23. It is not easy to define either determinism or randomness. The class of deterministic theories, if not well defined, is at least better defined than some notion of determinism defined überhaupt, as German metaphysicians say, but the various definitions do very little to advance any discussion of freedom of the will. Richard Montague's essay, "Deterministic Theories," remains to my mind the very best discussion. See Richard Montague, *Formal Philosophy: Selected Papers of Richard Montague,* ed. Richmond Thomason (New Haven, CT: Yale University Press, 1974).

24. Harari, *Homo Deus,* 101.

25. If a proposition is necessary, its denial is impossible. If determinism does not really *determine* something, it remains entirely a flabby concept.

26. Harari, *Homo Deus,* 36.

27. Harari, *Homo Deus,* 323.

28. Stephen Wolfram, "The Principle of Computational Equivalence," in *A New Kind of Science* (Champaign, IL: Wolfram Media, 2002). I am quoting from an advance copy of the uncorrected version of the book (Champaign, IL: Wolfram Media, 2001), 844. I sent Wolfram one of my books in the expectation that he would praise it; he sent me his in the same expectation. Neither expectation was justified.

29. Michael Jordan, quoted in Lee Gomes, "Machine-Learning Maestro Michael Jordan on the Delusions of Big Data and Other Huge Engineering Efforts," IEEE Spectrum, October 20, 2014, https://spectrum.ieee.org/robotics/artificial-intelligence/machinelearning-maestro-michael-jordan-on-the-delusions-of-big-data-and-other-huge-engineering-efforts.

30. For citations and a very professional discussion of the argument, see Solomon Feferman, "Penrose's Gödelian Argument," https://math.stanford.edu/~feferman/papers/penrose.pdf. This essay was originally published as "Penrose's Gödelian Argument: A Review of *Shadows of the Mind* by Roger Penrose," in the now-defunct online journal *Psyche,* vol. 2 (1995–1996), http://journalpsyche.org/archive/volume-2-1995-1996/.

31. Zoltan Istvan, quoted in Olivia Solon, "How Close Are We to a Black Mirror-Style Digital Afterlife?" *The Guardian,* January 9, 2018, https://www.theguardian.com/tv-and-radio/2018/jan/09/how-close-are-we-black-mirror-style-digital-afterlife.

32. Harari, *Homo Deus,* 319.

33. Harari, *Homo Deus,* 367. In a number of especially florid passages, Harari refers to Dataism as something like a religion. He is careful, as he is throughout his book, not to include himself in the congregation.

34. Wolfram, *A New Kind of Science,* advance uncorrected proofs, 4.

35. Scott Aronson, review of *A New Kind of Science,* by Stephen Wolfram, *Quantum Information and Computation* 1, no. 0 (30 July 2002), 95–108, arXiv:quant-ph/0206089v2.

36. For an account of the limitations inherent in deep learning techniques, see Gary Marcus, "Deep Learning: A Critical Appraisal" (2018), https://arxiv.org/ftp/arxiv/papers/1801/1801.00631.pdf.
37. Frank Rosenblatt, *Principles of Neurodynamics: Perceptrons and the Theory of Brain Mechanisms* (Washington, DC: Spartan Books, 1962).
38. Marvin Minsky and Seymour Papert, *Perceptrons: An Introduction to Computational Geometry* (Cambridge, MA: MIT Press, 1972).
39. Istvan, quoted in Solon, "How Close Are We?" Good old Zoltan!

13. A Flower of Chivalry

1. Guillaume le Maréchal (1147–1219), 1st Earl of Pembroke, knight, noble, and for a time protector of young Henry III and regent of England, served five English kings.
2. Georges Duby, *William Marshal: The Flower of Chivalry* (New York: Pantheon, 1985).
3. Duby, *William Marshal*, 152.

1. This and subsequent Abélard quotations in this essay are taken from Medieval Sourcebook: Peter Abelard: *Historia Calamitatum*, trans. Henry Adams Bellows (1922), https://sourcebooks.fordham.edu/basis/abelard-histcal.asp.

18. The Recovery of Case

1. Noam Chomsky and Howard Lasnik, "Filters and Control," *Linguistic Inquiry* 8, no. 3 (1977): 425–504.
2. Jean-Roger Vergnaud, personal letter to Noam Chomsky and Howard Lasnik, April 17, 1977, first published as "Letter to Noam Chomsky and Howard Lasnik," in *Syntax: Critical Concepts in Linguistics*, eds. Robert Freidin and Howard Lasnik (London: Routledge, 2006), 5: 21–34. The letter is also published as "Letter to Noam Chomsky and Howard Lasnik on 'Filters and Control,'" in *Foundational Issues in Linguistic Theory: Essays in Honor of Jean-Roger Vergnaud*, eds. Robert Freidin, Carlos P. Otero, and Maria Luisa Zubizarreta (Cambridge, MA: MIT Press, 2008), 3–15. Page references here are to the 2006 Freidin and Lasnik version.
3. See, for example, Hartley Rogers, *Theory of Recursive Functions and Effective Computability* (Cambridge, MA: MIT Press, 1987). Although not up to date, this remains a classical textbook.
4. Chomsky's review of B. F. Skinner's *Verbal Behavior* was famous from the moment that it appeared: Noam Chomsky, "A Review of B. F. Skinner's *Verbal Behavior*," *Language* 35, no. 1 (1959): 26–58.
5. It is a familiar enough experience for immigrant parents to fail completely to master a new language even as their children acquire it perfectly from other children or simply from the give-and-take of the streets; children can, and frequently do, learn four or five languages in this way.
6. Chomsky and Lasnik, "Filters and Control," 427.
7. Robert Lees, *The Grammar of English Nominalizations*, monograph published in *International Journal of American Linguistics* 26, no. 3, part 2 (Bloomington: University of Indiana Press, 1960).
8. Noam Chomsky, *Aspects of the Theory of Syntax* (Cambridge, MA: MIT Press, 1965).
9. Chomsky, *Aspects of the Theory of Syntax*, 3.

10. Randolph Quirk et al., *A Comprehensive Grammar of the English Language* (London: Longman, 1985).

11. Chomsky and Lasnik, "Filters and Control," 427.

12. Mark Baltin, "A Landing Site Theory of Movement Rules," *Linguistic Inquiry* 13, no. 1 (1982): 1.

13. Baltin, "A Landing Site Theory," 1.

14. Baltin, "A Landing Site Theory," 1.

15. Howard Gardner, "Encounter at Royaumont: The Debate between Jean Piaget and Noam Chomsky," in *Art, Mind, and Brain: A Cognitive Approach to Creativity* (New York: Basic Books, 1984).

16. Gardner, "Encounter at Royaumont," 17.

17. Gardner, "Encounter at Royaumont," 16.

18. Gardner, "Encounter at Royaumont," 17.

19. Gardner, "Encounter at Royaumont," 25.

20. Noam Chomsky, "Of Minds and Language," *Biolinguistics* 1 (2007): 19.

21. See Saunders MacLane and Ieke Moerdijk, *Sheaves in Geometry and Logic: A First Introduction to Topos Theory* (New York: Springer, 1992).

22. Noam Chomsky, *Current Issues in Linguistic Theory* (The Hague: Mouton, 1964).

23. Quoted in Alan Jay Levinovitz, "The New Astrology," *Aeon*, April 4, 2016.

24. Lees, *The Grammar of English Nominalizations.*

25. Chomsky and Lasnik, "Filters and Control," 430.

26. François Jacob, "Genetics of the Bacterial Cell," Nobel Lecture, December 11, 1965, published in *Science* 152, no. 3728 (10 Jun 1966): 1470–78. See also François Jacob, "Evolution and Tinkering," *Science* 196, no. 4295 (10 Jun 1977): 1161–66.

27. Quoted in Robert Berwick and Noam Chomsky, *Why Only Us* (Cambridge, MA: MIT Press, 2016): 16.

28. The Japanese example may be found in V. J. Cook, *Chomsky's Universal Grammar* (Cambridge, UK: Blackwell, 1988), 7.

29. Mark Baker, *The Atoms of Language: The Mind's Hidden Rules of Grammar* (New York: Basic Books, 2001).

30. The line is taken from G. K. Chesterton, "The Loyal Traitor," sec. 1, in *Four Faultless Felons* [1930] (London: Darwen Finlayson, 1962), 215:

As Aaron's serpent swallowed snakes and rods,
As God alone is greater than the gods,
As all stars shrivel in the single sun,
The words are many, but The Word is one.

31. Peter Rosenbaum, *Grammar of English Predicate Complement Constructions* (Cambridge, MA: MIT Press, 1967).

32. Joan Bresnan, "Theory of Complementation in English Syntax" (PhD diss., MIT, 1972).

33. Leonard Bloomfield, *Language* (London: Allen & Unwin, 1933).

34. Samuel Johnson, quoted in James Boswell, *The Life of Samuel Johnson, LL.D* (London: J. Davis, 1775), 2: 616.

35. Noam Chomsky, "Remarks on Nominalization," in *Readings in English Transformational Grammar*, eds. Roderick Jacobs and Peter Rosenbaum (Waltham, MA: Ginn, 1970), 184–21. See also Noam Chomsky, "The Amherst Lectures" (lectures, the Linguistic Institute, University of Massachusetts, Amherst, 1974).

36. Willi Hennig, *Grundzüge einer Theorie der phylogenetischen Systematik* (Berlin: Deutscher Zentralverlag, 1950); translated by D. Davis and R. Zangerl as *Phylogenetic Systematics* (Urbana, Illinois: University of Illinois Press, 1966).

37. Noam Chomsky, *Syntactic Structures* (Paris: Mouton & Co., 1957).

38. Henk van Riemsdijk, "Some Thoughts on Specified Ellipsis," in *Grammar in Focus: Festschrift for Christer Platzack*, eds. Lars-Olof Delsing, Cecilia Falk, Gunlög Josefsson, and Halldór Á. Sigurðsson (Lund, Sweden: Lund University, 2003), 258.

39. Scott Soames and David Perlmutter, *Syntactic Argumentation and the Structure of English* (Berkeley: University of California Press, 1979).

40. For these examples and related discussion, see Chomsky and Lasnik, "Filters and Control," sec. 2.2 ("Infinitival Constructions"), 456–58.

41. Chomsky and Lasnik, "Filters and Control," 435.

42. See David M. Perlmutter, "Deep and Surface Structure Constraints in Syntax" (PhD diss., MIT, 1968), https://dspace.mit.edu/handle/1721.1/13003, and David M. Perlmutter, *Deep and Surface Constraints in Syntax* (New York: Holt, Rinehart and Winston, 1971).

43. Chomsky and Lasnik, "Filters and Control," 433.

44. David Berlinski, "On the Origins of Life," *Commentary*, February 1, 2006, https://www.commentarymagazine.com/articles/on-the-origins-of-life/.

45. Kurt Gödel, "Letter to John von Neumann," March 20, 1956, https://rjlipton.wordpress.com/the-gdel-letter/.

46. Vergnaud, "Letter to Noam Chomsky and Howard Lasnik," 21.

47. Case had already been a central topic of discussion within generative grammar through the work of Chuck Fillmore, who systematically used it in his famous "The Case for Case." What Vergnaud did, however, is to place the phenomenon in a totally novel theoretical light within the EST, with ramifications that reverberate even in today's models. See Charles Fillmore, "The Case for Case," in *Universals in Linguistic Theory*, eds. Emmon Bach and Robert Harms (New York: Holt, Rinehart, and Winston, 1968), 1–88.

48. Vergnaud, "Letter to Noam Chomsky and Howard Lasnik," 21.

49. Vergnaud, "Letter to Noam Chomsky and Howard Lasnik," 22.

50. Vergnaud, "Letter to Noam Chomsky and Howard Lasnik," 22.

51. Noam Chomsky, *Lectures on Government and Binding* (Dordrecht: Foris, 1981), 49.

52. PRO is a pronominal determiner phrase, but one that goes unspoken.

53. PRO was the P&P (principles and parameters) successor of Rosenbaum's 1967 rule of "Equi NP Deletion." See Peter Rosenbaum, *The Grammar of English Predicate Complement Constructions* (Cambridge, MA: MIT Press, 1967).

54. Jonathan Bobaljik and Susi Wurmbrand, "Case in GB/Minimalism," in *The Oxford Handbook of Case*, eds. Andrej Malchukov and Andrew Spencer (Oxford: Oxford University Press, 2008), 44–58.

55. Bobaljik and Wurmbrand, "Case in GB/Minimalism."

56. Yen-Hui Audrey Li, "Abstract Case in Mandarin Chinese" (PhD diss., University of Southern California, 1985).
57. Noam Chomsky, *The Minimalist Program* (Cambridge, MA: MIT Press, 1995).
58. Vergnaud, "Letter to Noam Chomsky and Howard Lasnik," 22.

22. A Conversation with *Evolution News*

1. For the published version of the proceedings of the symposium, see *Mathematical Challenges to the Neo-Darwinian Interpretation of Evolution: Wistar Institute Symposium Monograph* No. 5, eds. Paul S. Moorhead and Martin M. Kaplan (Philadelphia: Wistar Institute Press, 1967).
2. David Berlinski, *Black Mischief: Language, Life, Logic, Luck*, 2nd ed. (Orlando, FL: Harcourt Brace Jovanovich, 1988).
3. David Berlinski, *The Devil's Delusion: Atheism and Its Scientific Pretensions*, 2nd ed. (New York: Basic Books, 2009).
4. Horace, *Epistles*, bk. 1, epistle 11: "Those who cross the sea change their sky, not their soul."

Credits

Cover image by Feiyuwzhangjie, "Chinese Calligraphy Character 'Happiness,'" 123RF (website), Image ID: 11750839.

Some of the material in this volume originally appeared elsewhere, and is used here with permission.

"Vienna" appeared in the now-defunct *European Travel and Life Magazine* (1980s). "A Conversation with *Le Figaro*" appeared as an interview with Catherine Nay & Meritens Share in *Le Figaro Magazine*, November 10, 2001.

"The Dangerous Discipline" appeared in *The Advent of the Algorithm* (New York: Harcourt, 2000) by David Berlinski. "Giuseppe Peano," "Sonja Kovalevsky," and "A Logician's Life" appeared in *One, Two, Three: Absolutely Elementary Mathematics* (New York: Random House, 2011) by David Berlinski.

"The Best of Times" appeared in *Inference* 1, no. 4 (October 2015). "The Recovery of Case" appeared in *Inference* 2, no. 3 (September 2016). "Godzooks," a review of *Homo Deus: A Brief History of Tomorrow*, by Yuval Noah Harari, appeared in *Inference* 3, no. 4 (February 2018). "The Social Set," a review of *Blueprint: The Evolutionary Origins of a Good Society*, by Nicholas Christakis, appeared in *Inference* 4, no. 4 (July 2019).

"A Conversation with Evolution News" appeared in five parts at *Evolution News* as "The Making of a Skeptic," September 22, 2009; "How I Came to Doubt Darwin," September 23, 2009; "Influences," September 24, 2009; "On the Darwinian Guild," September 25, 2009; and "On Religion, Teaching, and Life in Paris," September 28, 2009. Likewise, "Majestic Ascent" first appeared at *Evolution News* on November 20, 2011, and "A Flower of Chivalry," on December 16, 2011.

Index